Events in Book On[...]

Fourteen years had passed since The Destruction, which brought to an end Cai's faith in magic as a force in nature. His beloved pupil Gemma found that the benevolent world which contains Cai and her family is no longer enough for her. Turning her back on her royal heritage and on the convictions of those she holds dear, she follows the compulsion to sail to the recently discovered Southern Continent.

For Gemma is sure that magic still lives, but has no proof. No one will take her seriously, not even Arden, the sceptical adventurer who joins forces with her, but who scoffs at her beliefs.

In a world where alternate realities abound, where floating cities pass through camps at night, and where desert sands sing travellers to their doom, Gemma and Arden use their combined talents to save the strange and beautiful Valley of Knowing from drought and devastation. They come to know the true source of their dreams, the astonishing secrets of the desert stone, and discover that although magic is far from dead, its remnant, and the uses it must be put to, are frighteningly perilous.

Also by Jonathan Wylie

SERVANTS OF ARK
Book One: THE FIRST NAMED
Book Two: THE CENTRE OF THE CIRCLE
Book Three: THE MAGE-BORN CHILD

THE UNBALANCED EARTH
Book One: DREAMS OF STONE

and published by Corgi Books

The Unbalanced Earth
Book Two

THE LIGHTLESS KINGDOM

Jonathan Wylie

CORGI BOOKS

THE UNBALANCED EARTH BOOK TWO:
THE LIGHTLESS KINGDOM

A CORGI BOOK   0 552 13417 1

First publication in Great Britain

PRINTING HISTORY
Corgi edition published 1989

Copyright © Jonathan Wylie 1989

This book is set in 10/11pt Mallard
by Busby Typesetting

Corgi Books are published by Transworld Publishers Ltd.,
61-63 Uxbridge Road, Ealing, London W5 5SA, in Australia by
Transworld Publishers (Australia) Pty. Ltd., 15-23 Helles
Avenue, Moorebank, NSW 2170, and in New Zealand by Transworld
Publishers (N.Z.) Ltd., Cnr. Moselle and Waipareira Avenues,
Henderson, Auckland.

Made and printed in Great Britain by
Hazell, Watson & Viney Limited
Member of BPCC plc
Aylesbury, Bucks, England

This book is dedicated, with much love,
to The Quartet . . .

Christine and Clive,
John (again), and last (but very definitely
not least – in fact, she's usually first), Sue.

*   *   *

'For this relief, much thanks.'

Part One

THE WANDERERS

CHAPTER ONE

Why is it always so dark?

She had seen him several times now. On each occasion, hope had risen within her, only to be dashed away by the sheer impossibility of what she had witnessed. Sometimes she saw through *his* eyes, the scene blurred and frightening. Once, she had watched as he crawled, slowly and agonizingly, along a black, glistening tunnel. The only light came from a faint, sickly luminescence on the walls.

Then the others had arrived. She never saw them clearly, but knew that they brought with them fear and hope, suspicion and, above all, a palpable sense of difference. She could not see their faces – if indeed they had faces.

But this time felt different. He lay on his back, in a larger space than before. It was dry here; no water rushed by, no drips fell from the walls that surrounded him. In the dim, fractured light which came from above, nothing glistened and nothing moved. Only the constant darkness had any real substance.

The unbearable loneliness of her earlier glimpses was gone. Even the pain had lessened. Yet the confusion remained.

Where are you?

She held no firm beliefs about the continuation of life after death, but knew that others did. Yet surely it would not be like this. This was too cruel, too inconclusive.

No!

She shied away from the implication of her thoughts.

9

He is not dead!

Against all the evidence, against all reason, she believed it.

She returned her attention to the figure that lay unmoving below her. His eyes were closed, arms folded across his chest; she could not tell whether he breathed or not. The lower part of his body was covered with some sort of cloth.

The air about him was cool, still and silent, and she floated in it like the moon in the sky, a ghostly radiance that illuminated nothing. Whether this place was part of her world or another, one thing was clear. Wherever it was, the sun never reached this dismal realm.

Indeterminate black shapes entered her field of vision, and she tensed, filled with the helpless mixture of emotions that these alien presences always evoked. They moved towards the prone figure, appearing to bend over him and almost obscuring him from her sight, but they themselves remained infuriatingly obscure.

Don't hurt him!

It was a reflexive cry. She had no reason to distrust the mysterious beings, apart from her fear of the unknown. She could not tell whether they were corporeal or another form of life, and she could never make out a single detail of their appearance. They came and went in silence, shadows within shadow.

After a while, they withdrew, melting back into the darkness, their departure as unhurried as their arrival had been.

He had not moved, but there was a little more strength in his face, and the sense of pain was less marked. She sighed with relief. They had not hurt him. Perhaps they had even helped him! The bubble of happiness that welled up within her at this soon burst as her lack of real knowledge overwhelmed the small comfort.

Can't you give me a sign?

Her anguish was such that she almost looked away,

broke the contact. But her eyes were held captive by stronger forces. Whatever the price, she would pay it. However much grief came from her dark visions, they were worth every moment. The reason was simple.

I love you.

His eyes snapped open, and she experienced another surge of joy.

Can you hear me?

It was then that she saw the utter confusion in his green eyes. He glanced about wildly, though he could only move his head a little. Pain re-emerged in them both, and the vision faded.

I love you.

He was gone. It was over, and as she cried with relief at the end of her torture, she longed for the next time, the next contact.

It was all she had left now.

11

CHAPTER TWO

'I dreamt about Arden again last night,' Gemma told Mallory the next morning.

'I know,' her friend replied. 'I heard you. You sounded so distressed that I almost came to wake you up.'

'No!' Gemma was vehement. 'You must never do that.'

Mallory turned from her baking and looked at Gemma with a mixture of concern and sadness on her face.

'They're only dreams, Gemma.'

'No. They're more than that.'

The two women had been through this argument several times before. Mallory had logic and common sense on her side, but knew that she would never be able to convince Gemma of Arden's death until they could find proof. And there was virtually no chance that this proof would ever be forthcoming.

Arden had been lost in the high mountains, far to the south of the valley. He had disappeared at the same time as an entire mountain had been displaced, by a process which Mallory accepted but did not understand. It had involved magic, and had been initiated by Gemma. While the result had been joyous for the valley that was Mallory's home – returning a river to their parched and dying land – the effect in the mountains had been akin to an earthquake, centred on the very spot where Arden had been. Though Mallory and the inhabitants of a nearby village had searched high and low for him, they found only his horse and equipment; the man himself had vanished without trace. Gemma was alone in her belief that he had survived both the earthquake and its associated rock falls, as well as the tumultuous surge of newly diverted water.

Those events had taken place almost four months ago. For more than half the time since, Gemma had been back in the valley. She had arrived expecting Arden to be there, and was distraught when she heard Mallory tell of his loss. Since then, not even the miraculous revitalization of the valley and its special inhabitants had been enough to lift Gemma from her gloom for any length of time. She clung tenaciously to the hope that Arden would one day return. In her eyes at least, her dreams were powerful evidence that he was still alive – somewhere.

Mallory knew that she had to convince Gemma otherwise; the alternative was to watch her friend constantly torment herself. She left her work now, and joined Gemma at the kitchen table. She placed her hands, still covered with a dusting of flour, over Gemma's, and looked at her friend with concern. Gemma's naturally pale complexion had been darkened by her recent outdoor life, and her freckles were hardly noticeable. Her fiery red hair, so rare in these southern lands, fell to her shoulders. Soft grey eyes reflected guilt, regret and a measure of defiance. Mallory saw it all, and her heart ached. She had loved Arden dearly, in her own way, but her pain at his loss was nothing compared to Gemma's.

'Dreams come from inside your own head,' she said slowly.

'Ordinary dreams, yes,' Gemma replied instantly. 'But these come from *him*.'

'That's wishful thinking. You want to believe that Arden is still alive, so you conjure him up in this way.'

'If that were true, then why do I dream of him in such an awful place?' Gemma demanded. 'Why not somewhere pleasant, like the valley? That's where I'd *want* him to be.'

'Because dreams don't work like that,' Mallory said kindly. 'Who knows where we get the imagery from?'

'It's always so dark there,' Gemma went on, shuddering at the memory. 'Always.'

'You saw him in the tunnel again?'

'In a sort of cave this time. A big one. He was just lying there, not moving.' Gemma stared at her companion. 'There *are* caves in the mountains, aren't there?'

'Some, yes, but not where he disappeared,' Mallory answered firmly. 'We searched the whole area, you know we did.'

But Gemma was only half listening.

'I should have gone to look for him myself,' she said softly. '*I* would have known where he was.'

'Oh, stop torturing yourself,' Mallory ordered sharply, hoping to snap Gemma out of her deepening depression. 'We've been over that dozens of times. By the time you got back here, you were in no state to go *anywhere*. You're only just healthy again now—'

'That's not the point—'

'I haven't finished.' Mallory would not allow herself to be distracted. 'You weren't able to travel. The valley people couldn't leave here, and if the men from Keld couldn't find him in countryside they know better than anyone, what hope was there?' She stopped to take a breath, then continued relentlessly. 'Besides, it was already *too late*. By the time you could have got back there, he would have been missing for more than two months. If he *had* been injured by the earthquake, there would have been nothing you could have done to help him.'

Gemma said nothing, just stared at her companion, her face a mask.

Mallory tried again, her voice gentle now.

'Gemma, you have your whole life ahead of you. You have so many talents, and you mustn't waste them by

14

constantly feeling guilty and regretting the past.'
Mallory paused, but Gemma remained silent, and did
not try to deny the obvious. 'Accept what's happened,
and start looking towards the future.' She took a deep
breath. 'Arden's gone.'

Mallory's final words did not bring the instant angry
denial she had expected. Instead, Gemma just shook her
head, and smiled faintly.

'It's no good, Mallory. I'm as stubborn as granite.
He's alive.'

Mallory sighed, but Gemma's smile was such a
welcome sight – whatever the reason for it – that she
could not bring herself to argue further.

'If he *is*,' she said eventually, 'then he'll come back
to the valley. You know he will.'

Gemma nodded.

'So there's no point in plaguing yourself by worrying
about what you can't change,' Mallory went on, smiling
her encouragement. 'We'll keep you busy enough here
– take your mind off things!' She made as if to stand
up, but Gemma's next words kept her where she was.

'The black *things* were with him again.'

Mallory was intrigued, in spite of her misgivings.
Gemma's dreams seemed to have a logical progression.
At first, Arden had been in complete darkness, alone,
afraid, and in pain. There had been water everywhere,
though it could only be felt, not seen or heard. Later,
he had been moving in tunnels and shafts, with dim
light appearing in places. Then the 'others' had come
upon the scene, and shortly afterwards the dreams
had become far more vivid, though still confused.
Colour seeped into them, and pain had been replaced
by delirium.

Mallory wondered which remote corner of Gemma's
mind had produced the ambiguous black spectres.

'Do they mean him any harm?' she asked.

'I don't think so.' Gemma was puzzling something
out, trying to remember, and her look of triumph when

15

she succeeded was so delighted that Mallory could not help but grin back at her.

'He opened his eyes when I told him I loved him!' she exclaimed. 'He heard me!'

Oh, Gemma, Mallory thought despairingly. *Don't build yourself up for an even greater fall.* She didn't know what to say, but something of her thoughts must have shown in her face.

'More wishful thinking, eh?' Gemma asked, a sparkle in her eyes. 'It's all right, you don't have to believe me. I won't be offended—'

'It's not—' Mallory began.

'He talked to me once when I was in the kite,' Gemma interrupted. 'Perhaps he can do it again.'

Mallory had seen the beginning of Gemma's incredible flight from a plateau high in the mountains to the desert many leagues to the north, and had been told of Gemma's subsequent adventures, but had not heard this aspect of it before. Her surprise was obvious and Gemma hurried to explain.

'He gave me directions when I was lost – without his help I would never have been able to find the rocking stone.'

Whatever had happened, it was obvious that Gemma believed that he *had* spoken to her, and Mallory chose not to disagree. After all, Gemma did have remarkable powers; it had been her actions, on reaching the standing stone in the middle of the Diamond Desert, that had ultimately saved the valley. That same event had brought about Arden's probable death, and Gemma found this hard to cope with.

'We're getting closer,' she told Mallory now. 'Maybe we'll be able to talk to each other soon. That's why you must never wake me up. I might lose him.'

'Don't you think you might be deluding yourself?' Mallory asked, as gently as she was able.

Grey eyes stared calmly back at her.

'He'll come back. That's why I'm still here. Until I

can reason out some way of helping him, I'll wait.' It was as good a conclusion as any.

'Well, I've got something you can do now,' Mallory replied brightly. 'Go and tell Kragen and the boys that we need some potatoes for dinner.'

They stood up then, and Mallory returned to her baking. Gemma went to the door, then hesitated.

'Thank you for putting up with me,' she said quietly.

'Don't be ridiculous. I like having you here. We all do.'

Gemma smiled her thanks, and left.

'Gemma!' Mallory called after her. 'Don't wait *too* long!'

* * *

When Arden first brought Gemma to the valley, it had been a dusty travesty of its former green beauty. The river on which it depended usually ran from midwinter to late summer, but only every other year. Then it failed twice. Even the valley people's ingenious irrigation systems could not cope with four years of absolute drought, and their unique society had been on the verge of collapse.

But now the river had returned, brought about by Gemma's magical restoration of the powers of the rocking stone, and all that had changed. As Gemma walked across the fields in search of Mallory's husband, she could not help but notice the new growth that flourished everywhere. Spring this year was a joyous celebration of the renewal of life, and the summer would see the valley return to its former loveliness.

If only . . . she began, then made a determined effort to push the thought and its accompanying ache away. Mallory was right; brooding would get her nowhere.

She found Kragen and his two sons making adjustments to the sluice gates which controlled the water channels on the far side of the farm. They were so intent on their task that they did not notice her approach

17

until she was only a few paces away. Kragen glanced up and smiled, his deeply tanned face as welcoming as ever.

'Hello,' he said. 'It's good to see you up and about.'

His slow voice and steady manner were the outer form of his calm temperament. While he could not match Mallory's quick, instinctive intelligence, he had considerable common sense, and between them there were few problems that could not be overcome.

The boys were less reticent in their welcome. They liked Gemma enormously, and were delighted to have the valley's heroine staying with them. They had grown used to her bouts of melancholy, and learnt from their parents that there were times when it was better to leave her alone. This morning, though, their greeting was spontaneous and uninhibited. They clambered out of the stream, their bare feet covered with mud, and rushed to her side.

Jon, who was barely five years old, held up his arms and Gemma obediently lifted him up for a cuddle, heedless of the mess he was making of her tunic.

'My, you're getting heavy,' she remarked. It was not true. Both boys had been raised in times of hardship, and it showed. Jon had been a tiny baby at the beginning of the drought, and he was small and light for his age. Even Vance, who was seven, was too thin. However, they would soon see their home as it was meant to be, and their future was much brighter now. This was an enormous source of pleasure to Gemma.

Vance, who had contented himself with standing close by her side, asked, 'Are you going to help us with the gates?'

'Not this time. Your mother wants some potatoes dug. If you'll show me where they are, I'll do it – it's about time I started to earn my keep.'

'I'll help you!' Jon volunteered eagerly.

'Me too,' Vance added, then glanced at his father.

'Abandon your father in the mud, would you?' Kragen

asked, then, seeing the uncertainty on his son's face, he laughed and added, 'Go on, then. I can finish up here.' He looked at Gemma, and she knew he was wondering whether to refer to the previous night.

'I'm all right,' she told him simply.

Kragen smiled and nodded. 'Don't dig too many,' he said. 'They'll be much bigger in another month.'

The three walked back across the fields, one small hand in each of Gemma's. The boys kept up a lively chatter, pointing things out to their guest, and taking pride in identifying plants, trees and animals.

'That's a rook,' Jon said, pointing.

'No it's not. It's a crow,' Vance countered. 'You can tell by the way it flies.'

'Isn't that a rook, Gemma?' Jon asked.

'I don't know,' she replied diplomatically. 'They look the same to me.'

Any possible argument was diverted by the appearance of two rabbits which bounded out of one of the hedgerows and sped into a nearby copse. The boys watched them go with obvious delight. The valley people shared their home peacefully with the wild animals, and would not hunt them. It was only one of the many aspects which made it such a special place.

At the meal that night, there was a festive atmosphere. The potatoes had been ceremonially presented by Jon, and symbolized the revival of the valley, being the first of a new crop, and promising better things for the future. They ate no meat – something which Gemma no longer found strange – preferring to live off the abundance of grains, vegetables, nuts, fruits and herbs which the valley had once produced and would soon do so again.

When they had finished, the boys, though obviously tired, were in no mood to go straight to bed.

'Can we have a story?' Vance pleaded.

'Yes please!' Jon exclaimed, looking at Gemma. 'Tell us about the meyrkats.'

19

'Again?' Gemma was amused by their eagerness to hear her oft-told tale. 'There's not enough time to tell it all. Which part do you want to hear?'

'About when they put you to bed,' Vance replied, then quickly realized his mistake, and added, 'and the bit after that, with the Wanderers.' He glanced from Gemma to his mother.

'All right,' Mallory conceded. 'But when Gemma's finished, you both go straight upstairs.'

The boys nodded, then turned expectantly to Gemma.

'You remember how the meyrkats' singing helped me to move the stone?' she began. 'Well, after that I was awfully tired.'

'You were hurt too,' Jon put in.

'A little,' Gemma admitted, 'but the meyrkats took care of that. They licked my cuts, to clean them and make them heal quickly, and then they covered me with cloth from the sail of the kite. I slept under the stars while they watched over me, then, in the morning . . .'

She paused, trying to push away the recollection of that last vision in the monolith – the sight of Arden falling, falling into utter darkness – and the enigmatic message from the stone: *My brother has taken him.* Instead, she recalled the events that followed.

'That was the beginning of the green-time,' she said, as the memories came flooding back.

CHAPTER THREE

The enormous rocking stone towered over Gemma as she stood with her back to it, gazing out over the Diamond Desert. This was a forbidding wasteland of sand, brown stone and thorn-bush, which stretched for many leagues in every direction.

She looked at the three meyrkats who were waiting in front of her. The creatures stood no higher than her knee, even when upright on their hind legs. Each was covered with brown fur. They had small round ears and sharply pointed faces with darker circles of fur around their shiny black eyes; they looked rather like elongated squirrels, but the claws of their forepaws were built for burrowing, and their long tails were thin.

On first meeting the meyrkats, Gemma had discovered – to her amazement – that she could converse with them through mind-talk, in the same way as a wizard conversed with his familiar. By now she took this facility for granted, and even their notion of adding their own name at the end of each mental communication – something which had caused her not inconsiderable confusion at first – came as second nature to her, and she no longer heard it.

I have more wandering to do, Gemma told them.

Some of us will come with you, Ul replied.

Gemma leaned forward, her heart lifting at the meyrkat's words, and the prospect of their company. As she did so, she felt the first drops of rain fall on her outstretched hand. The few days of rain which came to the desert each winter – which the meyrkats called the green-time – had just begun.

That first shower did little more than lightly moisten the desert's surface, but even so, it was enough to bring forth an amazing variety of new smells, and the air for once seemed clear and fresh. The meyrkats were obviously delighted, and made small whistling sounds of happiness; in the distance Gemma could see more of them emerging from the clan burrow to frolic in the damp morning.

She returned her attention to the trio in front of her.

I have a long way to travel. Far beyond your territory, she said.

We know. There were Wanderers once. Now there will be again.

Ul's words held the wistful, romantic tone that Gemma had come to associate with her, but this time there was an added touch of excitement. *Even Od agrees,* Ul added.

Gemma looked at the male she had referred to, and smiled to herself. *That settles it then,* she thought privately. Od had always struck her as a traditionalist, rather stern and dogmatic. She had reason to be thankful for his strength of purpose during their singing the night before, however, and felt as much affection for him as she did for the others. He was, without doubt, the clan's expert on all matters relating to the rocking stone. His resonant 'voice' now sounded in her head.

I will remain, Od stated portentously. *The clan's promise must be kept. The singing will continue. But we are many now. Your return, Gem-ma, has been a sign. We have other duties. There will be Wanderers again.*

The clan will become two, the third meyrkat explained.

Are you sure that the division won't harm you? Gemma asked. She knew that the great strength of the meyrkats was their ability to act as a team, each devoting his or her own special skills to the good of the clan. Splitting them up would undoubtedly weaken them, and make them more vulnerable to the harsh environment. She was also worried in case she lost her ability to talk to them. Gemma was convinced that her magical ability was linked to multiple entities, and it was therefore the clan itself which enabled her to talk to the individuals within it, rather than the other way round. But this did not seem to worry the meyrkats.

The clan stands tall in knowing, Ul quoted.

We have claws enough. One burrow is no longer all we can dig, Ir added.

The green-time will make the wandering easier, Od said. *It is a good time for new beginnings.*

It is our destiny, Ul concluded.

* * *

Knowing that she was still too stiff and tired to travel far, Gemma spent the rest of that day taking stock of her situation. She had little enough in the way of supplies; no food, no water, no tools – not even a knife or a tinder box to light a fire. All she had were the clothes she stood up in and the wreckage of the kite. She cursed herself for being so unprepared, but reasoned that nothing had mattered to her save the attempt to reach the stone in time. It was only now, when she had done all she could in that respect, that she could turn her thoughts to survival and the next stage of her journey.

She made the best of what she had, building a make-shift shelter from the wood and material of the kite. While the rain was welcome, the nights would be cold and she had no wish to sleep in sodden clothes. Despite weighting it down with rocks and sand, the tent was not very stable, and it was obvious that a strong wind – let alone the sandstorms which often preceded the rainfall – would destroy it.

Helped by the meyrkats, Gemma dug a shallow hole and lined it with more cloth, hoping to catch rainwater overnight. Ox, the clan's leader, also showed her where water would gather in pools on the rock flats. The meyrkats worked hard, clearing these of sand and debris, though they obviously considered Gemma's concern about water – 'clear-rush' to them – to be unnecessary. Having to live without water for so long had clearly given them an entirely different attitude towards it. At last, even Gemma was convinced that water would not be a problem. She knew that – as a last resort – she could chew on the vile-tasting but water-bearing bulbous roots of the ubiquitous thorn bushes.

Her lack of food was a much more serious consideration. The fibrous roots could provide a little nutrition, but not nearly enough for the many days of travelling that lay ahead. The meyrkats had killed a snake for her, but she had no blade with which to prepare the meat, and no way of making a fire to cook it. Hungry as she was, Gemma found herself reluctant even to consider the snake as food. Throughout the day the meyrkats presented her with various alternatives – grubs and beetles, a massive centipede, a scorpion – but, much to their disappointment, Gemma found none of these titbits at all appetizing.

I could eat them if I was really desperate, she thought to herself, looking at the gifts and feeling rather sick, *but what I really need is a fire.*

She enlisted the meyrkats' help in looking for flints, but it soon became obvious that none of the nearby rocks was even remotely likely to produce a spark.

I could always chip a bit off the rocking stone, Gemma remarked in jest, and was shocked when her companions took her seriously.

The god-sky-fire-stone is one! Od exclaimed. *It must not be broken.*

It would not permit. Be angry, Ox added, and Gemma shuddered at the memory of the stone's wrath.

It was a joke! she explained quickly. *I didn't mean it.*

A few moments passed in confused mental silence.

A joke? Od queried, his uncertainty obvious. *What is a joke?*

Several of the meyrkats nearby stopped to listen to the conversation, and Gemma felt a wave of helplessness. A joke was something that made you laugh, and the meyrkats certainly seemed to understand laughter. She remembered her earlier games with the clan, when she had been demonstrating her link with them to Arden, and decided that the happy mental and verbal atmosphere that had been produced was their equivalent of laughter.

A joke is a story . . . she began, *told by one so that others can enjoy and be made happy.*

The meyrkats considered this.

But it is not true? Ox asked eventually.

It may not be, Gemma replied, sensing their bewilderment. *But if so, all know it.*

How? Od asked thoughtfully.

Reasons ran through Gemma's mind, but after a while they made little sense, even to her. She tried her best to explain; a joke could be the way something was said; when, where and to whom it was said; the fact that it was obviously absurd or made only inverted sense. In the end, though, she had to give up – her definitions were not being understood.

Here I am, stranded in the middle of a desert, talking about the philosophy of humour with a tribe of small furry animals, she thought to herself. The meyrkats sensed her amusement, but she wisely decided against trying to explain it. The clan was left a little more knowledgeable, but still puzzled and intrigued by this new aspect of the lives of men. Amongst themselves they decided to call a joke 'happy-lie-all-know', in keeping with their practice of giving long names to the things they did not understand. It became a sort of private challenge to them to invent a joke –

though Gemma was not aware of this until later.

She was determined to sort out the problem of her lack of fire. She organized the collection of kindling and deadwood from the thorn-bushes, and this was placed in her tent in order to keep it dry.

It was mid-afternoon when she remembered that she and Arden had camped here on two previous occasions. The memory shook her a little, and she felt saddened by the separation from the man she loved. *Feeling sorry for yourself won't help,* she lectured herself sternly, and, with her willing helpers, began to search for and excavate any debris buried on those previous visits.

Digging was the meyrkats' speciality, and they set about their task with great gusto. Soon, Gemma saw spurts of sand shooting from the new pits dug by teams of the creatures. She was astounded at the speed with which they worked, and delighted when one of the young males, Em, announced that they had found something. However, this turned out to be only the remains of an old fire, buried by the previous day's sandstorm, and it yielded only a few charred sticks. Em was so disappointed when he realized that this was not what Gemma needed, that she instructed him to take the sticks to her tent. She explained that they would help make a good fire once she got it started.

If I ever do . . . she added to herself.

Soon after that, there was better news. One of the clan's elders, a female named Av, whom Gemma remembered as a look-out specialist with incredible balance, called out that she had found 'hard rocks'. Gemma hurried over, and peered into the hole. It was indeed the rubbish that Arden had buried at the end of their last visit, and, among the debris, Gemma was delighted to see the broken shards of a green-glass bottle. She eagerly cleaned the slivers of glass with sand, remembering that the bottle had once contained the fiery liqueur from the abbey. A faint smell still clung

26

to it and she smiled, remembering the night when she and Arden had drunk the contents. Now she had something with which to prepare the snake meat and – hopefully – start a fire.

With some difficulty she achieved the former that afternoon, but intermittent showers continued until early evening, and when the sun eventually came out, it was too weak to produce enough heat to ignite kindling. Gemma decided to try again the next day.

She retired to her tent, and tried to sleep. The aching emptiness in her stomach – she had been without solid food now for two days and nights – and the departure of the meyrkats to the haven of their burrow left her feeling uncomfortable and despondent. Sleep would not come, and her thoughts turned to Arden and Mallory, and to the valley. Had she succeeded in restoring the river? What had the vision in the stone meant? She had no answers, and this made her all the more determined to escape from the desert. She *had* to find her friends again.

That night saw the first of the heavy rains; violent bursts that drummed on the earth and gushed along the runnels of rock and sand. Luckily, Gemma's tent survived the onslaught more or less unscathed. When she emerged in the early light of dawn, she was amazed to find the first green shoots of new life already poking up from the ground. In this environment, the plants could not afford to waste any time. *And neither can I*, she thought, feeling weak with hunger.

The early-morning air was moist and cool, and when the sun appeared it was pale and hazy. Gemma drank, then wondered if the meyrkats' burrow had been troubled by flooding. She inspected a few of the numerous entrances and found that, although some flash floods had passed close by, the doorways were designed so that the water was diverted from the burrow itself. Her respect for her companions rose another notch.

27

The meyrkats soon emerged and set to work. The green-time was important to the clan because, with the increase in plant life, there was a corresponding increase in the desert's animal population and food would therefore be plentiful.

As Gemma had nothing specific to do, except wait for the sun, she was asked to look after the youngest of the meyrkats – a task normally undertaken by one of the elders. She was honoured by their trust and enjoyed her babysitting duties, glad that she could repay them, in some measure, for all their help.

There were eight youngsters in her charge, the smallest one only a handspan tall. They played happily together, indulging in mock fights and mimicking their elders by carefully grooming each other. Gemma was so enchanted by their antics that she almost forgot the gnawing emptiness inside her. She kept a look-out for birds of prey, knowing that they were the meyrkats' greatest natural enemy, and at the same time watched as the sun climbed higher, and clouds moved in from the west. When one of the older meyrkats came to relieve her, she tested various pieces of glass to see which produced the best magnifying effect. She found one that was reasonably efficient but, to her frustration, it was nearly midday by the time there was a sufficient break in the clouds to allow her to make a proper attempt. When she stood up to collect the driest of her kindling, she felt dizzy and almost fainted, but steadied herself and returned to her chosen fireplace. Intrigued by what she was doing, several meyrkats came over to watch.

Gemma made a small ring of stones, and placed within it pieces of the charred sticks and wood from the kite, putting the smallest slivers at the very centre. Then she held the glass carefully, adjusting it so that a small spot of heat and light fell on to the kindling. The sun was at its strongest now, and this was the best chance she would have today. Light-headed with hunger and concentration, Gemma willed the fire to start. Her arms began to ache with the effort of keeping still, but there was as yet no sign of any smoke or flame.

Time passed slowly, and her frustration turned to anger. *Why isn't it working? Maybe the glass is too dark. Or the winter sun is too weak. Please!* Her head was spinning as though she were drunk. The meyrkats recognized her discomfort and shifted uneasily, not knowing how to help.

Then Gemma risked a glance up at the sky, and groaned as she saw the approach of a large black cloud. Not only would it blot out the sun, but if rain fell now she would have little time to cover her precious supply of dry wood. Fury erupted within her, directed at herself. *You started a fire in Newport big enough to burn down half a city. Do it again!*

She stared at the glass, her mind full of seething dark images. Reaching down into the black depths, she found the golden spark of power and let it flow to the surface. *Help me!*

A tiny wisp of smoke rose from the kindling, then, with an audible *whoosh*, the whole fire, slivers, sticks and embers alike, leapt into flame. For a moment, Gemma was almost too shocked to move, and she only came to her senses when her hands felt the pain of the fire and she smelt the smoke. Quickly, she withdrew her arms, dropping the glass fragment, and sat stunned, gazing at the blaze.

Then the cloud covered the sun, and at the same time Gemma became aware of a strange noise all around her. The meyrkats were singing, their voices interweaving in a discordant but oddly moving wail. Gemma gazed at them in wonder, and the song gradually faded into silence.

Did you do this? she asked, looking at Od.

No. But we called on the spirits of the fire to come forth at your command, he replied.

How?

The memories of fire were still in the black sticks, Od answered. *We sang for them for you to use.*

Gemma realized that he was referring to the charred wood from the old fire.

Then you did start the fire, she said.

No. That was your power, Od replied.

A few drops of rain began to fall then, and Gemma had to concentrate on protecting the fire. If a deluge should fall now, after all that effort . . . It didn't bear thinking about. She glanced up at the sky.

Thank you for your help, Gemma said. *Please bring me some more wood – quickly.*

The meyrkats hurried to do her bidding, and the blaze was soon roaring so fiercely that the animals refused to come too close. The rain stayed light, then died away, and Gemma got on with cooking the snake-meat on wooden skewers. Though the smell disgusted the meyrkats, it made her stomach knot in anticipation, and she burnt her mouth as she quickly appeased her hunger. Although the meat was tough and half-burnt, it tasted wonderful to Gemma.

That evening, she sat contentedly outside her tent, watching the meyrkats. She still did not fully understand what had happened earlier but was very grateful for it. She now had a full stomach – though she had been careful not to eat too much – and a day's supply of cooked meat at hand. She hoped the meyrkats would be able to provide her with more the next day, and planned to begin her trek to the valley the day after that.

She had explained this to Ox, and the clan was now busy with its own preparations. There was evidently a great deal of ritual involved in dividing a clan, but Gemma could only watch, and could not even begin to understand what most of it meant.

The fire had been split into two, and the original had been covered with stones and mud. Gemma was confident that the embers would still be hot in the morning. The second campfire was before her now, sending its comforting red light flickering over the scene before her; the puzzling movements of the meyr-kats, the looming presence of the stone, the water traps and thorn bushes.

Gemma remembered the earlier camps at this place. On the first occasion she had been near to death, and had been saved by Arden. During the second time, Arden himself had almost been killed by the stone's arcane violence.

He would be proud of me now, she thought. *I can cope, whereas a few months ago I would probably have just given up and died.* She longed to see him again.

CHAPTER FOUR

Gemma emerged from her tent the next morning to find the day bright and fresh. A few small clouds dotted the sky and there was a keen breeze blowing, but the new day lifted her spirits. Her battered body was no longer protesting, and she felt sharply alive. For a moment she thought of starting her journey there and then, but rejected the idea in favour of better preparation.

Her first concern was for the fire, but there had been little rain overnight and even the open campfire was still smouldering – another boost to her confidence.

The meyrkats were already up and about, and when they saw that she was awake, a group of them, headed by Ox, came towards her. They stopped a few paces away, and from the serious look of the delegation, Gemma expected a pronouncement about the division of the clan. Instead, there was a somewhat nervous pause, then Ox spoke.

Scorpions are blue and the sky is green, he announced solemnly, then he and his companions fixed Gemma with such fierce stares that she wilted under the combined intensity of so many jet-black eyes. Then she realized what was happening, and laughed. This caused an immediate reaction among the meyrkats – they glanced back and forth at each other, and made pleased piping sounds.

I make joke, Gem-ma. Yes? Ox asked.

Not quite, she replied, laughing all the more. *I don't think you've got the hang of it yet.*

This caused them much consternation, and Gemma

controlled her laughter with difficulty, hoping that she had not offended them.

But you laugh, Od accused, the confusion plain in his tone.

Yes, but . . . Desperately, Gemma searched her memory for a joke that would demonstrate what she meant. She soon came to the conclusion that it was impossible. *I can't explain,* she admitted finally. *I'm sorry.*

After a few moments, the meyrkats retreated. They were still puzzled, but decided to put the problem to one side and go in search of food. Gemma ate her breakfast, checked on the covered fire, and then went to inspect the new-grown vegetation to see if she could add anything to her meagre diet. She was again amazed at the rapidity with which the plants had sprung up. Some had even flowered, as if they had to compress the whole year and all of the seasons into just a few days. Brilliant reds and purples were added to the greenery that now festooned the desert. Even the drab thorn bushes carried light green buds.

She found several promising looking leaves, but had no way of knowing whether they were nutritious or poisonous. The meyrkats were little help, as they did not consider plants to be food. They did show her one that they used when stung by a scorpion, but Gemma was not sure how much of a recommendation that was. Bravely, she tasted a little, and found it bitter but edible; she suffered no ill effects. Another plant looked and tasted very much like a small onion, and she collected as much as she could find of both species before returning to her tent.

When she got there, she found that the meyrkats had produced another snake, much bigger than the other one. Gemma could not imagine how they had managed to kill it – it looked powerful enough to crush any of them. She set about the laborious business of preparing the meat, cooking some, smoking some more, and leaving a considerable raw portion for the hunters. It was well into the afternoon by the time she had finished, and she was tired and messy. She cleaned herself up with sand as best she could, then drank some water. When she returned, the meyrkats had produced another surprise.

'Eggs!' she said aloud, surprising herself with the sound of her own voice.

Gemma had no idea which bird or animal had produced the four large eggs, but was in no position to worry about this. She covered them in a mixture of mud and damp sand and baked them in the embers of her fire. She ate one with her meal that evening, finding it strong tasting and delicious. Her stores were now as complete as they could be.

As dusk faded into the dark of night, a large group of meyrkats, perhaps half the strength of the clan, gathered in a circle around the rocking stone. As the stars began to appear, they sang, and while no one would claim that the sound they made was beautiful, it had a resonant quality, a sadness, which touched Gemma's heart. She knew instinctively that these were the Wanderers, and that they were bidding farewell to the stone that their tribe had guarded for generations, to their territory, and to their home. The realization brought a lump to her throat and, once again, she found herself wondering why they felt she deserved such loyalty. As the sad song faded away into silence, tears were rolling down Gemma's cheeks.

Then a new song started, completely different this time. It was faster, high-pitched and discordant, and contained an undeniable element of excitement. Wiping the tears from her face, Gemma wondered what this song meant.

Od appeared at her side, as if in answer to her unspoken question.

What are they singing about? she asked.

They bid the god-sky-fire-stone farewell, and ask his

permission to wander, he replied solemnly. *Now they sing of the journey and the life to come . . . and of you.*

Me?

Of course. You are their territory now, Od answered.

* * *

'What did he mean, Gemma?' Jon asked from her lap. It was his standard question at this point in the story.

'I've told you that before,' she scolded him gently. 'It means that their home would be with me, wherever I went.'

'Then why didn't they come to the valley?' Jon persisted.

'Enough!' Mallory decided. 'You two – to bed!'

'Oh . . .'

'No arguments. It's late, and poor Gemma's voice will be worn out. She's been talking for hours.'

Gemma cleared her throat and coughed feebly, then smiled as the boys regarded her sceptically.

'Go on. Do as your mother says or she'll blame me when you oversleep tomorrow. There'll be plenty of time for more stories another day.'

'But it was just getting to the exciting part, with the bad men and the fighting,' Jon complained.

'You silly! That wasn't until much later,' Vance told his brother firmly.

'Go to bed!' Mallory ordered, not fooled by these diversionary tactics.

Gemma gave the boys a wry grin as they reluctantly headed for the stairs, recognizing their mother's ultimatum.

'I'd like to meet the meyrkats one day,' Jon remarked to Vance as they left the room.

'Me too.'

The three adults exchanged glances.

'I'm sorry. I got carried away,' Gemma apologized.

'You make a good storyteller,' Kragen replied.

35

'When you get fed up with saving the world, you should make it your profession,' Mallory said, grinning.

'I'd quite like to meet those meyrkats of yours myself one day,' Kragen remarked then. He had been as spellbound as his sons by Gemma's tale.

'I wish you could,' she answered. 'I miss them so much. But they can't come here any more than you can go to the desert.'

'*You* could go back to them,' Mallory put in.

'No. I'm not leaving the valley until . . .' Gemma sighed and looked down at her hands. 'Besides, I don't suppose I could find them now.'

'You underestimate yourself – and them,' her friend replied.

'Maybe.'

Then Gemma was quiet again, lost in her memories. Though she was no longer putting them into words, the images still flowed into her mind. It *was* a remarkable story.

For a moment, her thoughts went back to her own home, the island far to the north. After all this time, it now seemed utterly remote. *They wouldn't believe a tenth of what has happened to me*, she mused. *But then, a few months ago, I wouldn't have believed it either.*

She laughed softly, shaking her head.

'What's so funny?' Mallory asked.

'The idea of me saving the world!'

'Well, you haven't done too badly so far.'

'You know perfectly well that I've needed help at every step,' Gemma countered. 'I wouldn't even be alive now if it weren't for Arden. Then there was Jordan and his men in Newport, all of you in the valley, the mountain villagers, the meyrkats . . . On my own, I'm quite useless.' She paused. 'No. Worse than useless. I'm a liability!'

'Rubbish!' Mallory exclaimed. 'Tell that to those children you healed in Keld. If it hadn't been for you, they'd be dead by now.'

Gemma did not rise to the bait, but lapsed into silence and closed her eyes.

Mallory and Kragen began to clear away the debris of the meal, leaving their guest to her own thoughts. She was back in the desert again, with the meyrkats as they started their journey. Ever hopeful, she was recalling every detail, trying to ensure that she did not miss any clue to her future.

The only problem was that the most obvious clues filled her with dread.

* * *

The morning after the Wanderers' farewell song saw a flurry of activity. The meyrkats were in a state of high excitement, running hither and yon on stiff legs, their tails raised like battle standards. Gemma worried that they may not have any energy left for travelling, but then remembered that they would only have to keep up with her pace, and that was hardly likely to be too fast. She improvised a sack from the cloth of her tent, loading it with the tent poles and with as much food as possible. There was no way that she could take the fire – though she did include the glass and some blackened embers in the hope that their 'memory' would be useful again. Water was another problem, but she had no means of carrying it so she made sure that she drank her fill before pronouncing herself ready to go.

At her words, the meyrkats bounded towards her. Two groups emerged from the mêlée, and Gemma found herself looking at the Wanderers, those who would accompany her. She was delighted to recognize several familiar figures, then thought that she had mistaken the group, because foremost among them was Ox, the clan-leader. He sensed her surprise, and reassured her immediately.

Od is now the leader of the stone-clan. I will wander.

Gemma nodded her acknowledgement, not knowing what to say. With Ox was another male elder, Ed, and two of the older females, Ul and Av. The only other animal she recognized by name was Em, a young male. There were another seven adults and four young ones – though no babies – and Gemma was glad that the group was a diverse one, containing most elements of their society. The Wanderers would be a genuine clan.

The meyrkats were quiet now, and Gemma tried to find the appropriate words for the occasion, a speech to thank them for their help and trust. Then the entire clan suddenly burst into song. She had mistaken the reason for their silence; they were not waiting for her to speak, but had been merely drawing breath.

Two songs rose up, competing and clashing, as one clan became two. It would have been excruciating to most human ears, but to Gemma it was a beautiful sound; part farewell, part battle-cry, and part joyful exuberance. No words of hers could have portrayed that morning's mixture of emotions more accurately.

How can these little creatures affect me so? she wondered, then remembered the emotional link between wizards and their familiars. This led to another train of thought. Cai, her friend and mentor for so many years, had been a wizard, though he disowned the title now and claimed that magic was dead. Gemma knew this to be untrue, but perhaps it had changed even more than she had realized. *Could I be a wizard?*

Not long ago, she would have dismissed the thought as absurd, but now she was not so sure. While she did not have the control of the wizards of old, she *did* have latent magical ability. *I wish Cai were here now. Perhaps he could explain it to me.*

On more than one occasion since landing on the southern continent she had felt Cai's presence and had been able to converse with him – in spite of the great distance between them. While troubled, he had been able to help her, but had eventually abandoned her.

Gemma could feel no sense of contact now, but hoped that one day the link might be restored. Of all those she had left behind on that far northern isle, she missed him the most.

Her thoughts were rudely interrupted then as the meyrkats surged about her feet, their songs breaking up into a bewildering medley of calls and mental communication. The journey was beginning.

Goodbye! she called to those remaining, and was besieged by their answering farewells and good wishes. With a lump in her throat, Gemma gave a final wave, then turned and followed the Wanderers into the trackless desert.

They made good progress on that first day. A few rain showers fell, refreshing their spirits, but the temperature remained pleasant and the whole party was in a happy mood. After a midday halt, which the older meyrkats used to hunt, leaving the younger ones to rest with Gemma, they continued on their course to the south-east. They stopped shortly before dusk at a place where natural overhangs in the rock gullies provided the meyrkats with a temporary burrow, and Gemma erected her tent nearby, pleased with their day's travel. She had no way of gauging how far they had come, but her legs had survived the exercise without too many aches, and she had enough food for several days.

That night she dreamt of Arden for the first time. He was encased in stone, unable to move, in pain and alone in alien darkness. Even after she had been terrified into wakefulness, the awful images filled her mind, and the rest she needed so badly eluded her now.

Her own journey was to become a nightmare on the following day.

CHAPTER FIVE

Dawn gave no indication of what was to come; Gemma was thankful for the clear sky, and for the light breeze that blew away the darkness of her dreams. Her legs were stiff, but that wore off after the first hour of walking. Then the atmosphere of the day changed. A stillness settled over the desert, the air grew warm and humid, and, far to the west, ominous banks of cloud began to pile up.

Gemma felt an unseen menace, and found herself frequently glancing over her shoulder.

Will there be a storm? she asked the meyrkats.

The earth-dark is coming, Ul replied for the clan.

Not good for wandering, Ox added.

When will it come? Gemma queried, but the meyrkats had no conception of her measurement of time, so their replies were of little use.

Well, we'd better get as far as we can before it arrives, she told them, and their journey was resumed.

They had travelled only another half-league when Gemma felt a stir among the clan; Av, as always the sharpest look-out, had spotted the approaching storm.

Gem-ma, the earth-dark! she called, looking back to the west. Hot air swirled in gusts about them, ruffling the meyrkats' fur and Gemma's hair. She stared into the distance and saw what Av was referring to. This would be no ordinary storm. A brown mass, still far away but approaching fast, hung like a pall of smoke over the desert. As Gemma watched, it grew, sending spirals higher into the sky and obliterating everything in its path. What the meyrkats called the earth-dark, she knew as a sand-storm, and the realization filled her with dread. She knew just how violent the flying sand could be – her flight had ended abruptly amid such turmoil only a few days ago. It would be impossible to stand up, let alone travel, in the midst of such fury.

We must find somewhere to shelter, Gemma decided, but the meyrkats had already come to that conclusion, and had spread out, scouting the area. Gemma saw what looked like a gulley about a hundred paces ahead, and at the same time heard Ed give a high-pitched wail from that direction. The others all bounded towards him.

Gem-ma, a burrow! Ed's voice sounded urgently in her head and, with one last glance at the terrifyingly rapid approach of the storm, she ran.

The gulley was deep enough to provide Gemma with shelter if she crouched down. Better still, towards one end it grew progressively more steep-sided, ending in a miniature cave, and the clan were running towards this. Gemma followed, grateful for this piece of luck. She would be far too big to get inside the opening, but would be well sheltered, and with her body covering the entrance, the meyrkats would be completely protected.

After the animals were all inside, Gemma stored her precious provisions in the cave mouth and sat down, her knees under her chin, making herself as small as possible.

Are you all right in there? she called.

Of course, Ox replied. *This burrow is very deep.*

Then the first grains of sand whipped overhead; within moments the wind became a wild shriek and Gemma bent her head down to hide her face as darkness fell and the air howled. She sensed the meyrkats' concern for her, and reassured them. However, all communication stopped as the insanely loud noise of the storm made even thought impossible. Sand and grit covered Gemma's clothes and hair, and the gulley began to silt up, blocking the entrance to the cave. Gemma was not concerned, knowing that the meyrkats would be able to dig themselves out in a few moments. Then a new sound entered her consciousness, a rumbling beneath the roar of the wind and sand. Dimly, she recognized it as thunder, but could not look up to see the lightning. No rain fell.

Gemma seemed to have been huddled by the little cave for ever, but the storm showed no signs of abating. In the oppressive gloom the noise was a dominating presence, and it seemed to her that the world would never be quiet again.

A new sense of unease gradually penetrated Gemma's dulled mind, emanating from the clan, and though she did not understand their rapid communications, their sudden fear was obvious. It grew in strength until it reached panic level. Gemma cautiously opened her eyes, protecting them with cupped hands, in time to see claws scrabble through the sand that filled the cave's opening. She shifted out of the way as Ed emerged. He stepped aside to allow others to come out, but continued digging, widening the hole with frantic movements.

What's happening? Gemma asked fearfully.

Clear-rush, came the hurried reply. *Clear-rush comes.*

Gemma was bewildered. More meyrkats left the cave and climbed out of the gulley, disappearing from sight almost instantly.

Where are you going? Gemma called after them desperately, but received no clear answer.

Then she understood. Gemma heard it an instant before it arrived, but could not believe her ears. Water burst from the cave in an explosive surge that carried all before it. Meyrkats, sand, and her supplies were swept down the gulley, and Gemma herself was tossed helplessly in the churning foam.

Choking and spluttering, she forced herself to a stop

and pushed out of the stream, sliding up the side of the gulley on her back. Out of the water, she was exposed to the full force of the wind and flying sand; within moments, the back of her neck was stinging with pain, and she curled up in a miserable ball of shock and horror.

She could see none of the meyrkats, and such was her mental agony that she could not even call out to them with her mind. She gradually realized what had happened. The thunder she had heard *had* been from a storm, but the torrential rain had fallen far to the west, flowing into the underground cave systems which lay beneath the desert. The pressure of its flow had forced the water up into the passage that ended in the cave where the meyrkats had been sheltering. The water had become a geyser, and the sanctuary had turned into a trap. The ironic fact that water should present such a threat *in a desert* only added to the horror of the situation.

After what seemed like a lifetime, Gemma became aware of a slight lessening in the pressure of the wind on her back. The noise level was falling too, but the day remained as dark as ever. She called out to the meyrkats. *Ox? Av? Ul? Anybody!* There was no response, and her feeling of dread intensified. *Surely they couldn't all have drowned!*

Then, suddenly, the air cleared and the wind dropped even more. Gemma was able to lift her head, and watched as the sandstorm retreated, the new-born silence ringing in her ears. Black clouds hovered overhead, blocking out the sun, but no rain fell. The level of the water in the gulley had dropped unnoticed, and with every moment its flow grew less strong. Gemma took all this in slowly but was initially too stunned to react. Then a piping call sounded in the distance, and brought her to her senses.

Where were the meyrkats?

Painfully easing her cramped muscles into action, she

got up and set off along the side of the gulley. Before long, she heard more noise and headed towards its source. The clan was huddled together in a small hollow on the eastern side of the ditch, but as the water was now no more than a trickle, Gemma was able to cross over to them without difficulty.

The meyrkats did not move as she approached, but remained a tight group, their bedraggled fur pressing upon their neighbours. Gemma tried to count them but found the task beyond her. As she knelt down beside the group, several of the small creatures turned to her.

Are you all right? she asked.

Il and Ot are losing warmth, Av replied.

The clan stands together to share our heat, Ox added.

Can you help them? Ul asked hopefully.

Me? Gemma was taken aback, then began to wonder. She had been able to use healing skills to save the lives of two human children. Would meyrkats be so different?

Let me see them, she instructed and the meyrkats separated, letting her through. In their midst were two of the young ones, their fur plastered with water and sand. The support around them moved away, and they were placed gently on the ground. Gemma laid a finger on each tiny forehead, foreboding in her heart. She did not need her special awareness to know that they were already dead.

I can't help them, she said miserably, looking down at the pitiful bundles of matted fur. *They have no warmth at all.*

This announcement was greeted with despairing silence, and for the first time Gemma felt like an intruder. She stood up and walked away, leaving the meyrkats to their grief, and taking her own sorrow with her.

She found the remains of her tent further down the gulley. It had been ripped to shreds by thorn bush needles. She recovered a few pieces of smoked snake-meat, and tried to clean them as best she could. If the sun came out and she could dry them, they might be edible. The rest of her food, the charred sticks and the sliver of green glass had gone. Gemma's thoughts turned to her own prospects of survival; she had no shelter, no fire, very little food – and was still several days' journey from the edge of the desert.

Perhaps this place will kill me after all.

As that unhappy thought passed through her mind, she heard the meyrkats' voices raised in a song of mourning.

CHAPTER SIX

The sun broke through the clouds just as the meyrkats'
song came to an end, but did little to raise Gemma's
spirits – the storm had already done its damage.
She laid the salvaged strips of meat out to dry on
the branches of a thorn bush, and wondered what
to do next. The setback had been so sudden and
devastating that she felt near to tears; rational thought
was impossible.

Ox came bounding over towards her.

Ed asks for you, Gem-ma, he said. *The clear-rush has
bitten him.*

Translating this as 'the water has made him ill',
Gemma hurried back to the clan, its leader at her side.
She felt the tribe's conflicting moods – concern, relief
and acceptance, but was surprised that they seemed
to feel no sorrow, no grief. The bodies of the two
youngsters were nowhere to be seen.

Their song is over, Ox stated, sensing her unspoken
question. *The clan renews itself.*

While Gemma could not share this pragmatic attitude
to death, she understood and admired it in the meyrkats.
The dead were gone, and it was the living who
mattered; in the harsh desert it could be no other way.
Ed lay in the middle of the group, his eyes shut and
his breathing laboured. Flecks of foam covered his
mouth and nostrils. As Gemma watched him, Ed's voice
sounded in her head. She had always thought of him
as one of the most self-assured of the meyrkats, and full
of confidence – but now he sounded weak and unsure.

Is the earth-dark over? I can hear it coming. Is Gem-ma there?

I'm here, she replied. *You'll be all right soon.*

The animal's body relaxed a little at her words, but his breath still rattled in his throat. Feeling awkward and afraid, Gemma knelt down and placed a gentle hand on his chest. Closing her eyes, she willed her consciousness to expand to explore the small body. At first, she experienced nothing but pain and exhaustion, then her inner senses cleared and tendrils of awareness followed the lines of blood, bone and sinew within her alien patient. These lines were not as clear as those of the human children had been, but she was grateful for the knowledge offered to her. Ed's problem was obvious. His swollen stomach was filled with water, and sand blocked its exit. His lungs were also two-thirds full of water, and his heart was faltering under impossible stress. Life was ebbing from him.

Do something! Gemma ordered herself. *Now!* No action would be too drastic – there was nothing to lose.

So she applied pressure, tightened slack muscles, concentrating her effort then releasing it, while at the same time pushing down with her hand on his chest.

After a few moments, Ed made a funny gurgling noise, and water spurted forth in all directions – from his mouth and nostrils, and from between his legs. Gemma was showered with droplets, but was only concerned for Ed. She worried that in clearing the water she may have hurt him in other ways. She watched in agonized suspense as his breathing stopped. Then he took a deep, shuddering gulp of air and she felt a surge of elation. His eyes flickered open.

I am hungry, he said, then promptly fell asleep.

Gemma laughed aloud, much to the puzzlement of the spectators. She checked his breathing, which was now regular and strong, then stood up, her mood considerably brightened. The meyrkats watched her nervously.

You are not harmed? Ul asked hesitantly.

There was an odd inflection to her question, almost as though she believed Gemma might be offended.

Of course not. Though I must admit my patients don't usually piss on me. Gemma smiled.

There was an embarrassed mental silence.

Oh, she thought to herself, *so that's what they're worried about.*

The meyrkats were extremely fastidious about their toilet; in their terms, Ed had insulted her.

I am not harmed, she told them firmly. *I am delighted that Ed is well again. And all things are acceptable to achieve healing,* she added, trying hard not to laugh. The meyrkats appeared relieved by her words.

The clan grows stronger, Ox said. It was his way of thanking her.

There was no thought of any further travelling that day. As well as Ed, several of the other meyrkats had suffered hurts, though minor, and they were all very tired. Gemma felt as though every muscle in her body had been bruised. The fittest of the animals went hunting, and two helped in Gemma's search for and salvage of her supplies. They found some wood, but it had been drenched by the water; Gemma resigned herself to the lack of a fire.

It was from these helpers that she learnt how Ed had repeatedly pushed other meyrkats out of the water-filled gully, only to succumb to exhaustion. She felt doubly glad to have saved his life, and checked on his progress carefully when she returned to the clan.

The hunters were successful, and they all ate well that night. Gemma consumed one of her rescued strips – it was gritty but wholesome. She slept that night in the open, with the meyrkats all round her, and each took comfort from the other's presence.

The next day dawned clear, much to Gemma's relief – her tattered clothes were still damp and the night had been cold. She was glad of the prospect of resuming her journey, if only to work some warmth into her chilled limbs.

The night's rest had obviously rejuvenated the meyrkats and Gemma watched in amusement as they bounded along, occasionally darting off to explore something new. Their curiosity knew no bounds. Ed sought out Gemma as she trudged determinedly onwards, but then seemed reluctant to speak, so Gemma opened the conversation.

You were very brave yesterday, to rescue your clanmates from the clear-rush like that, she began.

They have told me . . . Ed interrupted, then his words came in a rush. *You are not harmed by my . . . act? I did not mean—*

Stop! Gemma commanded. *You mustn't be embarrassed. It happened because of what I did. And I'm glad, because it saved your life. Actually, now that you are well again, it seems very funny to me.*

After a pause, he asked, *Like happy-lie-all-know?*

Yes, she replied, smiling at his bewilderment. *The story of it is like a joke.*

This seemed to please Ed inordinately and he sped happily away towards his fellow creatures.

I wonder what their next 'joke' will be? Gemma wondered, laughing to herself.

* * *

For Gemma and the Wanderers, the next two days passed in a haze of fatigue and hunger. The last of her meat had gone bad, and in spite of all their efforts, the meyrkats had provided nothing that Gemma could bring herself to eat.

The steady, laborious march to the south-east seemed as if it would never end, and there were times when her progress seemed illusory, and the landscape unchanging. However, an hour before dusk, on the second day after the earth-dark, Gemma spotted mountain peaks in the far distance, and went to sleep that night with renewed hope in her heart.

As before, she slept curled within a hollow that the meyrkats had dug out for her, well away from any gulleys, and with the animals ranged all about her. They enjoyed the physical contact with her, despite the disturbances when she shifted in her sleep.

In the darkest hours of that night, Gemma dreamed of Arden again. It was a nightmare tinged with madness, and an overwhelming feeling of solitude. He was crawling, agonizingly slowly, down a dark, damp tunnel whose walls shone with a faint, unhealthy green luminescence. He crawled on and on, but nothing around him changed. The tunnel was endless, black and cold.

When Gemma woke up, she was shivering and depressed, and though she tried to rationalize the dream to herself, believing that she was superimposing her experiences on to Arden, this made her feel no better. She finally managed to get back to sleep, and was relieved when morning came with no repetition of the dreadful vision.

*   *   *

A day later, Gemma was moving by the force of her will alone. However, there were signs that meant they were approaching less arid realms. With the end of the rains, the desert flowers had faded as fast as they had bloomed, and the greenery was already turning brown, but here the plant-life was hardier – spiky grass, lush now after the rains, but also with the resilience of permanent growth.

Mountains were clearly visible to the east and south as Gemma and the meyrkats approached the foothills. The animals were now fully recovered from their ordeal and spent most of the time searching for food and water for Gemma. They were obviously concerned about her weakened state, but were at a loss as to how they could help her. At night they huddled close, sharing the warmth of their fur, but she still slept badly, feverish and afraid of dreaming. By day they took it in turns to walk beside her, lending encouragement and warning her of pitfalls. After a while, Gemma took their concern for granted, too exhausted even to express her gratitude.

That night they slept in a natural hollow on a bed of fibrous grass. The unaccustomed comfort helped Gemma slide into an exhausted sleep almost immediately. Some of the meyrkats joined her, but others remained alert, on guard. The moon rose, adding its serene and silvery glow to the glimmer of the stars.

For a while, all was quiet, but then one of the lookouts, on the edge of the group, heard a rustling and gave a quick bark of warning. Within moments, most of the clan was awake, looking about them with rapid glances from side to side. Gemma slept on, undisturbed.

Then the noise sounded even closer, and a group of wild dogs appeared over the rim of the hollow. Cruel eyes glinted above bared fangs, and large round ears twitched in search of prey. The meyrkats kept still and silent, but knew they had little hope of remaining unnoticed. Their thoughts were full of fear and loathing; this was an enemy they had not faced before.

Then the dogs moved forward, and the clan quickly took up defensive positions, their collective fighting spirit overriding individual terrors. At the same time, several appealed to Gemma to wake up, but her mind was too deeply asleep. Av quickly instructed the two remaining youngsters, who were kept firmly at the rear of the group, to wake her physically. They leapt to their task, scrabbling with their paws at her hands and arms, and shrilling in panic. Gemma grumbled and tried to push them away, but they persisted.

As she awoke, her mind was assaulted by a wave of such feral malevolence that she drew back instinctively,

51

hiding from the violence that it implied. At the same time, the meyrkats began to bark and wail their defiance at the enemy, and some even leapt into the air in a kind of insane, stiff-legged war-dance. Gemma looked beyond them, and saw the object of their fury and the source of her dread. The invading animals reminded her of hunting-dogs, but the only master these vicious creatures admitted to was their own leader. Their fur was mottled and blotchy, making them look diseased. They did not bark or yelp, but moved forward steadily and silently, fangs showing grey in the moonlight. They moved as a pack, and Gemma shuddered at the relentless ferocity of their thoughts. Although their meaning was too brutal and strange for her to make much sense of, it demonstrated once again her ability to 'hear' animals who lived in groups – though she could feel no affinity with these savages.

The leader of the pack was now only a few paces away, and his eyes swept the clan as though selecting his first victim. As Gemma rose unsteadily to her feet, she sensed the dogs' mounting hesitation. She had meant to add her own voice to that of the meyrkats, but her parched tongue was incapable of making any sound. Instead, she felt the fury boil within her.

Leave us alone! She put all the authority and anger she could muster into the unspoken command, hoping that it would have some effect. *Get away from here!*

A fresh surge of hatred washed back at Gemma, and the pack switched their attention to her, as if weighing up this new and unexpected opponent. There was hunger and a vindictive cruelty in their gaze which left her shivering. The dogs came on.

Leave us alone! she screamed silently. *Or I will destroy you!*

The pack's leader tensed to attack them, snarling his defiance. In desperation, Gemma reached inside the brute's mind, caught his thoughts and *twisted*. *Pain*, she gloated. *Pain!*

The wild dog yelped, shaking his head and flailing his paws, as though trying to ward off an invisible foe. The others shifted, snarling in consternation as the meyrkats' wails doubled in volume. Gemma was relentless, caught up in her own battle fury now. Abruptly, the pack broke up in terror and disarray, then ran howling into the night. The meyrkats chased after them for a few paces, then came to their senses and returned to the hollow.

All of a sudden, Gemma felt very ill. She doubled over, then sat down with a bump, her stomach heaving. The meyrkats were very quiet, watching her with awe. There was love, respect and gratitude in their gaze, but a new facet had been added to their regard for Gemma.

Fear.

CHAPTER SEVEN

Gemma was not able to get back to sleep that night; she felt wretched, and could not respond to the meyrkats' obvious concern. An argument raged within her, threatening to unhinge her already harrowed mind.

What I did was wrong. Magic should never be used to cause pain.

But they were evil, and could have killed us all!

They only acted according to their nature, as all creatures do. Magic is a force for healing, and you abused it.

I had no choice; I had no other weapon to use against them.

There is always choice. Beware. You may yet become an embodiment of the evil which made Cai reject his wizardry.

But I could not take the risk of their killing or mutilating my friends. What of their suffering? They have endured enough for my sake.

It was wrong. Magic should never . . .

And thus the bitter inner argument ran on.

* * *

Daylight brought Gemma some measure of solace. The clan had suffered no further harm and, from her previous desert crossings, Gemma guessed that they were within two days' journey of a village where she could hope to find a welcome. She roused the meyrkats and set out eastwards, keen to get there before her meagre reserves of strength ran out.

They had gone no more than a league when they came upon a road – little more than a track really – which ran parallel to the south-east rim of the desert. As Gemma paused, trying to remember whether she should continue into the hills or turn and follow the trail one way or another, she became aware that the meyrkats were feeling apprehensive. They had never before seen a road – of any kind – and this straight track was a source of fascination and awe to them.

Gemma was about to try and explain it, when her attention was drawn to a party of men on horseback, approaching from the south-west. Her first reaction was relief, but then something about the distant newcomers made her uneasy and she watched them closely, knowing that she had already been seen; she had no hope of outrunning a mounted man in this gently rolling terrain.

Grey-skins, Av commented.

Suddenly, Gemma's fear took form. These men were Grey Raiders, fanatics who blamed all the world's ills on the people who had been drawn to this continent from the northern isles. Gemma had narrowly escaped being killed by them when she had first landed in Cleve. Their hatred was unreasoning, and she knew that her red hair, so rare in the south, marked her as an obvious target.

Three of the grey-robed men broke away from the main group and galloped towards her. Gemma came to a quick decision – whatever her fate, the clan need not share it.

Scatter! Quickly, she told the meyrkats. *Hide yourselves. I'm not sure of our welcome here.*

The creatures disappeared; they too had been watching the horsemen's approach with some trepidation and were only too glad to escape the scene. Gemma sensed them nearby, hidden from sight but watching and listening uneasily.

The horses were drawn to a halt a few paces away, and as the three men eyed her curiously, Gemma stood her ground and faced them as boldly as she could. One of the men, evidently their leader, was thin and sharp-featured, with dark hair and shrewd grey eyes whose colour matched the coarse material of his clothes.

'You're a long way from home,' he remarked, his voice soft but slightly menacing.

'I am indeed,' Gemma agreed as heartily as she was able. 'And I'm very glad to see you. That bastard showman dumped me in the desert with no food or water! I'm lucky—'

The thin man held up his hand.

'Not so fast,' he ordered. His voice cracked like a whip, but there was a sparkle of amusement in his eyes. 'Where exactly are you from?'

'Originally?'

He nodded.

'Keld – in the mountains,' she replied, naming the village from whence she'd flown. One of the other men snorted derisively at her answer, but the leader silenced him with a gesture.

'And you were abandoned by a showman?'

'I'll tell you all about it,' Gemma replied, thinking hard, 'but can I have some water first? I'm parched.'

'Wray,' the leader said to one of his companions, snapping his fingers.

'But Aric, she's—' the other protested, but was silenced by a glance. Wray unfastened a water-bottle from his saddle-bags and flung it towards Gemma, his expression making it clear that he resented helping her.

Gemma picked the bottle up from the dust, unstoppered it and drank deeply, then returned it politely to the sullen Wray. She was watched silently by the horsemen, who showed no sign of dismounting. The rest of their party were now drawing close.

'Thank you, sirs,' Gemma said. The water had indeed been welcome, and it had restored her confidence a little.

'What is your name?' Aric asked, his tone almost gentle but fooling nobody.

'Princess Gemma!' she announced theatrically. 'That's my stage name, of course – no one's going to pay to see someone called Benetricia, are they.' She smiled, but drew no response.

'And what exactly is your stage act?'

'Performing animals,' she replied. 'At the moment it's meyrkats.'

'Meyrkats!' the third man exclaimed in disbelief.

'Yes,' Gemma retorted. 'I can tame anything.'

'Were they the creatures we saw running away?' Aric asked, and she nodded.

'They're a bit frightened of horses,' she said. 'Would you like to see them?'

'If we may.'

'Ed, Av, Em. Come to me!' she called, at the same time sending mental reassurances to the three, and instructions to the others to stay hidden. After a few moments, the trio emerged from their hiding place and bounded towards their mistress. Gemma noted the gasps of amazement from Aric's two companions with a degree of satisfaction. The leader remained outwardly unmoved.

'Remarkable,' he said. 'Why should such an unusual act have been abandoned so callously?'

'That scumbag tried to cheat me of my share of the takings. The audiences only came to see me anyway,' Gemma replied righteously. 'Then he tried to steal my animals, didn't he, my beauties. But they got away from him. I'd like to have seen his face when he found the empty cage.' She laughed hoarsely.

'It's lucky we found you,' Aric said. 'You're a long walk from the nearest village.'

'Oh, we'll survive,' she replied lightly, hoping that her weakened state was not too obvious.

'I still think you'd better come with us.'

'But Aric – her hair!'

57

'Shut up, Wray!' he snapped.

'What, this?' Gemma said, flicking her dusty locks nonchalantly. 'This is dyed, to fit my billing – the Royal Witch of the North. It actually looks quite effective in the lights.'

'Perhaps you can entertain us as we go,' Aric suggested, much to the disapproval of his companions.

'I'd be glad to,' Gemma replied, 'so long as you'll feed me and the troupe.'

'That's settled then,' he said with a tight smile.

'You can drop me at the next village. I'll be fine then,' she added, more in hope than expectation.

'We'll see,' was the ominous reply.

*   *   *

An hour later, Gemma was astride one of the twelve pack animals, jogging steadily along the trail to the north-east. She was accompanied by seven men on horseback, all of whom were armed. The three meyrkats bounded along on the edge of the road, trying to keep as close to Gemma as possible. They were obviously nervous in the company of so many large animals and men, but she was able to converse with them and keep their spirits up. The rest of the clan followed at a discreet distance, using their talent for blending in with the landscape, and remaining unnoticed.

Gemma was not sure whether Aric had been convinced by her story, but knew that his deputies, Wray and Yarat, were suspicious. The meyrkats themselves were the best disguise she had, and she made sure that they knew just how important they were.

Will you play some games with me this evening? she asked. *These men will like that.*

The tall-grey-skins are not clan-friends, Ed commented.

No. But for now we need their help, she replied. The food in her stomach was an unwelcome reminder of that very fact. *We'll leave them as soon as we can.* To herself she added, *If we can.*

We will play, Av said firmly.

As we played before, with you and Ard-en, Em chimed in.

That was obviously a happy memory for the meyrkats, but for Gemma it was a spark which inflamed her longing to see Arden once more. *Nothing* must be allowed to stand in the way of her return to the valley. Surely she would find him there. The meyrkats were silent, sensing her distraction, and she wondered about her immediate problem. Was she the guest or prisoner of the Grey Raiders? She knew that most citizens of Cleve regarded the grey-robed warriors as mad zealots, and she herself had first-hand evidence that they could be cold-blooded killers. On this occasion, however, she had been treated well, in spite of their obvious suspicion. She glanced ahead at Aric, who rode at the front of the party, and wondered what thoughts were hidden behind those cool, grey eyes.

Yarat brought his horse alongside Gemma's mule, and looked down at her. He was a big man, with a fleshy face and small dark eyes.

'You've pale skin for a traveller,' he remarked.

'I have the complexion of the mountains still, for all that I've journeyed far these last few years,' she replied.

'You haven't asked where we're going. Doesn't your destination interest you?' Yarat's stare was beginning to unnerve Gemma, but she replied steadily enough.

'What's the difference? Any place is better than the desert. And we can make a living anywhere.'

'Aren't you afraid you might run into your showman?' he asked.

'I hope we do!' Gemma exclaimed. 'I—'

'What was his name?' Yarat interrupted.

Gemma faltered, then covered her hesitation by spitting, as if in disgust.

'Barris,' she replied, picking a name from her past.

59

'Never heard of him,' Yarat responded.

'I'm not surprised. I was the only decent act he had.'

'Why were you in the desert? Not much of an audience there.'

'One of his short-cuts,' she said derisively. 'Barris would do anything to save a few marks.' Yarat's questions were fast becoming uncomfortable.

'A short-cut? From where?'

'We were playing our way round the villages in the foothills, then heading back to the coast for the new season.'

'Newport?'

Gemma shrugged, as casually as she was able.

'One town's much like another to show-folk,' she said wearily. 'As long as there's people there with money to be parted from.'

Yarat gave her an appraising look.

'Nice earrings,' he said. His tone was offhand, but Gemma could hear the avarice in his voice, and automatically raised a hand to touch one of the golden earrings, which were shaped like geese in flight.

'They were a gift from a gentleman who took a fancy to me,' she said, with a smile. It was true. They had been from Arden.

*   *   *

Gemma was glad when Aric called for the midday break, and she could dismount and stretch her legs. Her battered body now had another set of aches to cope with. After walking for a little while, she sat down with the meyrkats, apart from the others. Only Wray paid her any attention; he glanced nervously in her direction from time to time, as though expecting her to sprout wings and fly away. *I wish I could*, Gemma thought ruefully. She had given up the idea of trying to escape in open country and in daylight. She was still not sure whether she *needed* to escape.

Are the others all right? she asked her companions.

They are near, but hungry, Ed replied. *There is no stinger-food here.*

But there must be other things for them to eat, Gemma said. While she sympathized with the clan's plight, she was privately rather glad that they were not in scorpion country. *They must hunt now, while we have stopped.*

We are, Ox's distant voice replied, *but there is too much green here.*

I'll try to get you some raw meat, Gemma promised. There was little chance that the Grey Raiders would be carrying any fresh meat, but she might be able to get some when they reached a village or a farm.

One of the men was walking towards her now, carrying two bowls of food, and the three meyrkats edged away as he approached. He held out one of the bowls, and Gemma accepted gratefully.

'Do you have any raw meat?' she asked.

'No.'

'Better go hunt for yourselves then,' Gemma told the meyrkats, adding silently that she would call for them if they were needed. The three ran off gratefully, and the young man watched them go.

'Incredible,' he breathed.

'Thank you,' she replied. 'The main trick is getting them to come back.' He looked at her blankly for a moment, then smiled in response to her confident grin. He seemed about twenty years old, and appeared more open than the other soldiers Gemma had met; she realized that this might be a ruse to lull her into a false sense of security, and remained on her guard.

'May I join you?'

She nodded, and motioned to the ground beside her.

'I'm Dacey,' he said, once he was seated. 'Your name is . . .'

'Call me Gemma,' she answered. 'Most people do.'

He nodded, appearing almost shy.

If he's acting, Gemma thought, *he's very good.*

61

'How long have you been working with animals?' he asked.

'All my life – only now I get paid for it.' She laughed. 'Or I would do if showmen weren't such crooks.'

'I've never seen meyrkats before,' Dacey went on.

'We'll give you a show tonight,' Gemma promised, then decided to ask a few questions of her own. At least that way she wouldn't have to watch her words so carefully all the time. 'Why are you carrying all those swords? I didn't know there were bandits in this part of the country.'

'Oh, they're just for protection,' he said carelessly. 'We're traders, not soldiers really.' There was an odd inflection in his words that Gemma could not interpret. 'We don't see much action.' He glanced at Gemma's hair. 'You've put yourself in danger by dyeing your hair that colour,' he added. 'Some of the men think you're from the far north.'

'It's just part of my act,' she explained. 'Anyway, why is it so dangerous?'

'Because if you *were* from the north,' he replied, his tone matter-of-fact, 'we'd have to kill you.'

CHAPTER EIGHT

Gemma did her best to appear shocked.

'Perhaps I'd better change my billing!' she exclaimed.

'That would be wise,' Dacey replied seriously.

'Why—' she began, but at that moment her companion was called away. Gemma ate her meal and watched as Aric talked to the young man. Dacey did not return to her side.

The fact that even the youngest and most innocent-seeming of the Grey Raiders had talked of murder in such offhand terms, left Gemma all the more determined to escape when the opportunity presented itself. It was obvious that her story would not hold up for too long – sooner or later she was bound to make a slip. She decided to use what time she had with them to learn more of the mysterious raiders; Dacey seemed her best bet for this.

She looked for him as the party moved off, but he was stationed at the rear, and they had the length of the mule-train between them. None of the other men seemed inclined to talk to her, and so she resigned herself to waiting. Wray rode behind her for most of the afternoon and she could feel his intense gaze burning into the back of her head. Eventually she could stand the silence no longer, and twisted round to face him.

'What are you trading in?' she asked, indicating the bales strapped to the other mules.

'That's none of your business!' he snapped, and muttered something under his breath. Their eyes met, but Wray quickly looked away, making a strange sign with his free hand. Gemma realized that it was a gesture meant to ward off evil. *This man is dangerous,* she thought, *but he's having to control himself on Aric's orders.* A tiny devil within her decided to try and needle him into an indiscretion.

'Sorry, I'm sure,' she said caustically. 'It's easy to see . . .' She turned away, murmuring the end of her sentence deliberately so that he could not hear.

'What did you say?' he demanded.

Gemma did not reply, and remained facing away from him. Wray repeated his question, anger and even a little fear in his voice.

'I can't keep on twisting round,' she answered.

After a few moments, he brought his mount alongside hers.

'Answer me!' he ordered.

'I was just trying to pass the time of day,' she said. 'Why are you so touchy?'

'You don't fool me, witch!' he exclaimed. 'I know, even if the others are blind.' The fanatical look in his eyes turned Gemma's blood to ice, but she tried not to show it, firmly remaining in her chosen character.

'You're mad,' she told him. 'That stuff is only for the audiences. I'm no more a witch than you are.'

'Liar!' he shot back. 'Your kind comes to our land because you hear the music, the call from the South.' His voice was thick with hate and derision. 'We know all about it. Some of your friends were only too happy to tell us, before they died.' He smiled nastily, and for a while Gemma could not trust herself to speak. She deliberately tried to keep her face calm, knowing that this was precisely why she *had* journeyed to the southern lands.

'Do you hear it now?' he went on, suppressed fury working its way out. 'Your master's song from beyond the mountains?'

'You're out of your mind,' she responded, trying to

look and sound indifferent. 'I'm a show-performer, nothing more.'

Wray ignored her. 'We're heading the wrong way, aren't we?' he raged on. 'North. Away from the evil nest you want to share with the skyravens and all the other heralds of destruction.'

Skyravens? Gemma wondered. *What have they got to do with it?*

These were huge metallic birds which screamed overhead occasionally in this strange land, and were reputed to be able to kill you by just looking at you. Gemma herself had seen them destroy whole buildings in Great Newport. *Am I supposed to owe allegiance to the same master as the skyravens?* The idea was absurd, yet it chilled her. Her call did indeed come from the far south – as did the mysterious birds. Something of her confusion must have shown in her expression, because Wray began to gloat.

'Admit it!' he demanded. 'Tell me. Then we can put an end to this ridiculous charade.'

'You're the only thing that's ridiculous round here,' she said disgustedly, shuddering inside at the 'end' Wray was undoubtedly envisaging. 'Get away from me.'

Wray laughed, but then had to concentrate on controlling his horse, which had suddenly become jittery, fretting and prancing sideways. Looking down, he saw the three meyrkats risking life and limb by running in and out of the horse's legs. The commotion they were causing finally panicked his mount, and it reared. All Wray's attention was fixed on trying not to be thrown.

'Demon-spawn!' he shouted, as he was forced farther away.

Gemma's heart was in her mouth as her three small friends continued to run beneath the wildly stamping hooves. The disturbance had been noticed by other riders, and Wray's mount was soon brought under control. The meyrkats came bounding back to Gemma's

side, unharmed and mewing their pleasure. In the
distance, Aric and Wray exchanged angry words.

Tall-grey-one is not a clan-friend, Ed remarked
emphatically.

Thank you, Gemma said, relieved but still not understanding their actions. *How did you know—*

You wanted him to go away, Av replied simply.

The conversation ended as Aric rode up beside her.

'I apologize for Wray's behaviour,' he said, looking
at her appraisingly.

'He's a madman!' Gemma replied.

'There is much madness in this world,' Aric said.
'Some of it is necessary.' His calm statement left
Gemma feeling more unnerved than ever. 'He will
not bother you again,' he went on. Then he glanced at
the meyrkats. 'And please – no more demonstrations
like that.'

He rode forward without another word and Gemma
did not speak to anyone for the rest of the day.

The caravan halted at dusk, and the men erected three
large tents in the shelter of a rocky outcrop. Fires were
lit and food prepared; others tended to the animals and
carried the bales of cargo into a tent. Gemma watched
them curiously, wondering what the bundles contained.
When their preparations were complete, the raiders
settled down to their evening meal. As before, she was
ignored, and she suspected that Aric had told his men
to leave her alone. She could not fathom his motives.
His attitude seemed at odds with that of his men, but
his authority was unquestioned. Aric himself brought
Gemma her portion of food, and she thanked him.

'We have nothing for your animals, I'm afraid,' he
said, 'but we'll come to a village tomorrow.'

Gemma nodded, her mouth full.

'Perhaps you would perform for us tonight. Will there
be enough light from our fires?'

'We'll do our best.'

'Good.' Aric smiled. 'There are few entertainments

for travellers like ourselves.' He walked away, and Gemma thought briefly of trying to escape there and then, but rejected the idea. She was surely being watched, and would not get far.

The three meyrkats, who had disappeared soon after the party made camp, emerged from the deepening darkness.

The clan has had good hunting, Em said, in response to Gemma's enquiry.

We play games now? Ed asked, sounding almost eager.

Soon, Gemma replied, then thought about what they could do. She discussed her ideas with the meyrkats, but knew that they would have to rely on some improvisation.

All too soon, Aric came to fetch her. The men were sitting in a rough semi-circle, overlooking the two fires, and facing an open area beneath the rock wall. Someone had lit a couple of torches and placed them to either side of the 'stage' for further illumination. Gemma took her place in front of the men and surveyed their expressions, which reflected an odd mixture of anticipation, good humour and suspicion. Only Wray looked completely hostile and, as usual, Aric was unreadable.

'Gentlemen!' she announced confidently. 'Please take into account that our act is usually accompanied by music, enhanced by a stage and props, and illuminated by many lamps. Nevertheless, what you are about to witness is unique. Prepare to be amazed!'

She bowed low, then, straightening up, began to clap in a steady rhythm. From the darkness beyond the torches, the three meyrkats appeared. They bounced on all four stiff legs, their movements perfectly synchronized to Gemma's beat. They stared straight ahead, each tail erect and curled at the tip just so. The effect was so comical that several of the men laughed aloud.

Then the trio stood upright and turned to face the audience.

'Introduce yourselves!' Gemma cried and, in turn, each of the meyrkats sang a meaningless phrase, ending together on a high-pitched wail. There was more laughter as some of the raiders put their hands over their ears.

'I can see that you are no connoisseurs of music,' Gemma said; to the meyrkats she added in a stage whisper, 'Never mind, my beauties, we will be back among civilized audiences soon.' She clapped her hands, and the three went into a tumbling mock-fight, leaping over each other in a hectic whirl. Gemma left them to it, while giving the impression that she was orchestrating their movements. At her signal, they stopped, and were applauded.

'For our next sequence, we require the use of a sword,' Gemma announced, then marched forward between the fires to where Dacey sat. 'May I?' she asked, holding out her hand. The young man looked taken aback, and glanced over at his leader. Aric nodded, and Dacey slowly unsheathed his blade. He handed it to Gemma, looking worried, but she gave him no time for second thoughts. Striding back to the stage, she proceeded with the act. Each of the meyrkats leapt over the outstretched sword again and again, as she slowly raised it higher. Even Em managed some quite prodigious jumps. Emboldened by this success, Gemma went on to the next stage. She placed the tip of the sword on top of a flat rock so that she could hold it steady; Av then leapt up from the ground and landed on the flat of the blade, balancing perfectly and accepting her applause like a seasoned performer. Ed's unsuccessful attempt to emulate her was – whether by accident or design – even more popular. He got one foot on the sword, then did a sort of cartwheel and tumbled to the ground. When Gemma saw him bounce up again unharmed, she joined in the laughter.

She returned the sword to Dacey and felt the tension of the audience lessen immediately. She spotted a wine-skin, lying next to Yarat, and gave silent instructions to the meyrkats. They darted into the group of men, causing a few startled exclamations, and emerged a few moments later, dragging the wine-skin towards Gemma, their long fore-claws curled around its edges.

'Hey!' Yarat complained. 'That's mine!'

'I thank you for your generosity, sir,' Gemma said, bowing. 'The fires make this thirsty work.' She picked up the wine-skin, unstoppered it and drank deeply from the narrow spout, then threw the nearly empty container away.

After another display of acrobatics and dancing, Gemma ran out of inspiration and decided to call it a day. The meyrkats faced the audience once more, and repeated their short song of 'introduction'.

'Take a bow!' Gemma instructed.

The trio leant forward, but their bodies were not built for this stance, and they toppled over. After lying in the sand for a moment, they bounced up and left the stage to much laughter and applause.

'Bravo!' Aric called.

'They can't be real meyrkats.' Yarat's tone was sour, and the others quietened, looking towards their fat colleague. 'You could never get them to do that. These must be false.'

Gemma was furious, and glared at Yarat; at the same time she passed a new idea on to the meyrkats.

Think you can do it? she asked.

Of course, Ed replied, sounding positively eager.

Good. Let me know when you're ready. She turned back to Yarat.

'So you're the expert on animals here, are you? You certainly look as if you've eaten a few. Your horse could testify to that, no doubt.'

'Don't push your luck, woman,' he growled.

'Those are genuine meyrkats – as anyone with half a brain could tell you!' she retorted angrily.

'Then you're a—' Wray began, but his entry into the argument was cut short by Aric.

'Quiet!' he shouted. 'Accept the entertainment graciously, or remain silent.'

We're ready. Ed's voice sounded in Gemma's mind.

'What will it take to convince you?' Gemma asked Yarat. 'Perhaps I should ask them to piss on you from a great height.'

'Please!' Aric sounded pained, his distaste obvious.

'I'd like to see them try,' Yarat muttered angrily.

At this, Gemma clapped her hands and a thin stream of gleaming liquid shot out from the darkness on top of the rocks, splashing over Yarat's face and chest. He jumped to his feet, swearing and spluttering, reaching for his sword. He was restrained by his colleagues, who had great difficulty trying to control their hilarity. It slowly dawned on them and Yarat that the smell of the liquid was not as unpleasant as it should be, and all but the victim dissolved into laughter.

'You really should have been more generous with it,' Gemma said, smiling. 'It wasn't even very good wine.'

Piping sounds came from the darkness above.

CHAPTER NINE

Although she was very tired, Gemma lay awake that night, her mind too active for sleep. The meyrkats had been jubilant with the success of their performance and, for a while, so had she. She still could not fathom out how they had managed to drag the wine-skin up on to the rock without anyone noticing. And their aim had been miraculous!

You were wonderful, she had told them, and had felt the glow of their satisfaction in return. Ed was especially excited, because he had received a further insight into the nature of jokes. He knew now that the point of a joke could often depend on the misunderstanding, or the deliberate misleading, of those who saw or heard it. Remembering his own unfortunate and embarrassing episode when Gemma had healed him, he immediately saw the similarities – and the crucial difference.

It was clear-rush, but they thought . . . His words dried up, and the trio made the peeping noises Gemma now associated with laughter.

Actually, it was wine, she replied, then regretted her words as she had to explain to the meyrkats what wine was. After some confusion, they named it *taste-rush-make-happy*.

Now all of that earlier exhilaration had evaporated. While the show had been convincing, it was obvious that she was still regarded with suspicion and enmity. In effect, she was a prisoner of men who would kill her without compunction should they discover her true identity. She had no doubt that some of them were already prepared to condemn her, but were being held in check by Aric, for reasons of his own. It was not a comfortable thought.

Gemma looked again at the walls around her, and considered her chances of escape. The canvas was thick and strong, and was sewn to the groundsheet. She had nothing with which to cut it, and even if she had, the noise of her actions would surely wake her guard – the soldier who occupied the other half of the tent, beyond a makeshift screen. In addition, although she could not be sure of this, there would be guards posted outside, where one of the fires still burned brightly, its red light flickering over the tent walls. So her only way out would be through the flap at the far end, having to climb over her fellow occupant, and with other soldiers outside. It was hopeless.

Nor did she know how the meyrkats could come to her aid. The three 'performers' were outside, presumably with the rest of the clan. They would all do anything for her, but were no match for men with swords. And her own 'magic', which she was now beginning to accept, seemed just as impractical. What could she do? There was no group mentality here that she could influence as she had the wild dogs. There was no help from Cai, and her healing talents were hardly appropriate. What other resources did she have?

A small voice at the back of her mind reminded her that she was an attractive woman. Could she turn that into an advantage? After all, these men had been on the road for some time, with few 'entertainments'. She instinctively shied away from the idea, but wondered if the revulsion she felt could be put aside if it were the only way to save her life.

Her thoughts were interrupted by a scuffling sound as the tent flap opened and a man came in. Her heart thumped in alarm, but then she heard Dacey's voice and breathed a little easier.

'Time for your watch, Gerard,' he said.

'Already?' a sleepy voice grumbled. There followed the sounds of someone getting up and dressing.

'Any trouble from her?' Dacey asked quietly.

'Not a whisper,' the other answered. He left, and Gemma heard the tent flap being fastened once more. All was quiet for a while, and she got the impression that, like her, Dacey was listening hard. When he eventually broke the silence, she jumped nervously.

'Gemma? Are you awake?' he whispered.

She nodded, then remembered that he could not see her, and replied, 'Yes.'

'You have to get away,' Dacey said urgently and Gemma's heart missed a beat. Was there an ally here after all?

'Why?' she whispered back, controlling her voice with difficulty. The screen moved and his face appeared in the gap; even in the dim red light, Gemma could see that he was frightened.

'That trick with the wine was very funny,' he said, 'but it was a mistake. Sooner or later they're going to work out that you couldn't possibly have *trained* the meyrkats to do that. Yarat and Wray will want your blood – they don't like you much . . .'

'I've noticed.'

'And Aric can't hold them off for ever.'

'Why is he protecting me?' she asked.

'I don't know.'

'Come to that,' Gemma asked, 'why are you telling me all this?'

He paused and, in the silence, they heard footsteps outside. Dacey put a finger to his lips as they waited for the guard to move away, then they resumed their whispered conversation.

'I can't explain,' he said. 'It's better that you don't know.' This had an ominous ring, but Gemma was already out of her depth. There was danger at every turn, and she had no choice but to trust the young man.

After all, he could have betrayed her already if that had been his intention, and he was clearly taking a risk in talking to her like this.

'I'll try to help you,' he went on, 'but there is a limit to what I can do.'

Gemma nodded, feeling numb with fear.

'Dacey!' They froze as Gerard's voice sounded from outside. 'Where'd you leave the water?'

'By the stores tent!' he shouted back; his voice sounded excessively loud. He let the screen fall closed, separating them temporarily. He reappeared a little while later, but motioned her to remain silent.

'They're sitting just outside,' he mouthed, holding up two fingers, and shrugged helplessly. There was nothing they could do for now, and he withdrew.

Gemma found it impossible to sleep, but tried to relax, to get some rest at least. A dozen escape plans occurred to her, but each seemed so far-fetched that the process just left her feeling frustrated – and doomed. She began to despair, and had to lecture herself to keep from panicking. *I'm a survivor. Arden told me that, so it must be true.* This thought reawoke her longing to see him, and made her even more determined to get away. She went over her ideas again, trying to work out the most plausible avenue.

From time to time she heard snatches of conversation between the two guards. Most of it was uninteresting, centring mainly on how long it would take them to get back to the city, and on the bitterness of the brew they were drinking. Then they began to discuss Gemma herself, and she sat up, listening hard.

'She's scary,' one of them remarked.

'Don't be so wet, Caley, it's only a few tricks,' Gerard replied.

'Do you think she's one of the northerners?'

'Maybe. She won't like heading this way, if she is, and we'll find her out soon enough.'

'Do you think her hair *is* dyed? Wray doesn't think it is.'

'Oh, he just likes an excuse to kill people,' Gerard

answered, chuckling. 'He must be finding this trip really tedious.'

'The boss wants her alive.'

'Yeah, I reckon Aric's taken quite a fancy to her,' Gerard concluded. They both laughed, then went on to other topics.

Gemma wondered briefly what would happen to her if she was to hear the siren song while with the Grey Raiders. Would she be able to hide what she felt? *No sense worrying about that now!* she reprimanded herself.

Three hours later her eyelids were getting heavy, and she still had not come up with any solution to her problem. The sounds of movement outside made her listen intently, and she heard a murmured conversation between Dacey and Gerard, who had evidently returned to claim his bed. Dacey left, and she heard him greet Yarat, the current guard. Gemma came to a decision – Yarat was one of the men she felt she could both outwit and outrun.

She waited until Gerard had settled down, then lifted the screen and edged towards the exit.

'Where do you think you're going?' Gerard growled.

'I have to go outside.'

'What for?'

'Don't ask such stupid questions!' she snapped.

'God's teeth,' Gerard grumbled. 'Why on my time? I'll have to come with you.' Gemma said nothing. 'Orders,' he added, having the grace to sound rather awkward.

They went out. Yarat was sitting alone, near the fire, and he glanced up and scowled, but did not speak. Gemma marched off into the darkness, with Gerard a few paces behind. She couldn't see the second guard. Perhaps her luck had changed. After a few more paces, she stopped sharply, and gave a small scream. Turning round, she ran back towards the fire, past a bewildered Gerard.

'Wild dogs!' she yelled as she fled. 'A whole pack of them!'

Gerard glanced back into the night and thought he saw several pairs of eyes, reflecting the red of the fire. Terrified, he turned on his heels.

Meanwhile, Gemma had reached the fire.

'Wild dogs!' she told Yarat. 'Coming this way.'

The fat soldier scrambled to his feet just as Gerard reached them. 'There's dozens,' he gasped.

'Fire!' Gemma put in. 'They hate fire. Come on, before we're all eaten alive!'

She knelt down and grasped the unburnt ends of two blazing sticks. After a moment, the two men did likewise and took a couple of hesitant steps towards their invisible foes.

'Go forward,' Gemma urged. 'They'll run if we show them we're not afraid.' The men obeyed warily while she hung back, then, picking her moment, she turned and threw the burning branches at the tent which held the precious cargo. The sticks landed in a shower of sparks and a sudden leap of flame. Quickly, Gemma grabbed two more flaming pieces of wood, ran towards the store-tent and added them to the new fire. The two men saw what she was doing, and ran after her, yelling to their companions.

She dodged round behind the tent, and had the satisfaction of seeing it start to burn before she began to circle back in the darkness. Shouts and screams echoed as the sleeping men were roused and hurried to put out the flames. The pandemonium was so great that for a moment Gemma believed they had forgotten her, and she felt a thrill of hope.

She reached the horses, who were awake and whinnying nervously at the noise and flames, and managed to untether one with shaking fingers. Then she heard a soft cough from behind her, and turned slowly, to find the point of a sword almost touching her throat. Beyond it, she saw Wray's smiling face.

'Nice try,' he said.

CHAPTER TEN

The fire had been put out very quickly, and only the tent itself had suffered any real damage. Aric, who had been asleep inside, was unharmed, as was the cargo. Gemma had been forced back at sword-point, and tied up while the Grey Raiders decided her fate.

'Her actions prove her to be demon-spawn,' Wray stated, the loathing plain in his voice. 'She must die.'

Several of the others muttered their agreement, but were cut short by Aric.

'That is my decision,' he shot back. 'Do you question my authority?'

'Until now there has been no reason to. Why do you hesitate this time?'

'Do not presume that you know or understand everything,' the leader replied calmly.

'I have certain powers—' Wray went on.

'And I respect them,' Aric broke in. 'Your . . . sight, and that of your fellows make you invaluable to our cause. But . . . no, hear me out!' He held up a hand to forestall any interruption. 'It appears likely that she is indeed one of those to whom evil calls, but if that is the case, I have orders from the very highest powers to bring all such to them. Alive.' He paused, and glanced at his men, as if defying them to argue. A grim silence was his own answer. 'Taken logically, tonight's events only prove that she is a thief, with little respect for others' property. That is common enough in these degenerate days.'

77

'This is no common thief!' Wray burst out, pointing at Gemma with his unsheathed sword.

'I will not argue further,' Aric said, with cold finality. 'She comes with us to the caves.' He waited for any objections, but none came. 'We have suffered no harm,' he said eventually. 'The merchandise was not touched by the fire.'

'That would have been quite a blaze,' Gerard commented drily, and there were one or two low whistles as his colleagues contemplated the idea.

'Guard duties as before,' Aric ordered. 'And the rest of you get some sleep. I want to press on hard tomorrow.'

'What about *her*?' Yarat asked.

'Leave her where she is,' Aric replied. 'A little discomfort might teach her some manners.'

* * *

Gemma lay on her side near the fire. With the coming of dawn, she realized groggily that in spite of her misery and angry despair, she had actually dozed through the last few hours of the night. Her return to consciousness brought with it a wave of pain – her wrists and ankles were bound tightly, and her shoulder muscles were in agony. She tried to shift her position to ease the cramping, but only made things worse. She closed her eyes and lay still.

When she opened them again, she saw the three meyrkats standing close by her. She was horrified by this – she had told them to wait for her outside the camp, and had not thought to warn them when she was recaptured.

Gemma's horror deepened when she noticed a bow in Caley's hand, the arrow already nocked.

'Kill them,' she heard Yarat say, and her blood ran cold.

'No!' she yelled hoarsely.

Caley hesitated, while the meyrkats looked around, obviously confused and frightened.

'I'm not having the little bastards run around free,' Yarat insisted.

Then another voice entered the conversation.

'Put them in this,' Aric said. 'We'll take them with us. If they try to get away, kill them.' An empty sack, similar to those containing the raiders' merchandise, landed on the ground by Yarat's feet. He stooped to retrieve it, then advanced slowly upon the three meyrkats, who backed away, chittering nervously. Caley drew his bow and took aim.

Don't run, Gemma instructed the animals miserably. *If you do, they'll kill you.*

The skin will cover us? Ed asked uncertainly.

Yes, but it'll be all right. I'll get you out as soon as I can.

We will still wander with you? Av queried.

Yes, Gemma replied, her heart heavy.

Then we will take the skin, Ed decided. He took a step forward and Yarat pounced clumsily, grabbing the meyrkat by the scruff of his neck and stuffing him into the bag.

'Got you!' he gloated. Av did not resist, and was soon put inside, then Em astonished the soldiers by diving into the sack of his own accord. Yarat hoisted them high and looked at the wriggling shape with satisfaction. He secured the opening with a cord, and as he did so, Gemma felt a twinge of pain at the back of her neck. As the daylight grew, so the pain spread, becoming more and more intense, and making communication with the meyrkats extremely difficult. They were clearly in much discomfort, but their thoughts were confused and fearful. Although Gemma tried her best to reassure them, she felt little response. Grinning, Yarat put the sack on the ground, well out of Gemma's reach.

She lay and watched the unmoving bag while the men dismantled the camp and reloaded the mules, then her feet were untied and she walked stiffly, often stumbling, to her mount. Once she had been lifted on to the mule, her feet were tied together beneath its belly. For a moment, she thought that the meyrkats were going to be forgotten, but then Yarat picked up the bag and shook it, smiling maliciously. The animals wriggled uncomfortably as he attached them to another of the mules, which in its turn was made fretful by its moving burden.

'Keep still!' Yarat demanded angrily, and thumped the bag with his fist. Gemma almost cried out, and sent the meyrkats a desperate message though the pounding in her head.

Be still!

After a few moments they obeyed and Yarat left them alone.

The god is here. Fire burns. We cannot sing. Ed's voice was barely recognizable and Gemma heard it only faintly.

What's the matter? she asked. Each word made her head feel as though it was going to explode.

Earth-dark, Av responded weakly. *The sky is green.* She sounded amused, and as if she was on the brink of hysteria.

Why has such a short spell of captivity affected them so badly? Gemma wondered. After all, the meyrkats were used to the dark enclosed spaces of the burrow. *I wish I could think straight.*

Her wish was not to be granted. Her headache grew worse throughout the early morning, and she gave up the attempt to communicate with the meyrkats, abandoning herself to her own misery. Her arms were still tied behind her back and she was in constant fear of falling off, but the steady pace of her mount kept her stable. Every muscle in her body ached; her head was a solid mass of pain. Even thought became impossible.

The party travelled at the pace of the slowest mule. They left the trail for a time in order to avoid a village, and Gemma knew that Aric had changed his earlier plan. She would not be able to seek help from the people of the foothills.

An hour or so before noon, they came to a small valley, which was bounded on its eastern side by a small but overhanging cliff. Before entering the vale, Aric called for a halt.

'Is it clear?' he asked Wray.

'Yes, but there's activity here,' his deputy answered, staring intently at the cliffs. Gemma followed the line of his gaze, trying to work out what they were talking about. The overhanging rock formations looked unnatural somehow, but were too large to be man-made.

They rode on. The men were silent now, and glanced around constantly, as if in fear of being followed. Gemma soon discovered the reason for their apprehension.

'There!' Dacey cried, pointing up towards the cliff-top. Everyone followed his indication, and saw the mass of transparent blue flames, each the size of a man, that were congregating there.

Elementals! Gemma realized. She had encountered these awesome beings once before, and their activities then had filled her with fear. She knew from personal experience that they could take on any shape they chose, and were capable of moving at incredible speeds. They were usually associated with places greatly disrupted by The Levelling, and where the landscape had been drastically altered.

The elementals left their perch, and swooped down towards the horsemen like birds of prey. Wray's voice rang out in the silence, and Gemma turned to see him stand up in his stirrups, both arms pointing forward, his eyes blazing.

'I have power over you. Disturb us not!' he cried. At the same time, Gemma heard one of the captive meyrkats scream.

The gods come! Sing! The gods come!

Her head reeled, pain and bewilderment whirling her down into the black spaces of her mind. Flickers of light

81

burned within, and she realized suddenly that the raider's cargo, and the cause of the meyrkats' madness, was dragonflower seeds. The sack in which the animals were imprisoned contained a residue of the powerful drug. Fury erupted, pushing back the pain and opening new channels of light. Gemma felt her power surge, being fed to her from the crazed minds of the meyrkats. This was their only chance, and she hurriedly decided on her course of action.

The elementals had initially drawn near, but had been first slowed, then halted by Wray's command. They hovered in front of the nervous horses, their presence a wavering blue flame which was impossible to focus on.

'Let us pass,' Wray demanded. 'You cannot deny me.'

The flames withdrew slowly, and Gemma sensed that they did so reluctantly. They had only wanted to display friendship, and were unheeding of the terror their spectral presence inspired.

You need not go, she told them silently. *I welcome you.* Her greeting was instinctive, prompted by an awareness of their sadness and longing for companionship. She had no way of knowing what these strange beings were, or what motivated them, but their loneliness touched her heart. She fed conviction into her words, and knew that they were received. *I welcome you.*

Then several things happened all at once. The elementals sped forward once more, diving and whirling in a dance of joy. Horses reared in terror, mules ran in all directions, braying loudly, and the meyrkats sang, adding their discordant voices to the cacophony. Gemma detected other voices, and knew that it was not only the captive meyrkats who were singing. The rest of the clan had arrived, and were giving voice to their battle song. She saw them then, speeding between the horses and pack animals, and adding to the chaos. Wray's voice rose above the noise, but his fury went unanswered. Gemma had destroyed his power.

Several of the men had been unhorsed, and Gemma herself was hanging on for dear life. She knew that the ropes that bound her would drag her along the ground unprotected should she fall. Her mount was fretting, and she was enormously grateful when Dacey appeared at her side. He was on foot, and although he was bleeding from a cut over his eye, he managed to steady her on the mule before untying her feet and lifting her down to the ground.

'Dacey! Never mind her. Get after the mules!' Aric yelled angrily, and the young man hastened to obey.

Within moments, Gemma was surrounded by meyrkats. She felt one of them gnaw at the ropes which bound her wrists, and was soon free. She massaged the life back into her hands as she watched the mêlée about her.

Come, Gem-ma, Ox said. *We must wander quickly.*

Where are the others? she asked, looking round for the mule that carried her companions. She soon spotted it, but it was already some distance away.

'Come back!' she implored. *Can you catch it?* she asked the meyrkats, but before they could answer, three elementals swooped down to the retreating mule. It stopped, backed away from them, then turned and bolted towards Gemma. She yelled as it approached, and the frantic animal skidded to a halt. Gemma made soothing noises as she unfastened the bag, then knelt down and opened it.

Av and Ed emerged wide-eyed and shaky, but remarkably unscathed. There was no sign of Em, and Gemma's heart sank as she reached in and drew out his small body. He was stiff and cold; his neck had been broken.

His song will be sung, Ox told her quietly, as Gemma cradled the small corpse in her arms, unwilling to accept the fact of his death. *Now come!*

The clan leader's words roused her, and she glanced around. Men and horses were spread out all over the small valley, with the elementals still causing havoc.

However, three of them were hovering nearby, as if watching over Gemma. Abruptly, one sped away towards the cliff, where it disappeared. The other two soon followed.

A cave! Gemma realized. *Come on,* she said to Ox. *Gather the clan and go to the cliff.*

But we cannot climb such a thing, he replied uncertainly.

You don't need to. There is a burrow there!

Gemma ran towards the cliff, hoping that she would not be noticed in all the confusion. The meyrkats followed her, calling to each other as they went. The entrance to the cave was only half Gemma's height but she scrambled inside and was soon able to stand up. She was in a tall cavern, lit by the blue glow of the three elementals; they were deeper inside, and beckoned, as if inviting her to follow. The sounds of the meyrkats' noisy entrance echoed hollowly.

Gemma counted the animals. There were two missing.

Where are the others? she asked.

Their warmth has gone, Ox replied. They had been killed either by the soldiers, or by the maddened horses.

I will sing for them too, she told Ox sadly, then turned to the elementals once more.

'Thank you,' she said aloud, then, with the meyrkats trailing behind her, stepped forward into the elementals' cave.

CHAPTER ELEVEN

The blue flames led them deeper into the rock, down a narrow tunnel. Gemma had to pick her way carefully past the uneven floor and jagged walls, and hoped that her aching limbs would not let her down. The meyrkats seemed quite at home in the gloom, and one or two even scrambled ahead of her, checking for pitfalls. Ed and Av were still suffering from the after-effects of their debilitating confinement, and were being encouraged along by the others.

The elementals always stayed several paces in front, apparently intent only on their continued progress. As the tunnel began to slope upwards, Gemma wondered, for the first time, where they were going. *It's a bit late now to decide whether you trust them or not,* she chided herself, and climbed on. The incline became even steeper. Eventually, the elementals simply blinked out of existence and Gemma's heart stopped for an instant. Then she saw that their radiance had been replaced by a pool of daylight up ahead. The meyrkats hurried on, anxious now to see the sun again.

Sky-hole, Ox reported from his leading position. *Big-burrow entrance.* He was standing erect on his hind legs, looking directly upwards. Gemma joined him, and the other meyrkats clustered round them. Above their heads was a rock chimney, with a small patch of sky visible in the distance. There looked to be plenty of hand-holds, but in places the passage was very narrow.

Climb this? Ox asked tentatively.

Yes, Gemma replied firmly. *But first we rest for a*

while. Do you think the grey-skins are following us?

The meyrkats at the rear replied that there had been no pursuit, so Gemma sat down, glad of the chance to massage her sore legs. Ed and Av were brought over for her inspection, and she saw that although they were still disorientated and a little wide-eyed, they were recovering from their ordeal. She placed a gentle hand on each of their heads, hoping to calm them.

You were wonderful, she said. *I couldn't have welcomed the flames without your help and guidance.*

The gods came to us, Av told her. *Inside.*

I know. I felt it too, Gemma replied, remembering her dreadful headache. She realized that this was yet another parallel between the relationship of a wizard and his familiar, and hers with the clan. As well as the mental communication, there was also a two-way exchange of sensation; the dragonflower dust had affected her as badly as the trapped animals.

Now we can wander again, Ed remarked happily.

I'm so sorry about Em and the others, Gemma said. *We will sing for them.*

Yes, but not yet, she told him quickly, afraid that echoes of their song of mourning might reach the cave below.

A few of the more agile meyrkats began climbing, searching out the easiest route to the top, then guiding the rest of the clan. Gemma remained below, anxiously watching their ascent, and prepared to catch any that fell. When Ox reached the top, he clambered out and had a good look round.

No grey-skins, he reported, and gave the soft peeping call that indicated safety. Gemma breathed a sigh of relief, and began her own upward journey. She found it surprisingly easy, and was able to wedge herself securely every so often in order to rest. The only awkward moment came when she had to squeeze through a very narrow space, between two protruding slabs of rock. She panicked for a moment, not knowing

86

whether she would be able to get through, but determination lent her strength, and she emerged with only a few grazes and a slightly ripped tunic.

She joined the meyrkats, and studied her new surroundings. The cliff-top was about two hundred paces to the west, and all around her a grassy plateau stretched north and south. To the east was a wood, and the meyrkats were regarding this with awe. They had seen few trees on their wanderings thus far, and to have so many together – even bare of leaves – was overwhelming. Beyond the woodland, the hills rose even higher, and they could see in the distance the first range of mountains. None of it looked even remotely familiar, but Gemma longed to be there, knowing that somewhere to the east and south was the valley – and Arden.

A curl of smoke rose above the trees, and her heart leapt. If there was a farm or village nearby, then the beginning of her journey would be made that much easier. Then she realized that her ragged appearance was hardly likely to endear her to strangers, and she had no money with which to buy food or other supplies. The solution occurred to her; her act with the meyrkats could become real, and surely such entertainment would pay for a meal and a night's rest.

She gathered her friends together, and they set off. Although one or two of them cast wistful glances back towards the cave, Gemma would not let them linger.

And so they began a life as travelling show-people. They were successful almost everywhere; most villages and country taverns were only too pleased to see Gemma and her performing animals. She changed her name, and called the meyrkats monkeys, just in case word of their travels reached the ears of the Grey Raiders. Otherwise they travelled openly, always moving south and, whenever possible, to the east – asking each time they stopped whether the valley Gemma sought was nearby. After the first night, when the meyrkats stayed in the open in order to sing for their dead, they grew increasingly bold, often accompanying Gemma into the villages.

At first, Av and Ed were the main part of the act, but the others soon wanted to join in, and so the show grew longer, and more complex. Eventually, Gemma had little to do except make the announcements.

They travelled like this for nearly a month; although Gemma could tell that she was getting nearer to the valley, its exact whereabouts remained a mystery. Nobody she met had even heard of it, but this did not surprise her. She knew how isolated the valley was, and how its secret location protected its unique way of life.

During this time there were no sightings or reports of any Grey Raiders, and Gemma at last began to believe that she was safe, and that Aric and his men had continued north with their precious and deadly cargo. Her store of information about the Grey Raiders had grown because of her encounter, but she had many questions still unanswered, and was looking forward to talking to Arden about them. She longed for the day when she would at last see the mountain pass which would take her to him.

Her main worry was the health of the meyrkats. They were a hardy group, but were not used to the cold, wet weather of the upper hills, and often complained to her that there was 'too much green'. Their diet had of necessity changed, and eventually this began to have a harmful effect. It was obvious that a few of the animals were pining for the desert, in spite of their enjoyment of the new way of life.

It gradually became apparent to Gemma that they could not carry on this way. All her needs drove her eastward, while the Wanderers yearned to turn west. Gemma knew that asking them to attempt the mountain passes with her would be cruel – and possibly fatal. She also knew that they would follow her if she wished it, but she was healthier now, had a few coins in her pocket, and no longer needed their help to survive, as she had done in the desert. Gemma also knew that the meyrkats, as unrepentant carnivores, would not be suited to valley life.

Their inevitable decision to part company caused much heartache, but they were all convinced that their story was not over. Gemma and the meyrkats would meet again.

The last night together was spent in a cave. They had already made use of such shelters on several previous occasions when forced to sleep in open country, and the meyrkats felt at home in the underground darkness. Gemma had grown adept at making herself comfortable. Outside, the wind moaned and shook the trees, but in their rocky haven they were safe and warm.

The eleven surviving meyrkats gathered about Gemma, and moved close together, for comfort.

Where will you go? she asked them.

The clan had evidently discussed this at length, and Ox replied immediately.

Down. Towards the setting sun, he replied, then surprised her by adding, *We will explore the other burrows like this one.*

The various caves they had encountered had obviously made a greater impression on the clan than Gemma had realized.

We are Wanderers now, Ul added. *We will always wish to see new things.*

But we shall seek less green, less clear-rush, Ed put in, and received peeps of agreement.

I'm sorry you've had to suffer for me, Gemma said.

For a few moments there was no response, and she wondered if she had somehow offended them.

The clan stands taller in knowing, Av replied eventually. *We became Wanderers by our own choice.*

*   *   *

That night, Gemma dreamt again of Arden and, once again, the vision was different. Small furry shadows accompanied her, and she knew that the clan shared her dream. This felt natural; they were a part of her now.

The focus of her dream had changed. She was no longer restricted to one place, but could see many caves and tunnels, and halls of stone whose weird pinnacles of rock reached up from the floor and down from the ceiling. Crystalline light pulsed slowly, glowing then fading. Water churned through vast chasms, then spread serenely into huge, silent lakes, mirror-still. There was movement within the caverns, indefinable black shapes, shadows of ghosts, that glided within her sight.

And within all this came the precious glimpse of Arden. At various times he appeared calm, then troubled, smiling, then afraid. Pain accompanied each image, but it was deadened and made bearable for Gemma by the ever-changing patterns of her dream.

* * *

When she awoke, her clothes were clinging to the perspiration on her skin. In the pale dawn light she could see that she was being watched by eleven pairs of black eyes, and saw the dream reflected in each one.

The giant burrow, Ul said, filled with awe. *We have seen it!*

And the singing air, Ox added, equally reverential.

We will do your bidding, Av said.

What bidding? Gemma asked, bleary-eyed and confused. Conflicting emotions welled within her.

The Wanderers will find the giant burrow for you, Ox explained patiently.

The clan has told of it with each renewal, Ul said. *Now we shall see it.*

The meyrkats had worked themselves into a state of excitement, and Gemma realized that they believed her to have given them a task, and that this would make the parting much easier for them. Her dream had evidently triggered a clan-memory, and had revived a generations-old myth about the giant burrow – or underground caves. The Wanderers would now become true explorers, in Gemma's name. They were obviously so keen to begin that she could not help feeling a little hurt at their eagerness to depart, but was soon caught up in their exhilaration. When the time came to bid them farewell, she found it difficult to form the words.

Our clan will be smaller without you, Ox told her.

I . . . I'll miss you, Gemma said. *I can't thank you enough for all you've done.*

Gratitude was a concept not fully understood by the meyrkats, but they recognized her meaning well enough.

When we join again, Ed remarked, *we will have learnt some jokes for you.*

That would be nice, she replied, smiling.

There was little more to say. A short song, which mingled the sorrow of parting with the stimulation of a new adventure, brought tears to Gemma's eyes. Then, in a flurry of goodbyes, the meyrkats were gone.

Gemma sat down and wept, feeling the terrible wrench of separation. She cried for the sadness of the parting, for the happiness of their new purpose, but most of all, she cried for the loss of their comradeship. It left a gaping void within her.

Eventually she got up, dried her eyes, collected her few belongings and set her face determinedly towards the rising sun. Her mind was still in a turmoil over the meyrkats' departure, but she forced herself to think only of the goal ahead. She had already decided which mountain pass to attempt next, and, if that did not lead to the valley, there would always be another. And another. There was no room for failure in her thoughts now.

Twelve days later, after many leagues and several false sightings, Gemma crested a rise, hope welling within her, and looked down into yet another valley. In the distance she could see a woman, sitting on a boulder. As she watched, the woman rose, and glanced up in her direction. In that moment, Gemma knew that she was home. She ran down the hill, staggering from weariness, as the other hurried towards her, yelling her name. There were no doubts left now. For the time being at least, her wandering was over. Gemma ran on, stumbling now.

And fell into Mallory's welcoming arms.

CHAPTER TWELVE

As the last of the memories of her journey faded, Gemma recalled sadly that her exhilaration at reaching the valley had not lasted very long. She had immediately asked about Arden, but could see from Mallory's expression that the news was not good. Gemma opened her eyes now and looked across the kitchen at Mallory, who said in concerned tones, 'I thought you were asleep.'

'No, just thinking,' Gemma replied softly.

'You think too much. And I don't need to ask what about, do I?'

They smiled sadly at each other, then Gemma noticed that it was pitch-black outside.

'It's late,' she said, surprised.

'After midnight,' Mallory confirmed.

'You didn't have to stay up.'

'I know I didn't. You'd better get to bed now.'

Gemma nodded, and stretched as she stood up.

'I wonder if I'll dream about him again tonight,' she said. Although Mallory said nothing, her eyes told their own story.

'It isn't likely,' Gemma went on. 'I've been back in the valley over two months now, and I've only dreamt of him three times.'

'Just get some sleep,' Mallory said, concern for her friend showing in her face. 'Let the dreams take care of themselves.'

'Two nights in a row *would* be a bit much,' Gemma admitted, but even as she said the words, she hoped that she would see him again that night. This feeling persisted as she made herself ready for bed, and as she slid between the sheets, her thoughts fell into a familiar pattern.

She refused to believe that she would never again hold Arden in her arms, never argue with him about the existence of magic, never laugh together about the silliest of things. Most of all, she would not – could not – believe that they would not some day be able to lie together, as they should have done so many times, lovers at last as well as friends.

The nights were the hardest times of all. She and Arden had spent so many together, though chaste, and she missed the warmth and companionship, the sight of his face while he slept, the gentle touch of his hand when she had dreamt badly.

All this, and so much more, she would not forget. She felt so lonely without him – since their enforced separation, the strength of her feelings had become even more apparent. Arden was her love, and she refused to let him go.

So Gemma went to sleep with the familiar mixture of anticipation and fear in her heart, but awoke the next morning with no memory of her dreams.

As time passed, the pain of Arden's absence did not diminish. Rather, she learnt to store it away somewhere deep inside herself, to be brought out and examined only when she was alone. Those times hurt too much for her to be able to share them with anyone, not even Mallory, who also loved him.

Occasionally, she found herself able to laugh at an absurdity, and there was relief for her in that, but also a bitter regret because she could not share it with him. And yet life in the valley held undoubted compensations; Gemma could not imagine that there was a more pleasant place in this strange southern land. The beauty and peace that had been the hallmarks of the valley before the drought were returning in full measure

94

now as spring gave way to early summer. Nature rejoiced all around her, and, while this alone could not make her happy, some of the joy seeped into her being, raising her spirits a little.

At this time, Gemma also began to appreciate the serene atmosphere of the valley, which felt as though it were set apart from the rest of the earth, a self-contained world which neither needed nor welcomed interference from outside. She knew that this was in fact true in many ways. The valley was rarely visited, was almost unknown beyond its closest neighbours, and the valley people could not leave without their health suffering. However, the extent of the isolation of her new home was most emphatically confirmed by her realization that, while they had been here, neither she nor Mallory had ever heard the siren song from the far south – the unearthly impulse, half sound, half emotion, that she had learnt to distrust yet could never ignore. Somehow, the valley was protecting them from this potentially destructive influence, and she was grateful for the chance to rest, to wait and to make her decisions about the future. She knew that Arden would return to the valley if he could, and she could not think of anywhere she would rather wait for him.

And then there were the people. Now that the valley had grown healthy once more, their special qualities were made abundantly clear. They were hardly ever ill, and would eventually live to ages that Gemma considered incredible. Reaching the age of one hundred had not been uncommon before the drought, and even the very old among them tended to remain active. Though the recent hardships had meant an inevitable decline in both population and general health, the valley community showed every sign of regaining its former hardiness. But what really set them apart from anyone else Gemma had ever met was the 'knowing'. News passed among them without the need for the usual forms of communication. Anything of importance, witnessed by any one of them, would be known to all within just a few hours. Gemma spent much time puzzling over the nature of this ability. It was not a direct exchange, such as that between her and the meyrkats, but a sort of mental osmosis. It filtered out the private or irrelevant matters, but allowed information affecting them all to be broadcast throughout the community. Gemma did not share this common knowledge, making it all the more remarkable to her that she had been accepted as a welcome member of their society. However, she had reached the stage where she no longer found their uncanny ability unnerving.

Gemma's closest relationships were with Mallory, then with Mallory's immediate family, but there were several other people who had become important to her. Horan, Mallory's youngest brother, was a frequent visitor to their farm. He had been Arden's closest friend and had been with them for part of that fateful journey into the mountains. He shared Gemma's grief at Arden's disappearance.

Like his sister, Horan tried to exorcise Gemma's ghosts, to help her look instead to the future. He was always willing to talk, and it was in a conversation with him that she finally admitted that life might go on without Arden.

It was a glorious day in early summer, and they were walking between the fields of Kragen's farm and the nearby woods. The valley around them was a splendid patchwork of green and gold, and the crystal-clear air was filled with birdsong. They reached the river and sat on the bank, watching the precious, life-giving water sweep past.

'It's been almost a month since I dreamt of him,' Gemma told Horan quietly.

He put an arm round her shoulders and gave her a brotherly hug. He found the sadness in her voice almost unbearable but knew that only time – and help from her friends – could heal her hurt. They were silent for a while.

'You think he's dead, don't you?' she asked eventually.

Horan was surprised by her directness – she had never been so blunt before.

'Gemma, it's been five months since he disappeared,' he reminded her. 'If he's still alive, I can't see what has prevented him from getting back here – or at least sending us a message.'

After another long pause, Gemma sighed and shook her head.

'I wish I *knew*,' she said. 'Sometimes I think that would be easier than hoping.'

'Of course it would,' he replied gently, 'but you have to face the fact that we may *never* know what happened to him. The mountains keep their secrets.'

My brother has taken him, Gemma thought, remembering the words of the rocking-stone. *If only it could have been more specific!*

'It's not fair!' she burst out. 'We loved each other. And this wasn't our destiny,' she trailed off miserably. Tears were brimming in her eyes and Horan hugged her close again.

'There are other people who love you, Gemma,' he said, knowing his words to be inadequate, but unable to remain silent in the face of her anguish.

'And that I love,' she replied wearily, 'but it's not the same.'

'I know,' he admitted.

'Do you?' she asked. 'You've never married.' It was almost an accusation.

'I've got plenty of time. I'm only thirty-eight,' he replied, smiling bravely. 'A mere sapling.' When Gemma did not respond, he went on, 'And you're not much more than half my age. You've got your whole life ahead of you.'

'There'll never be anyone like Arden,' she said. 'Whether he's dead or alive, I'll always love him, and he'll always be with me.'

Horan had no answer to that.

Later, they walked back to the farmhouse, savouring the sights and smells of the lovely afternoon. There was another visitor waiting for Gemma. Ashlin was sitting in the kitchen with Mallory and Kragen, and stood up, smiling nervously, as they came in and exchanged greetings. Ashlin was twenty years old, though he looked younger to Gemma, belying his age as most of the valley people did. He had also attempted the journey into the mountains, returning with Horan and Kragen when ill-health forced them back. His obstinate courage had earned Gemma's respect, especially as most of his friends had felt he was foolish to make the attempt at all. He gave the impression of being timid and – by valley standards – frail, but Gemma had seen the strength of character behind that façade, and knew that he was stronger than he looked.

He had been a frequent visitor since her return to the valley and, though initially reticent, they now knew each other well. Gemma was aware that Ashlin's regard for her was rather more than friendship, and at times bordered on hero-worship, but he was intelligent and sensitive, and she enjoyed his company.

'You're certainly in demand today,' Mallory remarked, grinning.

'And you shouldn't be surprised,' Kragen added. 'Any young man with an ounce of sense would be queueing up to spend time with a beautiful girl like you.' He glanced at Mallory. 'If I didn't already have the most wonderful wife in the world, I'd be joining it myself.'

'Is that how he courted you, Mallory?' Gemma asked. 'With such outrageous flattery?'

'Partly,' her friend answered with a smile.

'You know *perfectly* well that I meant everything I said,' Kragen protested.

'I never knew these muscle-bound farming types had such a pretty way with words,' Horan commented.

'You're pretty solid yourself, brother dear,' Mallory put in. 'In more ways than one.'

'A mere sapling,' Gemma said, exchanging grins with Horan. She always enjoyed the genial war of words between Mallory and her brother, and it felt good to be part of such a family. And Kragen's flattery – outrageous or not – had lifted her spirits.

Ashlin, who had been listening to all this with some embarrassment, cleared his throat and spoke for the first time.

'I had hoped that you would come for a walk with me,' he told Gemma.

'But she's only just got back!' Mallory exclaimed. 'You'll wear the poor girl out.'

'I'd love to,' Gemma said quickly, seeing how shy Ashlin looked. 'With all this wonderful food that Mallory keeps forcing down me, I shall be as fat as a pig by the end of the summer if I don't get plenty of exercise.'

Ashlin's expression mirrored his pleasure and relief.

'You're not too bad at this flattery business yourself,' Mallory said. 'See you later.'

As Ashlin and Gemma left, Mallory and her husband exchanged glances.

'I hope she knows how fond he's getting of her,' Mallory said.

'She knows,' Horan replied. 'And she'll let him down gently if he gets too serious.'

'She could do worse,' Kragen put in, then, seeing the look on his wife's face, he added quickly, 'Not for some time of course, but . . . she'll get over it one day.'

'I hope so,' Mallory said, but did not sound convinced. She looked at Horan, but he just shrugged. 'For her sake, I hope so.'

Outside, Gemma and Ashlin were walking away from the river, towards the wilder areas on the lower slopes of the encircling mountains.

'You . . . you don't mind me coming to see you, do you?' he asked.

'Of course not,' she replied. 'I enjoy your company. You know I do.' It was true. He was tactful and never mentioned Arden, but they often had long discussions on other, safer topics – the valley and its inhabitants, the construction of her kite, the desert and the meyrkats. Above all, he loved to talk about magic. It was a subject which obviously fascinated him and, while he took the shared knowledge of the valley for granted, he never wearied of hearing about Gemma's experiences with individual wizardry, or of advancing theories about the nature of magic in general. He already knew about Gemma's idea that her talents were connected with groups – and her encounters with the wild-dog pack and the elementals bore that out – but he found it difficult to reconcile this with other facts.

'If magic no longer depends on, or can be controlled by a single mind, then how do you explain what you accomplished when you were quite alone?'

It was a question they had discussed before, but had never answered to their satisfaction. Now, as they walked on one of the grass-covered hills that overlooked the valley, Gemma gave the only answer she could.

'Perhaps I'm the exception.' It sounded feeble, but she could think of no other explanation.

'Why, though?' Ashlin asked eagerly, and went on, not waiting for a reply. 'You can heal, raise fires, smash things to pieces when you're angry, communicate with animals – and you were the one who finally understood the floating city and what you'd found there. It's obvious that you're special – but why?'

'I don't feel very special most of the time,' she told him. 'And I've had help all the way along. Even when I've been physically alone, there have been others to guide me – especially Cai.'

'But not at the rocking stone.'

'No, but the meyrkats—'

'The meyrkats helped, but their singing had failed in previous years. You restored the spell,' Ashlin

100

interrupted. 'It's as if you've been chosen to play an important role, by someone – or *something* – that we can't envisage.'

'Then I wish they'd show me the script!' Gemma responded, laughing now. 'It would save an awful lot of bother.'

'Was there something that happened before The Levelling,' Ashlin went on, serious still, 'which might have given you unique powers?'

Not before, Gemma remembered. *During*. She had always been reluctant to talk of her part – as a seven-year-old girl – in the wizards' ritual that had brought about The Levelling, or The Destruction as it had been known on her home-isle. Her memories of that fateful day were confused, and ever since Arden had refused to believe her story, it had been even more difficult for her to remember it clearly. But she *had* been there, at the epicentre of that fearful cataclysm, within the reach of a power more awesome than anything she could imagine. The Earth-Mind had been forced awake for a few moments, and had destroyed the evil that was threatening to overwhelm the entire world – but at the cost of thousands of innocent lives. Perhaps that experience *had* made her someone special, and had cast her in this confused leading role.

She thought of trying to explain all this to Ashlin. After all, his enquiring mind deserved some consideration, as did his concern for her, but in the end she could not bring herself to do it. Her explanation was too complicated, too vague.

'I don't know,' she said. 'I was only a child then.'

Ashlin hid his disappointment, and they walked on in silence for a while.

'You'll always be special to me,' he told her softly, then, having made this outright confession, seemed to lose the use of his tongue. Gemma waited, but eventually had to speak.

'Ashlin, I like you very much, but you must know—'

'Oh, I do!' he said quickly. 'I'm sorry – I shouldn't have said anything.'

'Don't be sorry. Just be my friend.'

'Always,' he replied solemnly.

The rest of their walk passed either in silence or in a determinedly light-hearted discussion of the plants and animals around them, both taking delight in the new life of the valley. At the farmyard gate, Ashlin took his leave, and Gemma went inside, with some relief, to find Kragen preparing their evening meal.

'No more suitors yet?' he asked innocently.

For a moment Gemma did not know whether to laugh or cry, but the twinkle in the farmer's eye was too mischievous, and won her over.

'Don't mock me!' she laughed. 'It's not like that for me, and you know it.'

Kragen was delighted to see Gemma's good humour, and his broad smile showed his feelings plainly.

'Chop them up for me, will you?' he asked, pointing to a pile of onions. 'They make me cry.'

'Call yourself a man?' she teased, but moved to do as he had requested. 'Where's Mallory? You usually leave such awesome tasks to her.'

'She's upstairs, asleep.'

'That's not like her. Is she all right?'

'Of course,' he replied. 'Just a bit tired.'

Gemma set about her task and, to her chagrin, soon found the tears streaming down her face. Kragen's eyes watered in sympathy, and when their glances met, they burst out laughing. Mallory came into the kitchen at that moment and stared at them, confused.

'What's the matter?' she asked. 'Has Ashlin upset you?'

Gemma held up an onion in reply, and Mallory realized her mistake.

'Reduced to snivelling heaps by a *vegetable*,' she mocked. 'Better let someone competent back in the kitchen.'

*   *   *

The next morning brought news of another, far less frequent visitor. The boys had gone out to play after breakfast, but reappeared almost immediately.

'Mum! Kris is here! Kris is here!' they yelled, as they burst into the kitchen.

Kris was undoubtedly the strangest inhabitant of the valley, and the most wonderful. Gemma did not know his age, but he stood no higher than a ten-year-old because his spine and limbs were grotesquely deformed. His clothes were generally black and shapeless, flapping as he walked. When he moved, his legs and arms seemed unco-ordinated and Arden had once described him, though not unkindly, as looking like an enormous wounded crow. Yet he retained his independence, constantly travelling the length and breadth of the valley. But strangest of all were Kris's eyes. They were yellow, and glittered like imperfect crystal; the pupils were vertical slits, like a goat's.

In spite of all this, his physical appearance was not the reason for Kris's unique position in the valley community. He brought with him an unfailing warmth and good humour, touching all about him with love. And he had extraordinary psychic powers, being able to create visions and, on occasion, predict future events. He was regarded with warmth and affection, and every household kept a place for him at table and a spare bed, in case he should choose to visit them.

He had lain in a comatose state during the drought, but even then Gemma had felt his kind spirit, and his guidance. He had recovered when the river flowed once more, and had now resumed his wandering life.

Gemma had seen Kris a few times since her return to the valley; indeed she had sought him out, hoping that he might be able to help her find Arden. But he could not, and could only offer her his unique welcome.

Gemma and Mallory went out to meet him now, and he was soon installed in the kitchen. The whole family enjoyed his presence, told him all their latest news, and asked questions of him in return. Although Kris could not speak, he communicated with his own special sign language – which Gemma was just beginning to learn.

'He has a message for you,' Mallory told her abruptly, and everyone turned to look at Gemma, their faces curious.

'What is it?'

As the bird-like hands fluttered briefly, too fast for Gemma to follow, Mallory looked shocked.

'What is it?' Gemma repeated insistently.

'He says there's a man coming, looking for you,' Mallory said.

Gemma's heart leapt.

'Did he say who?' she demanded.

'No,' Mallory replied. 'Gemma . . . don't build your hopes too high.'

'When's he coming?' Gemma asked, ignoring her friend's advice.

'This afternoon.'

CHAPTER THIRTEEN

Kris had not been able to see which direction the man would be coming from, but Gemma believed that it would be the southern end of the valley, where the trail to the high mountains began, and wanted to go there immediately. Mallory dissuaded her, pointing out that, in fact, he could arrive from anywhere. In any case, she assured Gemma, the whole valley was now on the lookout for his approach and they would be sent word as soon as the visitor was spotted.

So Gemma agreed to stay where she was, but Mallory then wondered if keeping her there had been such a good idea. Once Kris had left, and without his calming influence, Gemma was unbearably tense, and paced up and down restlessly.

'Why don't you go outside?' Mallory suggested. 'You're like a caged animal in here.'

'No. I want to stay with you,' Gemma replied quickly. 'So that when you know—'

'Then I'll go out too.' Mallory marched to the door and opened it. 'Come on.'

Gemma glanced around the room, as if thinking she had forgotten something, then followed her friend into the yard. They strolled around the nearby fields, talking occasionally, until midday.

'Nothing yet?' Gemma asked, for the tenth time.

'I'll tell you as soon as I hear!' Mallory exclaimed, almost losing her temper. They decided to go back to the farm, and found Kragen sharpening a scythe in the yard. The sound grated on Mallory's frayed nerves and she was about to ask him to stop when he suddenly put his tools down and looked at her. They knew.

Gemma glanced from one to the other.

'Where?' she demanded.

'The northern end,' Mallory replied. 'By Winder's place.'

'To the west of the ravine,' Kragen added. 'They must have climbed the trail over Raven's Crag.'

'They?' Gemma asked quickly.

'Two men,' Mallory went on, as more information filtered into her mind. 'On horseback.' Then her face fell – there was no easy way to break the news. 'Gemma, it's not Arden. I'm sorry.'

Gemma closed her eyes, and took a deep, shuddering breath. For a moment Mallory thought her friend was going to faint, and reached out to support her, but she remained steady, and when she spoke, her voice only shook a little.

'Do you know who it is?'

'No. They're strangers.'

Gemma's eyes opened again, and when Mallory saw the pain locked away behind them, she wondered for the first time whether Kris's prescience was such a good thing. It would have been better for Gemma if the strangers' arrival had been unannounced, rather than to have raised her hopes so cruelly.

Kragen left his scythe, and joined his wife.

'Shall we ride out to meet them?' he asked softly.

'No,' Mallory decided. 'They'll be here soon enough.' To Gemma she added, 'Come inside.'

A short while later they were sitting quietly in the kitchen, drinking herbal tea.

'Who else could be looking for me?' Gemma asked eventually, then, as the obvious answer occurred to her, she asked 'What are they wearing?'

'Travelling clothes. Not grey,' Mallory replied.

'The raiders have never been seen in this area,' Kragen added. 'And Winder would not have directed

106

them here if he sensed that they meant you any harm.'

'I don't believe anyone with evil intent could ever find their way to the valley,' Mallory said thoughtfully. 'How else have we remained so isolated and peaceful?'

Kragen nodded. 'Whoever they are, you're safe here,' he told Gemma. 'Don't worry about that.'

Just over an hour later, Vance came to report that four horsemen were approaching, Winder and his son Rulon having accompanied the two strangers. They all went outside to watch them arrive. Gemma thought that one of the newcomers looked familiar, and as they drew nearer she realized who he was, and a small portion of her earlier disappointment was replaced by a genuine gladness.

'Hello, Hewe!' she called. He waved back, and Gemma explained to Mallory and Kragen, 'He's a friend, one of Jordan's men from Great Newport. You remember, I told you about them, and about the Underground.'

The horsemen were only a few paces away now.

'At last!' Hewe exclaimed. 'It's the witch from the northern isles!' His broad grin stifled any objections from Gemma's friends. 'If I'd known how hard it was going to be to find you, I wouldn't have bothered!' He dismounted and walked towards her. 'Burned down any cities recently?' he asked.

'No,' Gemma replied, smiling as she gave him a brief hug. 'But I *have* managed a few other things.'

'So I see,' Hewe commented, looking around. 'I can see why you and Arden felt this place worth saving. Where is he?'

Mallory tensed at the question, but Gemma remained composed.

'It's a long story,' she replied softly but firmly.

Hewe's scarred face grew serious. He glanced at the others, and Gemma introduced him to Kragen's family. Hewe shook hands with all four, much to the boys' delight, then turned to his own companions.

'This is Dale, a colleague from Altonbridge.' The man

he indicated was slim and wiry, his dark hair cropped short. He bowed slightly in greeting. 'And I expect you know Winder and Rulon,' Hewe went on. 'They were kind enough to guide us here – though I rather suspect that they were anxious to keep an eye on two disreputable-looking characters like us.'

Winder was about to protest, then saw the twinkle in Hewe's eyes and admitted the truth of his words.

'We get few visitors here,' the farmer said. 'Fewer still who would ask after Gemma.'

Hewe nodded, not at all put out.

'Why are you looking for me?' Gemma asked.

'That's another long story,' he replied.

'Come inside, all of you,' Mallory said. She had been worried by the newcomers' sinister appearance – Hewe was wearing his usual black – but Gemma's ready acceptance of them had put her mind at rest. 'Talking is much easier with something to wet the tongue.'

'I won't argue with that,' Hewe replied, and they all trooped into the farmhouse, except for Winder and Rulon who, seeing that all was well, excused themselves and rode back home.

Gemma was prevailed upon to tell her tale first and did so, beginning with the journey up into the high mountains. She described her flight, and, with Mallory's help, told of the restoration of the river. Then she described her long trek with the meyr-kats, and her capture by the Grey Raiders. She was telling them about her escape when she noticed Dale nodding, as if in agreement. She looked at him questioningly.

'Please go on,' he said, but Gemma's curiosity had been roused.

'Has this ever happened before?' she asked.

'We've suspected for some time that a few of the raiders can control elementals to some extent,' he replied. 'And you've just confirmed our other report.'

'What other report?'

Dale and Hewe exchanged glances.

'Dacey is one of our own men,' Hewe said, 'and his story tallies with yours exactly. He'll be glad to know that you got away safely.'

'So *that's* why he tried to help me!' Gemma said. 'He even warned me not to admit that I was from the north.'

'He'd have liked to help you more,' Dale went on, 'but he was in a rather difficult position.'

'That's putting it mildly,' Hewe added. 'Your involvement with the elementals was something completely new, and one of the reasons we were so keen to find you.'

Gemma ignored that, and pursued her own line of enquiry.

'Why were the Grey Raiders carrying dragonflower seeds?'

'That's what Dacey was trying to find out,' Dale replied. 'The other discoveries came as a bonus.'

'We still don't know why they're doing it, or who they're trading with,' Hewe went on, 'though I'll wager the Guild is mixed up in it somewhere.'

'The Guild?' Kragen spoke for the first time. 'That's the government you're pledged to overthrow?'

'Yes, and the sooner the better,' Dale replied, sounding angry and determined.

'You haven't finished your story, Gemma,' Hewe said.

'There isn't much more to tell,' she responded. 'After we climbed out of the cave, we spent some time earning our living as entertainers . . .'

'I'd like to have seen that,' Hewe laughed.

'Then the meyrkats and I split up, and I found my way back here. That's when I heard about Arden.' She swallowed hard. 'I've been here three months now.'

'That's the most incredible story I've ever heard,' Dale said, shaking his head in amazement.

'I told you she was special,' Hewe remarked.

'Not you too!' Gemma laughed, thinking of Ashlin's words. 'Right, I've finished. Now will you tell us why you've come searching for me?'

'That's easy,' Hewe replied. 'We've come to ask for your help. And to tell you that we're not the only ones looking for you.'

CHAPTER FOURTEEN

'Who are the others?' Gemma asked quickly.

'There's the raiders of course, but you already know that,' Hewe answered. 'And the Guild.'

'Haven't they forgotten about me yet?' she asked wryly.

'Well, they did for a while, but the situation has changed recently – and not for the better.' Hewe paused, marshalling his thoughts. 'I'd better start at the beginning. Can I have some more beer? This could take a while.' Mallory obliged and Hewe thanked her, then took a large mouthful.

'When you left the city, the Guild was in a state of turmoil, in spite of the brave face they put on it for the public, and nobody knew whether Mendle was dead or alive. If he *was* alive, he was in hiding, and no one knew where. With the major supplier of the niceties of life gone . . .' Hewe saw that Kragen and Mallory looked puzzled, and hesitated. 'I mean such delights as dragonflower seeds and other drugs, violence to order, and women as slaves and for sex,' he explained briefly. 'With him out of the picture, there was bound to be a power struggle to get hold of such a profitable business, and for a while this suited our purpose – they were so busy fighting amongst themselves that they forgot about making the rest of us suffer.

'Lunket was still Overlord at this stage, though Quillan and his faction were pressing him hard, so I assume that he had gained the biggest share of Mendle's trade. He didn't last long, though. The skyravens

111

returned about three months ago, and the Overlord's palace was blown to pieces, with him inside.'

Gemma shuddered at the memory of the screaming metal birds and the devastating explosions that followed in their wake.

'Our first thought was to arouse the Underground, strike immediately while the Guild was still leaderless, and get rid of them once and for all. But the raids had surprised us as well, and we weren't prepared. By the time we were ready, it was too late – there was a new Overlord, and the Guild appeared united behind him. It all happened so quickly that we should have known there was more than politics involved. The strangest thing of all was that no one, not even the senior Guild members, knows what the new leader's name is. Either that or they're being unbelievably tight-lipped about it in public – and to what purpose? Anyway, whoever he is, his methods became clear soon enough.

'We lost many of our people; some of them were killed, some taken prisoner, and some have just disappeared. Our whole organization is in jeopardy, and we've had to lie low. I've never seen Jordan so close to giving up.'

'Oh, but he mustn't!' Gemma exclaimed, startling everyone. Hewe's words had reminded her of something from her experiences in the floating city, something which had been inadvertently omitted from her earlier, hurried narration. 'The revolution can succeed!'

'How can you know that?' Dale asked.

'It's written in a book in one of Shanti's libraries,' she replied eagerly, and Hewe and his colleague exchanged glances.

'Explain that!' Hewe said, his eyes suddenly intense.

'Each of the libraries contained books which were almost the same, but different somehow,' Gemma told them. 'We discovered that you couldn't move any of the books from one library to another. They contain alternative histories, and, more to the point, alternative futures.'

'Go on.'

'One of the books contained a footnote which described how Jordan had overthrown the rulers of Cleve and set up his own government.' Gemma paused, and her face lost some of its eagerness. 'Only the equivalent volume in the other room didn't have the footnote.'

'So you know the revolution *might* succeed,' Mallory pointed out. 'It's *not* hopeless.'

'I'd like to do a little reading in that library myself,' Hewe said quietly. 'I wonder . . . could you find it again?'

'If we're *meant* to find it we will,' Gemma replied, and she sounded so certain that no one doubted her.

'We'll put the word out,' Dale said, 'but it may not be as easy as all that.'

Hewe thought for a few moments, then continued his story.

'Things looked pretty bad, and the new Overlord's power was growing all the time. The Guild would do anything for him – and you know how ruthless they can be. Even when rivalry and wholesale corruption kept them divided they were a formidable enemy. Now that they seem to be acting as one, they're even more dangerous.'

'Tell them about the new palace,' Dale put in.

'I was just coming to that.' Hewe paused. 'Pretty soon, a new building was under construction on the site of the ruined palace. The guards rounded up hundreds of craftsmen – masons, smiths and woodworkers, as well as general labour. They were given no choice; anyone who argued was soon persuaded. By something subtle, like the murder of one of their children. And once they began work, no one ever saw them again. The whole area is sealed off.

'We haven't been able to see what they're doing, but judging by the amount of raw material that's being taken in, it's going to be huge.'

'There are all sorts of rumours, of course,' Dale said.

'One of which is that the central tower will be a hundred storeys high.'

'That's impossible!' Gemma exclaimed. Even the tallest tower on her home-isle was less than a quarter of that height – and it had been built using the fabled wizardry of ancient times.

'Maybe,' Hewe said. 'Anyway, it's only hearsay. More importantly though, it's obviously more than just a building. There've been all manner of strange noises and vibrations coming from inside the construction area, and there have been reports of strange, impossibly bright lights – as well as ghosts and all the other favourites of gossip.'

'No one knows what's going on, but anyone with sense is afraid of it,' Dale said grimly. 'Of course, the Guild are all for it, claiming city enterprise and other such nonsense. The real reason though, is that they're making piles of money by supplying all the materials, and by creaming off the best of the artisans' work for their own profit.'

'They'll realize their mistake eventually, but by then it will be too late,' Hewe said. 'When their usefulness is exhausted . . .' He shrugged eloquently.

'But where do I fit into all this?' Gemma asked. 'Why are the Guild looking for me?'

'Because the new Overlord issued a list of people he wanted to "interview" just a few days after he came to power. Most of them were madmen – prophets and such like – but all had some interest in magic or the elementals; blue flame devotees, self-proclaimed wizards, and so on. Quite a lot of them went voluntarily, and have never been seen again. But a few of the names were obviously political. At the top of the list were six people for whom a large reward would be paid should they be brought in alive.

'Jordan was one of them. You were another.'

Gemma shivered, a cold draught raising the hairs on the back of her neck. From what Hewe had said earlier, she had been expecting something of this nature, but the importance that had so obviously been attached to her capture made her feel dizzy and afraid.

'Why?' she whispered.

'You do have something of a reputation, you know,' Hewe replied evenly, 'and they are obviously interested in magic.'

'And some in the Guild have very long memories,' Dale added. 'Especially those who were hurt in your fire. But even more than that, your efforts disrupted trade for some time – and in their eyes that's an unforgivable sin.'

'I told you before that no good ever came of arson,' Hewe remarked, a wry smile creasing his broad face. 'So you see – you qualify for that list on both counts – magic and politics.'

'That's not all, I'm afraid,' Dale said, his face serious. 'They found out somehow that you were Arden's companion, and so they're looking for this valley as well.'

There was a stunned silence.

'I'm glad you found it first,' Mallory said eventually, in a small voice.

'What all this boils down to,' Hewe said firmly, trying to be practical, 'is that the Underground is going to have to strike – and soon. We'll be all but helpless before long, and the reasons we had for getting rid of the Overlord and the Guild are doubly true now. And, even if you dismiss their sudden interest in all things magical, it's clear that the struggle we face is more than just political. There are signs of that everywhere. Jordan's seen it coming for a long time – he even spoke of it to you last autumn – but there are things now that are obvious to everyone.

'The blue-flame wall to the west is getting closer; we know that for a fact. Whole chunks of land are disappearing behind what looks like a huge mass of linked elementals. The blue-flame sect is gaining converts every hour. They believe that the end of the world is

115

upon us, and claim to have found some old texts which prove it – though no one that I'd believe has seen them.

'There's an island off the coast which keeps disappearing – literally. Some of our own people have seen it, and one was actually on the island when it vanished. When he eventually got back to the mainland he was babbling and crying, completely insane.'

'So the fisherman was right,' Gemma said, remembering the man's attempt to convince the crowds in Newport.

'Of course,' Hewe recalled. 'That was at Arden's trial, wasn't it?'

Gemma nodded, her face set.

'In short,' Hewe went on, 'the world's cracking up, and Jordan is convinced that the rise of the new Overlord at this time is no coincidence. We'll be fighting more than a corrupt government, and most of the people who admit to magical talent now are mad.'

'Something very strange is happening,' Dale began.

'And that's why we need your help,' Hewe concluded.

CHAPTER FIFTEEN

They talked on long into the evening. Mallory prepared a meal which was eaten thankfully, but nothing interrupted the flow of words. The boys, their eyes wide at the tales they were hearing, hovered unobtrusively, hoping to avoid being sent to bed.

Hewe and Dale gave more details about life in Newport and Altonbridge, and it became clear – not that the group in Mallory's kitchen had needed any proof – that the Underground's planned revolution was necessary, and had been so even before these latest developments. The Guild had been a legal tyranny for decades, allowing a few rich and powerful men to live in luxury while many people suffered in abject poverty. The sheer scale of the injustice described by the two visitors was almost beyond belief.

'The more I hear, the more I realize just how fortunate our sheltered lives have been,' Kragen said. 'How can men and women live like that?'

'For the most part, they have no choice,' Dale answered. 'That's what our organization is pledged to change.'

'They never *will* have a choice if we don't act soon,' Hewe added grimly. 'If we are to succeed, we'll need all the help we can get.' He looked at Gemma once more.

'You still haven't told me how I can be of use,' she said.

'You've got your magical talent,' Mallory told her. 'Even you have to admit that now.'

'Yes, but I can't direct it, or call upon it at will,' Gemma protested. 'I've only ever accomplished anything when I've been furious, or drugged – or both! Or else when someone has helped me.'

'Your talent is strong,' Hewe said. 'Even if it is a little wild . . .' He grinned. 'It would still be of great value to us. We have few enough people who are capable of wizardry, enchantments or whatever, and who still have a sane head on their shoulders. It's a rare combination these days.'

'There are others?'

'A few, and they'll help you all they can. You won't be alone.' Hewe paused. 'Jordan believes you to be very important, and I'm not about to argue with him. He's been right too often about matters like this – and everything you've told me backs up what he says.'

'Perhaps the saving of this valley was just the first step in the journey that fate has planned for you,' Mallory said. Gemma shook her head, not liking the idea at all, but her friend went on. 'First of all, you were called to this continent, then you found the stone and Arden, and survived the desert. *You* deciphered the secrets of the floating city, and brought life back to this place. But that *wasn't* what you came to the south for. You're meant to go on; waiting around obviously doesn't suit you. It would be good for you to have a purpose again.'

In the silence that followed, Mallory noticed her sons, trying to hide behind their father's broad back.

'You two!' she exclaimed. 'Get to bed!' She marched round the table and ushered them out of the room.

'Is Gemma going away, Mummy?' Jon asked as he and his brother were herded up the stairs.

'I don't know, little one,' his mother replied, following in their reluctant footsteps.

The three men looked at Gemma, and she wilted under their combined scrutiny.

'You don't *have* to decide now,' Hewe said eventually,

118

'but I must get back to Newport as soon as I can, and I'd like you to come with me.' He waited, but Gemma still said nothing. After a while he went on, 'This valley is a haven for you now, and I understand your need for it, but eventually – if what is happening is as serious as we believe – it won't be safe *anywhere*, not even here.' He sounded uncharacteristically gentle. 'It's your choice, and I wouldn't blame you if you decided to stay. This place is at least partly invisible to the outside world.'

'You found it, though,' Gemma said quietly.

'That could be because they were meant to find you,' Mallory said as she came back into the room.

'Let's not look for significance in *everything*,' Hewe replied. 'We may have just been lucky.'

'And yet if you can find me, then so can others,' Gemma said. 'And so therefore just by being here, I put the whole valley in danger.'

'No!' Kragen exclaimed. 'This is your home now – you will *always* be welcome here. A threat to you is a threat to us all, and one that we would be willing to face. Our safety must not be a factor in your decision.'

'Well said!' Dale commented, looking at the farmer with increased respect.

'I only wish,' Kragen went on, 'that some of us could come with you – if you should decide to go.'

'So do I!' Gemma exclaimed, smiling for the first time in hours. She glanced at Mallory. 'You were all right in the mountains. Do you fancy a trip to Newport?'

It was only a light-hearted suggestion, and not meant seriously, but Kragen looked worried, and Mallory did not respond.

'I was only joking!' Gemma told them quickly, looking anxiously from one to the other. Then Mallory grinned, and the moment passed.

'I was only all right as long as you were with me,' she said. 'I fell apart soon enough after you flew off.' She paused. 'Besides, I can't go now.' She went to stand

119

by Kragen, and Gemma suddenly knew what her friend was about to say. The next moment proved her correct.

'I'm going to have a baby,' Mallory told them, and her husband took her in his arms.

'That's wonderful!' Gemma exclaimed, delighted for them.

'Congratulations,' Hewe said.

'Thank you,' Mallory mumbled from the depths of her husband's embrace. 'Sorry about the timing of this announcement.'

'Good news is always welcome,' Dale said.

Gemma went to hug Mallory, but was a little tentative at first, not knowing how delicate her friend was.

'I'm not made of glass,' Mallory said, laughing and holding Gemma tightly. When they drew apart, the two women still held hands; without conscious effort, Gemma looked 'inside' Mallory and checked on the progress of the unborn child. Then she suddenly realized what she was doing and withdrew, embarrassed, to find her friend looking at her intently, a smile on her face.

'Well?' Mallory asked.

Gemma could not meet her gaze.

'She's fine,' she whispered.

'She?' Kragen asked. 'Are you sure?'

Mallory had no such doubts over Gemma's prediction.

'We'll name her after you,' she told Gemma delightedly. 'Would you like that?'

'I'd be more than honoured,' Gemma replied quietly. 'I'm sorry – I didn't mean to pry.'

Mallory took her hands again and held them tightly.

'I'd have been upset if you hadn't,' she said. 'You're a healer, Gemma, and there's no reason to be ashamed of that, or to think of it as prying.'

'After all, that's the one aspect of your magic that you can control,' Kragen added, understanding now.

Gemma nodded, then her instinctive awareness spread once more. She felt an embryonic life pulse beneath her touch, and for a moment she saw an image of the future child, looking down upon the world from a great height, as if she were standing on top of a mountain. The vision faded, then was gone, leaving Gemma with no notion as to its meaning. Something of her bewilderment must have shown in her face, because Mallory was quick to ask her what she had sensed.

'I don't know exactly,' Gemma replied, 'but she will be special.' She was absolutely convinced of that, but could not explain why, and felt oddly reluctant to talk about what she had seen.

'But she *is* healthy?' Kragen asked.

'Yes.' Gemma released Mallory's hands. 'She's perfectly healthy.'

'When will she be born?' Hewe asked.

'In about six months,' Mallory replied.

'I wish I could stay to see her born,' Gemma said. A silence descended on the room at her words.

'I'm coming with you,' she told Hewe, 'but I have two conditions. The first is that the Underground keeps in regular touch with the valley. If Arden does ever get back here, I want to know – and I want him to know where *I* am.'

'Agreed,' Hewe said. 'What else?'

'We get this business over within six months,' she said, smiling now. 'So that I can be here to see my namesake born.'

'I'll do what I can,' he replied with a grin, but they both knew that this was something beyond any individual's control.

'When do we leave?'

'The day after tomorrow,' he suggested. 'At first light. Will that give you enough time to prepare?'

Gemma nodded. She knew they needed to hurry, but was grateful for a day in which to say her farewells. No amount of time would be enough for her to feel confident in her own abilities; she would just have to

121

trust her intuition – and the aid of her friends.

The next day passed in a flurry of activity, though it seemed to Gemma that everyone else was doing all the work, while she sat quietly in the eye of the storm.

Her horse was brought from Elway's farm at the southern end of the valley. Arden had supplied Gemma with Mischa when he had rescued her in the desert, and she had ridden her ever since. Saddle and harness were prepared and the few items she needed were packed into two small bags. Hewe refused the offer of provisions, saying that they were better travelling light, and would eat at village taverns or wayside inns.

Mallory cut Gemma's hair short, and sewed a veil onto the back of a leather hat so that what was left of the tell-tale colour would be hidden on the journey.

Dale spent much of that day talking to the people who lived at the northern end of the valley, learning all he could of the passes and routes to the outside world. Meanwhile, Hewe learnt as much as was possible of the valley itself, ready to report his findings to Jordan.

By noon, everyone in the valley knew of Gemma's intended departure, and she received many visitors, who wished her well and promised her a warm welcome on her return. However, one of the callers had a different message. Ashlin appeared even more nervous than usual when he joined Gemma and Mallory in the farm kitchen, and before either of them could speak, he made a sudden plea.

'I want to come with you! Please, let me come with you.' His words tumbled out so fast and he looked so apprehensive that the two women were taken aback, and it was several moments before Gemma spoke.

'Why do you want to come?' she asked eventually.

'Because I know what you're doing is important, and I want to help,' he replied eagerly. 'And . . . and I . . . you mean a lot to me.'

'But you can't leave the valley – you'll be ill,' Mallory pointed out.

'You were all right when you were with Gemma,' he responded. 'Perhaps this time I will be too. And I promise I won't be a burden to you, Gemma. If I *am* ill, I'll leave you and come back here. After all, I *was* able to lead Kragen and Horan back from the mountains – they were much worse off than me,' he concluded persuasively.

'Do you have any idea of what we're going to do, what you'll be getting into?' Gemma asked.

'I'm not afraid of danger,' he replied defensively.

'No one is questioning your courage,' she said. 'We know you better than that. But even *I* don't have a proper idea of what we're facing, or how we can hope to overcome it. You've never been anywhere like Newport – it's a huge, ugly, frightening city – and that's on a good day! Now there's going to be fighting as well, and nothing in your life can have prepared you for that.'

'I'll take my chances,' he said, sullen now.

Gemma was silent, considering.

'I appreciate your offer,' she said at last. 'And I'll be happy for you to come with us – so long as you realize that I may not be able to protect you from the travelling illness. If that happens, you'll be on your own.'

'Of course,' Ashlin replied, and a broad grin spread over his face.

'Then go and find Hewe and ask his permission to join us. Tell him I'd like you to come.'

'Thank you!' he said, almost shouting. 'Thank you!' He left, almost tripping over the door rail in his haste.

'Do you think that's wise?' Mallory asked quietly.

'Who can tell?' Gemma replied. 'I'm not even sure I know what *I'm* doing!'

CHAPTER SIXTEEN

The first four days of their journey passed uneventfully; although they met a few people, nobody questioned Gemma's identity. Ashlin's health remained good, in spite of the fact that they were now many leagues beyond the boundaries of the valley, and his confidence grew with each new day.

The group had left the valley by crossing Raven's Crag and travelling down the same precipitous path that Hewe and Dale had climbed two days earlier. After an hour's descent, Gemma had looked back, but could see no trace of the way they had come. The cliffs looked impassable – yet another example of how the valley protected itself from the outside world. The only gap in the rock wall was where the river emerged from a sheer-sided chasm, and the water tumbled forth in a series of waterfalls and rapids. Had the river not been running, the ravine would have been a jumble of boulders, impossible for horses and extremely difficult for men. Two leagues further on, the river was joined by another, and it was beside this joint flow that the party now rode.

They had left Kragen's farm at first light, and were thus able to reach their planned shelter by nightfall. It was an isolated holding, and it had been the farmer's complete lack of knowledge of or interest in the land which lay only a day's journey to the south of his home that had spurred Hewe to investigate further. On this occasion, their host showed no surprise at the increased number of the party, and accepted without question the story that the cliffs had proved an impenetrable barrier.

They followed the river for the next few days, stopping to rest at taverns in villages which grew in size and prosperity as they moved further north. Then, on the fourth day out of the valley, they turned away from the river as Dale led them to a lone house in a tree-filled hollow. Before they had even had a chance to dismount, the door opened and an old woman came out to greet them. Her hair was white and she leaned heavily on a stick, but her eyes were bright and her smile warm.

'Good,' she remarked. 'I could do with some company.'

'Where are those boys of yours?' Dale asked.

'My sons travel a lot – as you well know,' she retorted, then glanced at Gemma. 'You found her then.'

'Have you ever known us to fail?' Hewe asked, grinning and spreading his hands wide.

'You should know better than to ask an old woman like me about the failings of men,' she replied. 'Well, don't just stand there!' With that she turned and went inside, and the others followed.

'As these two mannerless ruffians haven't seen fit to introduce me,' she went on, as they settled themselves, 'I'll do it myself. I'm Adria. You, I presume, are Gemma and Arden.'

'No. I'm Ashlin,' the young man replied. 'Arden's—'

'Arden's missing,' Gemma said firmly. The mention of his name had been a shock to her but she refused to let it show. Adria looked at her thoughtfully.

'They tell me that you have talent,' she said.

'I think they're right,' Gemma replied. 'But I don't know how to use it properly.'

'Tell me all,' Adria said, sitting back in her chair.

The subsequent conversation lasted several hours. For the most part, Adria was content to listen, asking only an occasional question. She was especially interested in the spell within the rocking stone, the floating city, and Gemma's encounter with the elementals. The

125

three men took little part in the recital, but added a few details here and there. After a while, it grew dark outside, Dale lit lamps and found them all some food.

When Gemma finally brought her tale to a close, she was very tired, and her throat was sore from talking so much, but Adria still seemed alert and eager for more.

'This magic inside your head,' she began. 'How do you see it?'

'Like golden sparks or flashes, within a great darkness,' Gemma replied. 'The light is very elusive.'

'And you have to give in to the blackness in order to find the light?'

'Yes. How did you know that?'

Adria ignored the question.

'And you can be helped by anger, or by dragonflower seeds?' she asked.

'Apparently. I've no idea why.'

'Didn't those wizards in the north teach you *anything* about magic?' the old woman asked.

'No. I was only a little girl, and they saw no need.'

'Fools!' Adria said disgustedly. 'All men, I suppose?'

'All except one, and she disappeared during The Levelling.'

'Come here, child.'

Gemma did not mind being addressed so by Adria. She knew that there was more to the old woman than met the eye, and had already come to admire her feisty spirit and forthright nature. So she obediently went over and knelt before her hostess, who then placed her hands on either side of Gemma's head. She rested her thumbs on Gemma's temples, and the other cool fingers probed gently behind and below her ears. Adria closed her eyes and remained perfectly still for so long that Gemma wondered if the old woman had dozed off. Then the black swirls of unreason began to rise within her, still frightening in spite of her knowledge of what lay beyond. She allowed herself to sink into them,

126

somehow knowing what was required of her. The familiar golden sparks appeared, flying chaotically in all directions.

'Magic is energy,' Adria said calmly. 'It is present in us all, but only a few have the ability or the patience to master it and put it to any use. An arrow can kill a man but only when given energy by the archer and his bow. It is the energy, not the arrow, that kills. So it is with magic, except that its application is infinitely more subtle. The man or woman with the skill to direct and concentrate their own magical power, and to gather it from other sources, has a rare and special talent. These people were once called wizards, but it seems that that term is frowned upon nowadays.' She paused, and Gemma realized that a small measure of order had come to the chaos in her mind. She felt quite relaxed, yet the golden flashes were still there and she was actually beginning to see a pattern to their movements, a structure to their power. She sank ever deeper into her trance, and Adria's words continued.

'You have many sources from which you can gain power. For others it has been objects or places which have retained the vestiges of magic from past events; blind sources of nature, random and unpredictable. Or, in the cases of utmost evil, from the minds of fellow men. But for you ... it is something new ... something I do not understand.'

There was silence for a few moments. Gemma was still very relaxed, her breathing slow and deep.

'Try this,' Adria said abruptly.

Light exploded in Gemma's mind, a fountain of golden flame where before there had been only sparks. She felt as though she was floating, lighter than air, yet so strong that she would be capable of anything.

'Learn from this. Remember.' Adria's voice sounded through the blaze and Gemma struggled to obey, but she was so intoxicated that her mind danced on, unable to concentrate.

127

Then suddenly the euphoria ended. Adria removed her hands and sank back into her chair, leaving Gemma dazed and blinking. The old woman looked grey and tired, but was smiling faintly.

'How did you do that?' Gemma began, but Adria held up a wrinkled hand.

'I'll tell you in the morning,' she said, her voice weak but determined. A few moments later she was fast asleep, and Hewe carried her gently up to her bed.

* * *

Very early the next morning, Gemma knocked softly on the door of Adria's bedroom. Dawn was breaking outside, but sleep was no longer possible; there were too many questions waiting to be asked.

'Come in, Gemma,' Adria called softly. The old lady was sitting up in bed, a lace shawl around her shoulders, and her hands folded neatly in front of her.

'Did you sleep well?' she asked, and smiled when Gemma nodded. 'That's one advantage of the boys being away so much. I always have plenty of room for guests. I usually rattle around this old house like a solitary dried pea.' She chuckled, then said, 'Enough of my grumblings. I suppose you have some questions.'

'Yes, but I hardly know where to begin.'

Adria waited patiently.

'Are you a wizard?' Gemma asked eventually.

'Goodness, no!' she replied. 'I have no magical power of my own. My talent is to recognize it in others, and sometimes to help them a little.'

'What you did to me last night—'

'I did nothing to you. I merely showed you the channels you should pursue. You produced all that energy – and it was quite a remarkable performance!'

'Could you show me again?'

'There's no need. You'll remember when you have to,' Adria said. 'Besides, I'm still worn out from my efforts. Are you trying to finish me off?' She smiled, but Gemma was more puzzled than ever.

'I don't understand.'

'You will,' the old woman said confidently. 'You have an incredible talent, and the laws of nature demand that you should be able to utilize it. Accept it, and learn to trust it. Until now, you've only been able to channel the magic by the force of your anger, or by outside means. When you can do it from will-power alone, you'll be something to be reckoned with.' She laughed. 'It's almost enough to make an old woman want to travel again.'

Gemma was floundering. *Will-power?* It did not seem possible that that was enough, yet Adria seemed to take it for granted.

'Where does all this energy come from in the first place?' she asked.

'Now there you have me,' Adria answered, her face serious once more. 'Magic is like any other form of energy. It can't be created from nothing, and it has to be paid for. But you . . . you appear to accept it from a linking of minds – many, not just two—'

'Like the meyrkats?'

'Yes. Or the valley people. But your acceptance of it *does not diminish them*. If anything, from what I've heard, it is a mutually beneficial transaction.' Adria sighed. 'The ultimate source must be somewhere . . . but I don't know what it can be. These groups are important, they're the means by which your magic is often manifested, but you're *also* capable of acting alone – or so it seems.' She shrugged, obviously puzzled, then her eyes twinkled. 'We're both in the dark. But we won't tell the men that. We don't want to disabuse them of the notion that we women know everything.'

Her laughter was infectious and, although Gemma was still confused, she could not help but join in.

* * *

They went on that morning, leaving Adria still in bed. Gemma was concerned, but Dale assured her that there was nothing to worry about. He and Howe had gone up to talk to Adria, and had satisfied themselves that she would soon be up and about.

'She's a tough old bird,' Dale remarked, 'and she's used to being on her own. To tell you the truth, I think she prefers it that way.'

'What about her sons?'

'They spend a lot of time away from home; they're messengers and collectors of information for us,' Hewe replied. 'They're good men.'

'Although their most recent news *isn't* good,' Dale put in.

'What news?' Ashlin asked, eager to learn all he could.

'More trouble in Altonbridge,' Dale answered. 'It would appear that the new government in Newport has decided our citizens don't pay enough taxes, and has been taking measures to rectify the situation. Many of those not willing – or able – to pay have been killed, or have simply disappeared.'

'The outlying villages have also been affected,' Hewe added. 'We'll have to watch our step from here.'

'It's a mess,' Dale concluded, 'and I want to get back to the city just as soon as possible.'

The anxiety in his voice was all the persuasion the others needed to spur their mounts into action.

* * *

They rode without speaking for the most part, and Gemma's thoughts drifted. She mused over Adria's words, and took little notice of where they were going.

When you can do it from will-power alone . . .

Will-power is something you certainly never lacked, a voice inside her head remarked.

130

Cai? she exclaimed in delight. *I thought you'd abandoned me!*

No, Gemma. You left me behind, the ex-wizard returned.

How is it possible for us to talk like this when you're so far away?

You're the one who's far away, he replied. *I haven't been able to sense you for months.*

I've been in a very special place. Hiding from the outside world. Gemma reflected privately that this had been both a good and a bad thing. While she had not been able to communicate with Cai, neither the Grey Raiders nor the Guild had been able to find her – and she had not been disturbed by the siren song of the south.

But you've come out now? Cai said.

I have to. There are some people I must help. Am I doing the right thing?

You are beyond my guidance in such matters, he answered. *Follow your own instincts.*

It's good to hear you again, Gemma told him.

Cai did not respond for a few moments, but when he did, she felt the glow of pleasure unspoken behind his words.

You're only open sometimes, even now. I had a vivid dream of you last night – it felt as though your spirit had reawoken.

She told him briefly of her amazing encounter with Adria.

Ah, he responded. *A latentor. I've heard of such. Heed her teachings well, Gemma.*

You could have taught me. It was half accusation, half regret for missed opportunities.

No. My belief was shattered, and no one can teach from such a position.

Can it never be renewed?

Perhaps you can do that, he said quietly.

How? she asked, eager to help.

131

By being Gemma, he replied enigmatically. *I must go – my own world is calling. Goodbye.*

Wait! she cried, but he was gone. In the sudden internal quiet, the pounding of the horses' hooves seemed very loud.

'Are you all right?' Ashlin sounded worried. 'You're awfully pale.'

'I'm fine,' she replied, wondering whether she and Cai would ever reach a true understanding of each other.

'If there's anything I can do . . . anything at all . . .' he persisted.

Gemma looked at the young man fondly. She liked and respected him, and was comforted by his concern, but he could never fill the aching gaps in her life left by Cai and Arden. That was beyond the power of any man.

CHAPTER SEVENTEEN

They reached Altonbridge after four days of arduous
travelling. Dale went on ahead, entering the city alone
and leaving the other three to wait at the inn of a nearby
village. Hewe and Gemma were both anxious to begin
their journey westward, along the coast to Great
Newport, and felt it wiser not to risk entering the walled
city. Gemma had learnt a great deal about Altonbridge
during their journey. A larger city than Newport, it
owed its size and prosperity to its location at the mouth
of the River Alt, and to the fertile plain which surrounded it. In contrast to Cleve's capital, its business
was trade – by land, sea and river – rather than politics
and reliance on historical advantages. However, it had
been ruthlessly exploited in recent years by Cleve's
ruling Guild and by the Overlord in Newport. Here too,
corruption and injustice had become the norm. There
were the same appalling shanty towns outside the city
walls, the military guards who administered the rule
of corrupt laws, and the same extremes of poverty and
decadence. Because of this, the Underground had had
no difficulty in attracting new recruits; when the
uprising began in Newport it would be followed by
similar action in Altonbridge.

Dale did not return to them but instead sent a
messenger, Croft, with a detailed report of how things
stood in the city. Hewe listened grimly as the courier
told them of the way the situation had deteriorated still
further since his last visit. The Guild's 'tax-collectors'
had made their mark, appropriating goods as well as

money, and transporting everything back to Newport under heavy guard. A number of people had been taken as slaves, and the Underground's organization had come near to breaking point. Dale sent word that they were regrouping, and that he was confident that victory could still be theirs.

Hewe had obviously expected this much, but what followed left even his sanguine spirit shaken. During the last month, the city had suffered three attacks by skyravens; on each occasion, huge explosions had killed or injured hundreds of people, and destroyed many buildings.

'There doesn't seem to be any reason behind it,' Croft told them. 'There are no obviously specific targets – it just seems like sheer vindictiveness, as if they were using us as a test for whatever awful weapons they're currently using. How can it benefit them to flatten small shops and people's homes?'

'Have any of the Guild merchants suffered?' Hewe asked.

'Yes. One of their warehouses was flattened. They took it out on us, of course,' Croft replied bitterly. 'The one thing that *does* seem safe is the city wall. That hasn't been touched, and neither have the bastards who man it and call themselves soldiers.' He took a deep breath. 'And there's more.' He began to tick items off on his fingers. 'One: there's been a marked increase in the amount of elemental activity near here. They've even been seen at sea. Two: it seems that news of our plans has reached the east. There've been few ships come in recently, and those that *do* come act nervously and leave fast. And the coast road has been practically empty for days.'

'Have there been any ships from Quaid?' Gemma asked.

'Not many,' the messenger replied, surprised. 'That's hundreds of leagues away.'

'Why do you ask that?' Hewe queried.

'Because Quaid was the place mentioned in the same book that had the footnote about Jordan,' she told him.

'Well done,' he said, and turned to Croft. 'Make sure you learn as much as you can from anyone from Quaid.'

The messenger nodded, then asked, 'Was that the book in the floating city?'

'Yes,' Gemma replied.

'That was the third point. Dale has passed the word out, and if anyone in our network sees it, we'll hear pretty quickly.'

'Good. Anything else?'

'Just that if you're travelling by the coast road, watch out for demons.'

'What!'

'I'm only reporting what we've been told,' the man said defensively. 'Apparently, they always come at night, screaming fit to burst your eardrums. There've been too many sightings to ignore.'

'We'll worry about demons if and when we meet them,' Hewe said. 'What about the Grey Raiders?'

'They've been quiet lately. Rumour has it they're busy elsewhere.' He waited for a few moments, ascertained that they had no more questions, then said, 'I'll be getting back now. Dale says you're to go as soon as you can. Leave Altonbridge to us – we won't let you down.'

'I know you won't, and we appreciate your help. Let's hope the next time we meet will be in happier circumstances,' Hewe replied.

'Goodbye. Good luck.' With that, Croft was gone.

'Good luck!' Gemma called after him.

'We should be able to reach Newport in about seven or eight days,' Hewe told her. 'And by the sound of things, that won't be a moment too soon.'

*　　*　　*

The great coast road ran the length of Cleve's northern seaboard, linking Altonbridge with Great Newport and

135

the third city, Clevemouth, far to the west. For most of its two hundred leagues it stayed close to the ocean, as its name implied, but for the first part of their journey, it took Hewe, Gemma and Ashlin overland, and due west. Here the road traversed good farming land but avoided the salt-swamps to the north. It was only three days later, when the Diamond Desert pressed in from the south, that their course took them in sight of the sea. There were no villages here, but Hewe led them to a small abandoned stone cottage which was hidden from the road.

'It's not much,' he said, 'but I've slept here before and it's a roof over our heads.'

'Shall I gather some wood for a fire?' Ashlin asked, eager to help. His health was still good, and he was growing in confidence as his knowledge of the outside world grew.

'We've made good time,' Hewe remarked later, as they sat round the fire, watching the sparks fly up into the black night. 'With luck we'll reach Newport in another three days.'

'It's a better road than I remember,' Gemma said.

'It gets worse from here on,' Hewe replied. 'The land's not as flat, and we have to make a few detours between the rocks and the sand dunes.'

'Where was it that you first landed in Cleve?' Ashlin asked Gemma.

'It must be somewhere near here,' she replied. 'The landscape's beginning to look familiar. Let's hope we don't get the same reception from the Grey Raiders that I did then.'

'We seem to have been lucky so far,' Ashlin remarked. 'No raiders, and no soldiers either.'

'Almost *too* lucky,' Hewe said thoughtfully.

'What do you mean?' Ashlin asked.

'The road's awfully quiet – even the Guild's convoys seem to have stopped. And that *never* happens. What do they know that we don't?' The flippant question could not hide his underlying worry. Gemma was about to try and reassure him when the music that had first called her to the southern lands began again, filling her head with its sweet longing. Losing all interest in the conversation, she stood up and turned to face the south, her eyes rapt.

'What's the matter?' Ashlin asked, worried.

'Don't you hear it?' she asked, her voice dreamy. 'I have to go.' She moved forward, but Hewe's bulk blocked her path. When he reached out and took her by her shoulders, she thought for a moment that he was going to shake her. But his grip, though firm, was gentle.

'If you go south from here,' he said softly, 'you'll be alone in the desert – and lost. And this time, there'll be no Arden to rescue you.' He was hoping to shock her back to reason, and was rewarded when her eyes flashed at the mention of Arden's name. Behind Hewe she could see Ashlin hovering uncertainly, his face a mask of concern.

'But you don't understand!' she wailed, covering her ears with her hands. 'It drives you mad. I'd forgotten how strong—'

'You beat it before,' Hewe said calmly. 'And we're here to help you.'

'I didn't beat it,' Gemma replied, her eyes wide. 'I only postponed its victory.'

'You turned the kite away from it,' Ashlin reminded her.

'Only because I had to get to the stone. That was too important to give up on,' Gemma said.

'Your task now is just as important,' Hewe said. 'We need you, Gemma.'

As she looked at him, he saw the pain and incomprehension in her soft grey eyes.

'Arden told me that it was just the sound of the wind in underground caves,' Gemma said, as though trying to convince herself.

'It's all things to all men,' Hewe replied, 'but if you follow it now, you'll die.'

'Fight it, Gemma,' Ashlin said, then his face suddenly creased with pain and he began coughing.

'I *am*,' she told him.

'Good girl,' Hewe said. 'Does it help if we talk to you?'

Gemma nodded. They sat down, and Hewe began to tell her all about his earlier travels, occasionally prompting her to speak, and generally keeping her mind occupied. They discussed their visit to Adria, and Gemma tried to recreate the feeling of relaxed power that she had experienced then. This helped her a little. The fire died down, unheeded, until only a few red embers glowed in the darkness. Hewe had his arm around Gemma's shoulders, trying to lend her comfort and strength. As they talked, their heads together, they did not notice Ashlin, who was now curled in a ball, coughing silently as his chest burned.

Finally, deep in the night, Hewe felt Gemma's body relax suddenly and she lay back thankfully.

'It's stopped,' she whispered, her voice hoarse. Moments later, she was asleep. Hewe covered her with a blanket, glanced at Ashlin who also appeared to be sleeping, then went to check on the horses. When he was satisfied that all was well, he built up the fire again, and prepared to sit out the remainder of the night on guard. He could not risk Gemma sneaking away while he slept.

It was a sorry-looking trio that set out the next morning. Gemma was worn out by her night's struggle, Hewe had had no sleep at all, and Ashlin was silent and pale. He had fallen asleep eventually, but the pain in his chest was still there. He made no mention of it, however, and the others only assumed that he was as tired as they were.

They rode on, moving slowly now due to the rougher terrain and their own fatigue. The day grew hotter, and Hewe called a halt shortly after midday.

138

'If I don't get some rest soon, I'm going to fall off,' he said, 'and the horses won't thank us for riding them in this heat.'

They found some shade under a rock overhang, and Hewe was soon asleep. The others dozed fitfully, Ashlin taking comfort from Gemma's nearness. His coughing had stopped, and the pain was gradually diminishing. He dreaded the thought of having to return to the valley alone, and hoped that his burning chest would soon ease.

After resting for two hours, they roused Hewe and went on. They had had the road to themselves for a day and a half now, and so were surprised when they spotted a man a little way ahead, walking towards them.

'What's he doing out here, alone and on foot?' Hewe wondered aloud, but Gemma didn't hear him. The solitary figure looked suddenly familiar. She spurred Mischa into a gallop, leaving her companions to gape at each other in astonishment before hastening to follow.

As Gemma drew nearer, she grew more certain of the newcomer's identity, and her heart leapt for joy as her mount pounded down the sandy trail.

'Arden!' she yelled, wanting to wave, but not daring to take a hand from the reins. 'Arden!'

It *was* him. His fair hair was longer than she remembered, and he was walking with a slight limp, but his dark, rugged face and the way he carried himself were unmistakable. It *was* him!

As Gemma brought Mischa to a skidding halt, Arden stopped a few paces away. Sand flew and the mare whinnied as Gemma flung herself from the saddle and ran towards him, her arms stretched wide in welcome. He watched impassively as she approached, and something in his green eyes stopped her in her tracks.

'Arden, are you all right?' A sudden cold fear touched her heart, but she refused to let anything crush the exultation she felt at having found her love again. She was confident that she could heal him of any ill; they were united again, and nothing else mattered. She took a step forward.

'No!' Arden raised his hands as if warding off unwanted attention. 'They are not demons!'

Gemma almost cried out – she had so longed to hear the sound of his voice, but his words made no sense.

'Arden! It's me, Gemma.'

At first, he did not react, then a small smile touched his lips, and Gemma could hardly contain her happiness as she closed the gap between them.

Then his whole face changed in an instant, grew indistinct, and wavered like a heat haze. Within moments, his entire body was shimmering, losing all substance, and Gemma watched with mounting horror as the elemental returned to its natural form. Then the blue flame-like being sped away, and the road was empty once more.

'No!' Gemma's voice cracked, and her legs gave way beneath her. She knelt in the sand, her mouth open and her eyes staring wildly. 'Arden!' It was a long, drawn-out scream of despair, a tortured plea against the wanton cruelty that had allowed her such joy, only to tear it away so cruelly. Her breath came in dry, agonized gulps, and she did not hear Hewe approach her from behind or feel his hand rest gently on her shoulder. By then her body was shaking violently, her mind a blank void of denial and disbelief.

CHAPTER EIGHTEEN

They travelled no further that day, and set up camp on a small beach. It was hidden from the road by a low cliff, and Hewe virtually carried Gemma down to this place of relative safety, leaving Ashlin to follow with the horses. Both men had witnessed the elemental's impersonation and subsequent flight, and though they had been shaken by it, they could only imagine the traumatic effect it had had on Gemma.

She had not spoken since the incident, and had not reacted to their concern. As the afternoon wore on, her shaking lessened and she began to cry silently. The two men tried in vain to comfort her, holding her and talking softly, but with little effect.

Eventually, they managed to persuade her to accept a cup of hot broth which Ashlin had brewed from their meagre supplies. She sipped it tentatively, her eyes fixed on the sinuous flame of the campfire.

'It's cold,' she said, a little while later.

Hewe and Ashlin saw that she was shivering, so Hewe fetched a blanket to protect her from the sea breeze. He draped it around her hunched shoulders.

'Is that better?' he asked.

She nodded, still not taking her eyes from the fire.

'Why did it do that?' she said, in a small voice.

'I don't know, Gemma,' Hewe replied. 'Nobody knows why the elementals behave as they do.'

'It was so wonderful to see him again . . . I love him, you know.' A little more strength crept back into her voice, as if she was daring him to dispute her statement.

'I never doubted that for a moment,' Hewe replied gently, then glanced at Ashlin. The young man sat quietly, grieving over Gemma's heartbreak but also over his own forlorn love for her. *What strange creatures we humans are*, Hewe thought. *To desire so much, and to suffer so for it.* He smiled ruefully; it was not often that he cast himself in the role of philosopher.

'And now he's probably dead,' Gemma went on miserably. 'It would have been better if he'd left me to die in the desert.'

'Don't say that—' Hewe began, but Ashlin interrupted him.

'I don't think he's dead.' His voice was an odd mixture of hope, excitement and uncertainty. As Gemma looked at him, there was a spark of life in her eyes for the first time, and Ashlin looked down as if he were reluctant to go on.

'Why not?' Gemma asked.

'What . . . what we saw earlier . . . it *was* him, wasn't it?' he asked.

'Of course it was!' Gemma's eyes were brimming again. 'I'd know him anywhere.'

'In every detail?' Ashlin persisted, in spite of the warning looks he was getting from Hewe.

'Yes. His hair was a mess and he was limping, but otherwise he was the same,' she answered.

'What are you getting at?' Hewe asked pointedly. He could not understand why Ashlin was pursuing a subject that must be so painful for Gemma.

'Elementals can take any form they choose, right?' the young man went on, more confident now.

'Yes, but—'

'Do they invent shapes, or do they *copy* them?' Ashlin asked. He paused to let that thought register, then added, 'How can the elemental have created such an exact replica unless it had seen Arden? The *real* Arden.'

'You think so?' Gemma exclaimed, sudden hope welling within her.

'His hair would have grown since you last saw him, and it's possible that he could have hurt his leg,' Ashlin replied, basking in the warmth of her new regard.

'He could be near us now!' Gemma exploded. Hewe was worried. She had grasped at Ashlin's theory, embracing it as the truth, and although he hated to throw cold water on her enthusiasm, he knew he had to put Ashlin's suggestion in perspective.

'There is nowhere round here that he could be,' he told Gemma. 'Besides, you know how fast the elementals move. It could have come from leagues away.'

Gemma looked at him resentfully, but acknowledged the truth of his statement.

'You're right,' she conceded, although it was clear that she would not completely give up her new-found hope. Hewe steeled himself and went on.

'The elementals do copy shapes,' he said, 'but that could have been Arden at some time in the past.'

Gemma's face fell.

'I hope you're right, Ashlin,' Hewe said as the young man glowered silently. 'There's every chance that you are. But you have to face the possibility that it was an illusion and nothing more.' He noted with satisfaction that while Gemma appeared to accept his words, she was not returning to the arms of shock, arms that had held her in their numbing grasp all afternoon. Ashlin was also recovering his composure, and it was he who broke the ensuing silence.

'What did he say to you?'

' "They are not demons",' Gemma quoted. 'Whatever that means.'

'Could it be a message?'

'If it is, I don't understand it.'

'What do demons look like?' Ashlin asked.

'I don't know,' she replied.

'Let's hope we never find out,' Hewe said.

* * *

The rest of their journey passed uneventfully. Three more days' riding brought them near the outskirts of Great Newport, which looked much the same as Gemma remembered it. The great grey walls were stained in places, and were surrounded by the squalid hopelessness of those too poor to gain admittance. From a distance they could see no sign of the new tower that was being built by the Overlord, but a pall of smoke hung over the city like a grey shroud.

They had left the coastal road some leagues back, and had ridden cross-country, hoping to avoid the patrols of Guild soldiers who would – for a price – escort travellers through the hostile shanty town to the safety of the city gates. Gemma knew from past experience that once there, more money would need to change hands before anyone was permitted to enter the city of a thousand vices.

'We'll wait here until dark,' Hewe said. 'It'll be much safer getting in then.'

So they rested, and watched the sun go down from the shelter of a small copse. As the lower rim of the majestic orange ball touched the far horizon, Ashlin stared hard, then said, 'There's a blue ring round the sun! Do you see it?'

Squinting, Gemma could indeed see that the sun was surrounded by a blue circle, with a fainter green one within that. She had seen this corona before, but it had never been so strong. A shiver ran down her spine, and she glanced at Hewe.

'It's getting closer all the time,' he said. 'That's the blue-flame wall we're seeing,' he explained to Ashlin.

'What will happen when it reaches the city?' the young man asked, but Hewe didn't answer.

A little while later, as the sky darkened, another form of illumination came, this time from the city. Crackling flashes of blue-white light reflected off the smoke cloud overhead, resembling inverted lightning.

'The tower?' Gemma asked.

144

'The tower,' Hewe confirmed. 'Time to go.'

They rode as far as the shanty town, then left their horses in the care of one of the silent inhabitants, who showed no sign of surprise at their arrival. Hewe led Gemma and Ashlin through the maze of hovels, picking his way carefully but confidently in the half-light.

He's like a cat, Gemma thought. *And this is his territory.* She followed as quietly as she could, and Ashlin walked just behind her, his eyes drawn to the horror of the way in which these twilight people were forced to live.

They entered one of the dark dwellings, and Hewe rapped out an obvious signal on an inner door. This opened a few moments later, and as they were ushered inside, faceless men moved a table and opened the trap door beneath. Hewe went down first, warning his companions that the steps were worn and slippery in places. Gemma descended into the utter blackness of the true underground, grateful for the presence of the men in front and behind her. At the foot of the steps, they came to one of the straight tunnels which Gemma remembered from her earlier visit. A faint light shone in the distance, glinting off the damp walls and floor.

'We'll wait a moment until your eyes get used to the light,' Hewe said. Then he led them into the gloom, passing several side tunnels, and hearing unseen creatures scurry away. The tunnel branched, and Hewe led them on, turning right then left.

'Not far now,' he told them.

A torch glowed in its bracket a hundred paces away. Before they reached it, two men stepped out of the shadows and blocked their path, their silhouettes showing that they carried knives.

'Is this how you greet long-lost friends?' Hewe asked jovially, but the reply was ice-cold.

'If you're a friend, then you'll know today's password.'

'Egan, is that you? It's Hewe, man! I've been away three months – how am I going to know today's

145

password?' Gemma could hear the dangerous under-currents of anger in the big man's voice.

'How did you get in here without the password?' the other man asked.

'Because the men outside the walls aren't so dense as you are!' Hewe exploded. 'They can recognize a friend when they see one!'

His inquisitor stiffened, but the man called Egan put a hand on his arm.

'It's all right, Ambros. That's Hewe all right – I recognize his temper.' He waved them forward. 'Who's that with you?'

'Gemma and Ashlin,' Hewe replied. 'Hasn't word reached you?'

'It's been pretty chaotic here of late,' Egan said. 'We knew you were coming, but had no idea when you'd arrive.'

The two sentries inspected the newcomers as they drew closer to the torch.

'I'm sorry for the poor welcome,' Egan went on. 'Things have been rough, and we can't afford to take any chances.'

'That's all right,' Hewe responded. 'I shouldn't have got so angry, but it's been a long journey and I need to see Jordan.'

'Then you're out of luck,' Egan said. 'No one knows where he is.'

'What?'

'Paule's inside. Maybe he can tell you more.'

'I don't believe this,' Hewe said, shaking his head.

'Go on in,' Egan urged.

'By the way, what is today's password?' Hewe asked as he ushered Gemma and Ashlin forward.

'Fish-hook,' Egan replied with a grin. 'But we haven't caught anyone yet.'

'Your jokes don't get any better,' Hewe groaned.

They came to a door a few paces beyond the torch and Hewe repeated his earlier signal, rapping quickly

146

on the wood. A spyhole opened, then they heard bolts being drawn back, and the door swung open.

'Welcome home,' Paule said cordially.

'That's better,' Hewe muttered, and pushed the others ahead of him.

* * *

'So you see,' Paule concluded, 'quite a lot has happened since you left, but nothing has really changed. The new Overlord is still a mystery – albeit an unpleasant one – and the reasons for getting rid of him, and of the Guild, are stronger than ever. We've been under a lot of pressure while you've been away.'

'So it seems,' Hewe remarked. 'We've got to do something about this new palace, or tower – or whatever it is – before half the population gets swallowed up by it.'

'Now that you're here we'll be able to strike as soon as Jordan gets back. There's no point in waiting much longer.'

'Good.' Hewe was obviously pleased by the prospect of some action. It was clear now that a bloodless revolution was not going to be possible – if indeed it ever had been. After a moment, he added, 'Why didn't Jordan leave word about where he was going? It's not like him to disappear like this.'

'He's been off on mysterious errands of his own before,' Paule reminded him.

'But surely not when the situation has been as critical as this!' Gemma put in. 'If I didn't know him better, I'd call it downright irresponsible.'

Paule and Hewe exchanged a smile over her claim to know their leader well, when she had only met him twice, even if she had been in his presence for a few hours.

'Well, we just have to trust him,' Hewe said. 'He's never let us down before.'

'He'll be back,' Paule added firmly. 'In his own good time. Just like Hewe here. There's no controlling them.' He grinned, but Gemma would not be humoured, and he gave up the attempt at levity. 'We're very grateful that you're here, Gemma – and for the information you've given us,' he went on. 'Adria sent word via her sons, so we already know about the floating city. There haven't been any sightings reported yet, but that doesn't surprise me. It would appear from what you told me that those librarians don't exactly encourage interruptions of their work.' He smiled as Gemma nodded in agreement. 'What it *has* done, though, is prompt us to start looking at our own records, at the libraries here in Newport.'

'What good will that do?' Gemma asked. 'That will only tell you about the past.'

'Not if you believe what the blue-flame sect are saying,' Paule replied.

'Those madmen? What have they got to do with it?' Hewe was mystified.

'They may not be quite as mad as we'd thought,' Paule said. 'But that's beside the point. What *is* important is that they've been claiming for some time now to have found references in an ancient book which predicts our current situation with uncanny accuracy.'

'I know that,' Hewe put in. ' "The end of the world is nigh".'

'That's about it,' Paule agreed. 'What's interesting is that our revered Overlord has apparently started to take it seriously. He's been making contact with the blue-flame sect, and has had an enormous number of books taken in to the new palace. He can't have found what he's looking for yet, because the process is still going on.'

'So what can we do about it?'

'We've made a few contacts ourselves among the archivists, and acquired a little knowledge,' Paule replied. 'It appears that this book is probably hidden

148

in a secret vault beneath the laughably misnamed Halls of Justice.'

'And?' Hewe prompted.

'Well, is there anyone who can match us for expertise in matters subterranean?' Paule asked with a grin.

'You've found it?' Gemma exclaimed.

'We have,' he admitted. 'But there's a problem.'

They waited expectantly.

'The vault is protected by some sort of living shield,' he went on. 'I've seen it myself, and it looks like a miniature blue-flame wall. Someone has harnessed the power of a number of elementals, and put them to work most effectively. Nobody can get in, and therefore the book – or books – can't be taken out.'

'So knowing where the book is doesn't actually help us,' Gemma said.

'Maybe, maybe not,' Paule replied, looking at her seriously now. 'This is where we need your help.'

* * *

Standing in front of the pulsating blue screen, Gemma could feel its power, its solidity. *How can I hope to breach that?* she thought hopelessly. The elementals that she had influenced during her escape from the Grey Raiders had been living entities, warm and real. This was cold, hard and unyielding.

Have you forgotten Adria's lesson so soon? Cai rebuked.

Gemma felt a surge of relief at his presence – remote though it may be – but still could not fathom how to proceed.

This was created by someone with an incredible amount of power, she said. *I can't possibly match it.*

I doubt that, he replied. *Just relax, and let us all help you.* Though his voice faded, his calming influence remained.

All? Gemma wondered, but obediently sank into the blackness of her dreams. Sparks appeared, joined, and grew in strength. They formed magical banners that flew in the wind of her mind. Lines of power weaved in and out, strengthening and building until a fountain of light burst forth.

She took the fountain and moulded it, coaxing, and bent it to her will. *By will-power alone.*

A door opened in the blue screen, its edges crackling with opposing forces – old and new, cold and warm, dark and light.

Gemma stepped through the door and it snapped shut behind her, leaving Cai and his welcome support on the other side. She stood now in a marble chamber, whose floor and ceiling were marvellously smooth, its walls covered with intricate carvings. All were illuminated by a soft, yellow light. The room was empty except for a marble table at the far end; a man was standing before it, his back to her, bent over as if he was studying something on the table.

Gemma walked forward a few steps, then stopped as the man straightened up and turned round.

'Welcome, my dear. I have been expecting you.' His voice, smooth as velvet, held hints of amused malice. Gemma could not ask who he was – she had lost the use of her tongue.

The man's face was covered with a shiny metal substance as smooth as the marble on which they both stood. Black holes were all that she could see of his eyes and mouth.

'We have much to discuss,' he said.

And the metal lips did not move.

Part Two

THE LIGHTLESS
KINGDOM

CHAPTER NINETEEN

Arden found it difficult to remember what the sunlit world looked like; it had faded from his mind, and had been replaced by pain and confusion. Time had no meaning in this dark realm. He could not differentiate between day and night, and although logic told him that he could only have been underground for a few days, it seemed as though he had always lived in this damp, silent gloom.

And yet the darkness was not total. Every so often, a seam of crystalline rock gave off a faint glow, allowing Arden to make out a few details of his surroundings. He could not tell whether this was refracted light from far above, or whether it came from inside the rock itself, and he didn't care. He knew that without it, he would have gone quite insane. As it was, this subterranean world was already filled with nightmarish creatures, brought into existence by his fevered imagination. Utter blackness would have made them all too real.

* * *

The manner of his arrival remained a mystery to Arden. After the mountain had moved and the river had been diverted back to the valley, he found himself stranded on a tiny island amid the newly surging waters. His doomed attempt to swim to safety led him to the entrance of a small cave just above the spray, and he crawled inside, his body bruised and near to exhaustion. He lay there for a moment, catching his breath, and was about to stand up when a wave of water surged over the cavern's rim. Before he knew what was happening, Arden found himself slipping deeper into the mountain, his scrabbling hands able to find no purchase on the smooth wet surface of the rock. As he slipped further, so the downward slope increased and his fall accelerated relentlessly. The light of the entrance receded, and Arden felt as though he was being swallowed whole. Frantic now, he clawed at the stone, but to no avail.

His last vision before the darkness of the earth engulfed him was of Gemma, horrified, shouting his name.

The water chute swept him down, faster and faster, into utter blackness. He whirled helplessly, arms and legs spinning in a never-ending cartwheel, waiting in terror for the jagged rock that would rip him apart, or the boulder which would bar his way and end his life as it ended his fall. Yet neither came, and the smooth tunnel sucked him on, as if it had been designed for just this purpose.

Arden accepted his fate; beyond hope now and barely able to think or breathe, he no longer tried to slow his progress, and was content merely to protect himself as best he could. He had no idea how far he had travelled, or how far he was beneath the surface of the earth, but it gradually dawned on him that his descent was slowing. The upwards pressure on his back and stomach told him that the slope was levelling off, though he was still pushed from side to side.

And then, suddenly, he was weightless, thrown into the air by a quick upturn of the rock. For an instant he hung in darkness, then plunged downwards once more.

What now?

Unprepared and unprotected, he hit the water with a crack, his body pummelled by a hundred liquid fists. Water streamed into his mouth, his nose, his ears. One

154

of his feet hit a rock, and the searing pain in his leg left him even more disorientated.

He floundered, senses reeling, and desperately needing to breathe, but could not immediately tell which way was up. As he gulped down the inky water, cold attacked him from inside and out. Forcing himself to relax, he floated upward for a moment, and struck out for the surface, trying not to scream as he felt the agonizing pain in his injured leg.

When he burst from the water, drawing a huge gulp of air into his lungs, Arden saw sparks of light whirl before his eyes like shooting stars. Although he coughed and spluttered, his world remained totally silent. The shock of immersion in the icy water had made him deaf.

As he calmed himself, he could see that some of the white sparks no longer moved but shone steadily, like the lights of a distant city. He floated, paddling with his arms and one good leg, knowing that if he didn't find dry land soon, he would drown.

I'm still alive! Perhaps the gods are saving me for something special.

The irony of the old saying almost made him laugh aloud, but he gulped it down, fearing the onset of hysteria.

His eyes gradually got used to the gloom, and he was able to make out a ledge of rock above the water line. As he swam gingerly towards it, his left leg dragged behind him. The numbness was spreading now, and he could feel nothing below the knee.

He heaved himself slowly and painfully from the water and crawled away from the edge. To his astonishment, the rock on the far side of the ledge was warm, and he huddled against it gratefully.

He felt his injured leg. There was a swelling just above the ankle, and he could not move his foot. Although Arden could not be sure, all the evidence indicated that he had cracked his shin-bone.

Just my luck, he thought. *To survive that murderous*

fall, and then to get hurt after a relatively soft landing!

It occurred to him now that the wild water-slide that had brought him to this place could not have been entirely natural. Water could indeed smooth rock, but surely not on such a massive scale; the bends and curves could almost have been designed so that a man might make the helter-skelter journey in safety – provided he knew what to expect. The final upturn which had flipped him into the underground lake was too perfect a device to be accidental.

And yet who – or what – could have constructed such a formidable slide? No miner in Arden's world would have been capable of such a feat.

It was a mystery, but one which boosted his spirit. He had survived many perils since making his way into the world at the age of fourteen and, though he knew his present situation to be desperate, he had long ago learnt never to abandon hope. He would make every effort to escape from this subterranean dungeon; he certainly had reasons enough. He had always believed that the cruellest thing about men dying in battle was the fact that they would never know if their side was victorious. Had they given their lives in the pursuit of ultimate success, or was their sacrifice in vain? His battle had been to save the valley and, while he believed with all his heart that this had been accomplished, he could not rest easy until he saw the proof for himself.

But his main reason was Gemma. If she had survived her incredible flight and succeeded in literally moving a mountain for Arden's sake, then the least he could do was live to see her again.

'We are destined to be together,' he said aloud, then shivered as he realized that he could not hear himself speak. He shook his head to clear the water from his ears, but the silence remained. Somehow, that was harder to accept than the steadily throbbing pain in his leg.

To distract himself from this sudden disability, Arden

began to study his surroundings, as best he could. His eyes had grown accustomed to the meagre light, and he was able to pick out certain details. The cavern was large, but the shelf on which he lay was the only part of the floor above the water line. The black depths looked impenetrable, but the surface moved, glinting coldly as a ripple caught the reflection of pinpoints of light far above. Currents swirled and eddied slowly, but Arden could not tell whether the water was flowing like a river, or reacting to more mysterious forces. The rock beneath him was uneven but worn, and he wondered if the water ever rose above his position. This was not a comforting thought. He was fast becoming drowsy, and the effects of exhaustion and shock, combined with the warmth of his resting place, made the idea of having to move extremely unwelcome.

As far as he could see, the shelf ran the entire length of the cavern in both directions, but it was impossible to tell whether it led to other caverns, tunnels or solid rock. Even so, Arden concluded that there must be an exit from the cavern. The air seemed fresh enough – and the water had to go *somewhere*. He could just make out the hole through which he had fallen. It would be impossible to return that way, but he reassured himself that where one route existed, others could also be found.

Looking up, he could see faint seams in the rock structure, which appeared to be the source of the sparks of light. Strange inverted pinnacles of rock hung down from the unseen roof, pointing like gigantic fingers as water dripped from their tips, eerily silent. Even in his predicament, Arden could appreciate the half-seen wonders of the cavern, and longed for a lamp with which to illuminate them.

Eventually, the warmth and the darkness of the cavern combined with the demands of his aching body, and he slept – in spite of the pain in his leg.

When Arden awoke, his clothes were dry and the dull

red ache above his ankle had subsided, but his stomach was complaining bitterly; he had eaten nothing for some time. There appeared to be rather more light, and he knew that it was time to try and escape. He had nothing with which to splint his leg, so he improvised, removing his belt and wrapping it round the swelling as tightly as he could, in an effort to minimize the ankle's movement.

Water first, he told himself, and moved slowly towards the edge of the rock shelf. Leaning over, he cupped his hands and lifted the cold liquid to his lips. After a careful taste, he drank his fill. Although he felt refreshed, the movement had awoken protests from every bruised and stiff muscle and, for a moment, he doubted his resolve.

'Which way?' he asked aloud, and this time was able to hear the faintest whisper of sound. Although it was only a shadow of his voice, he was encouraged by the thought that his hearing was returning, and shouted incoherently, making his head buzz.

There was absolutely no way for him to tell which would be the best route, so he chose at random. He began to crawl, and soon discovered that his leg was less painful if he moved backwards, pulling himself along with his arms, and pushing with his right leg. However, this meant that he could not see where he was going, and he had to stop frequently, twisting round to survey the prospect in front of him.

Before long, the ledge narrowed and the ceiling became lower. Here and there, crystals shone with a soft glow which seemed incredibly bright to Arden, and which illuminated the stalactites and the slowly moving water to his left. Ahead was darkness, but by now Arden could feel the gentle pressure of moving air, and his spirits rose immeasurably. There *was* a tunnel!

As he inched his way forward, trying to track down the source of the hope-giving breeze, he realized that he was moving over an increasingly rough surface.

Although his progress slowed, he forced himself on, and at last found what he was looking for.

The entrance to the tunnel was a jagged hole, about half the height of a man. Inside it was pitch-black, but Arden's probing fingers were able to confirm that the tunnel sloped upwards. The draught of air grew stronger; he took several deep breaths, then pressed onwards into the darkness.

The tunnel narrowed and the going became even rougher. There was no light at all. The jutting rocks gave Arden plenty of leverage, but were also hazardous – his injured leg caught against unseen projections several times, and he gasped as pain shot through his body. On each occasion he calmed himself slowly, forcing himself to breathe deeply and think only of his progress towards the world above; the world of sunlight and greenery, the world of the valley – and of Gemma.

At one point, the tunnel grew so constricted that he feared he would not be able to get through – and knew with a dreadful certainty that if that happened, it would be the end of him. Unable to turn round, and with his fractured leg useless, he would not have the strength to return to the cavern. However, he was able to force himself on, and the constant flow of air helped keep his hopes up. During one of his increasingly frequent rests, he craned his neck round to look ahead – and almost cried out for joy when he saw a tiny pin-prick of light in the distance.

The next few hours passed in an agony of frustration. However hard he tried, his progress was deadly slow, the far-away light beckoning like an unattainable star. Arden was sweating, in spite of the cool air, and was now parched and ravenously hungry. He had no way of knowing how long his struggles lasted, but eventually his tired limbs ran out of energy and movement became increasingly difficult. He had to rest more and more, dozing fitfully at times, and waking with a start as fearful images exploded inside his head.

159

At last the light ahead grew in size and began to take form. Arden recognized it as the outline of an opening into another cavern. It was not the outside world – he had known that to be an over-optimistic hope – but at least it would be better than this nightmare tunnel. He climbed on doggedly until he found himself at the bottom of a small, near-vertical shaft, which formed the last part of the tunnel. Although the entrance to the new cavern was only a few paces above him, Arden was exhausted now, and the climb was beyond him. So he slept, restless and feverish, huddled against the wall.

When he awoke, his lips were cracked, and his tongue was stuck to the roof of his mouth. Desperate for water, he thought longingly of the lake below, yet knew that he could only go forward now. Levering himself upright, he began to climb. There were plenty of handholds, but his weakened state and useless left leg meant that it was a painfully slow business – and he knew that if he fell, he would die.

With one last, exhausted effort, Arden pulled himself on to the floor of the cave and lay flat on his back, gasping for breath. Above him was an enchanted landscape of fantastic rock formations; between them, veins of crystal glowed in varied hues – green, blue, yellow.

He smelled water, and searched for it with eager eyes. He could not hear the sounds of dripping or the gurgle of springs, but he saw them glinting on one wall and crawled towards them as quickly as he could. The rock was covered with a green, moss-like growth which gave mysterious glints to the trickling water. Arden sucked forth the moisture gladly, ignoring its bitter taste, then splashed his face and arms. He relaxed for the first time in what seemed like an age.

However, the water sat heavily on his stomach, and he knew that he needed food. He pulled away a handful of the green stuff, but it disintegrated at his touch and flowed away, leaving only a few tiny morsels which were sour and unappetizing. Disappointed, he searched for something else to eat, and noticed a group of strange rock formations on the wall beyond the water. Semi-circular projections, light on top and dark below, covered the surface in astonishing profusion. Arden had never seen any stone like it, though it seemed strangely familiar. Curiosity forced him across to them, and he discovered that they were not rock at all, but were soft and spongy to the touch.

Fungi! he thought, gazing at them in wonder. *Thousands of them.*

He broke a piece off, and sniffed it carefully. Some fungi are edible, while others are deadly poison – and he had no way of telling which this unknown species might be.

If I don't find food soon, I'll die anyway, he told himself and took a small bite. The flesh was firm and moist but virtually tasteless, neither pleasant nor unpleasant. Arden swallowed, and waited. His stomach went into a riot of long-delayed digestion, but otherwise he felt no ill-effects. On the contrary, his spirits rose, so he took another, larger mouthful, chewed quickly and swallowed once more. Several bites followed in quick succession, and his feeling of well-being grew; he could feel the energy course back into his limbs with amazing speed and, most remarkable of all, the pain in his leg all but disappeared.

After a while, he began to feel bloated, so he stopped eating and turned to look at his surroundings, feeling a glow of satisfaction at having solved his most immediate problem. The light was stronger here than in the lower cavern, but it was still too dark for him to be able to see all the cave's recesses. However, he *could* see several openings in the rock and knew that he had plenty of opportunities for exploration. His confidence rose even more.

He noticed a circular patch on the wall above him which was bare of the fungoid growths. It looked as though there were markings in this space but he could not make them out from where he was sitting. He peered long and hard, eventually deciding, as he felt so much better, to stand up and get a better view.

Slowly and carefully, he levered himself upright until he was standing on his right leg, with his back braced against the fungi. Then he pivoted to face the wall.

The drawings were crude but unmistakably human, and Arden rejoiced in the knowledge that other men had obviously been here before him. If they had come and gone, then so could he. It was only after thinking this that he took in the details of the markings. All around the lower rim of the circle were small human figures. The upper border was decorated with a curious set of symbols – wavy lines, jagged peaks, and what looked like flames. However, the drawing was dominated by a single central figure, and it was that which drew Arden's attention.

The limbs and torso were stick-like in comparison to the creature's large round head, but each hand carried a half-moon shape, clearly meant to be the fungi. The face was dominated by two huge staring eyes: these held Arden's gaze hypnotically for a few moments. Then his attention moved down to its mouth, where a long black tongue hung from twisted lips, reaching below the chin. The effect was grotesque, like a child's drawing of a nightmare foe, and Arden was torn between laughter and disgust.

So that's what you get for eating the mushrooms, he thought, feeling suddenly faint.

He lowered himself carefully to the ground, sitting on the floor with his back against the wall.

It only took a few moments for the monsters to arrive.

CHAPTER TWENTY

He saw them first out of the corner of his eye, movement without substance. As soon as he turned to look at them, they disappeared, mocking his slowness. He heard voices, then animal howls and heavy footsteps, but when he called out, his own cries remained inaudible.

'Who are you?'

An echoing susurration joined the noises in his head, as if the caverns had measured his voice and found it wanting, swallowing the words as the mountain had swallowed him. He was afraid.

What is happening to me?

He felt no pain from his injured leg. In fact, his entire body no longer seemed a part of him – it would not respond to his commands, and allowed him only the use of his eyes. Each dark recess of the cavern became the lair of ghastly creatures; it was only a matter of time before they began to advance on their helpless victim.

Then the worm emerged, and, deep inside himself, Arden screamed. The monster's body was as wide as a man's, and as it slithered into the centre of the cavern, its front portion rose into the air, standing taller than a horse. Its segmented trunk was a dull, slimy green – but the abomination's head was the worst sight of all. Though the creature had no neck, its face was human, and Arden found himself gazing helplessly into the eyes of his father.

'You're dead!' he screamed, sickened.

'Not here,' the monster replied, smiling maliciously.

'But I killed you.'

'You will never be rid of me,' the worm stated calmly. 'And I have your mother still.' A long green tail swept round from the darkness, bringing with it a crumpled pile of flesh and cloth. Arden watched in horror as his mother's head rose from the broken mass to gaze blankly at him.

'Don't you want to greet your beautiful mother?' the beast asked. 'Neither of you could escape from me, in spite of all your efforts.' The creature shook with mirth. It was his father's cruel laughter, and Arden could only stare as the pitiful bundle of humanity in front of him began to char and spit, cloth burning, flesh dissolving. His mother turned to ash before his eyes. Soon, only a sticky black stain remained, glinting evilly on the cavern floor.

'You did that to her,' the worm remarked offhandedly.

'She was already dead when I burnt the house,' Arden shouted back. 'It was you I killed!'

Mocking laughter was the only response. Arden closed his eyes, but the sickening images did not disappear.

'You will never be rid of me,' his father said again, then vanished, and the cave was plunged into darkness.

* * *

He was in a tunnel, struggling towards the light but never getting any closer. Far above him, the sun shone, there was laughter and song, the sounds of running water and wind rustling the summer leaves. But none of this reached Arden's world, a world of unending despair.

He climbed on, knowing that his efforts were hopeless, and felt the shaft grow narrower, the rock press in towards him. Then he could not move – the stone bound him on every side, the light still unattainable, far above him. The rock held him fast, flowing ever closer about his body.

His last sight before it closed over his head was a glimpse of Gemma's face, far above, looking down the shaft that was now being sealed for ever. He tried to call out, but could not. The light faded as he was encased in stone.

* * *

Arden gradually regained control of his mind. As the last of the hallucinations faded, he slept, too exhausted to dream. He was hungry again, but he counted his empty stomach a blessing.

When he next awoke, he crawled to the water, drank, and splashed his face, trying to forget the nightmare visions that had held him in their grip. His leg was hurting again.

He looked up at the circular drawing, and understood now why it was there. This place had been a source of fear and veneration to the artist – whoever that had been. For all its dark crannies, the cavern was a place where nobody could hide.

As Arden steeled himself to continue his quest for freedom, he ruefully inspected the rents in his clothes, caused by his efforts so far. Before leaving the cavern, he looked once again at the innocent-seeming fungi. They now inspired in him a feeling that was a mixture of awe and revulsion, but he perversely believed that they had saved his life – although at a price. He broke off several pieces and stuffed them into his pockets, muttering an apology for the desecration of the place.

The exit of the first tunnel Arden tried was impossibly narrow, and the second proved impassable when he was faced with the rim of a vertical-sided chasm. He threw a stone into the invisible depths, counting twenty heartbeats before he realized that he would not be able to hear it landing. He could not climb round the walls of the deadly drop, and so was forced to make another laborious return journey to the cavern. There he rested and drank before resuming his exploration. The first two exits had been chosen because they sloped upward, and for their perceptible draughts of air. His next option was the largest he had tried – and also the darkest. He moved cautiously, but was relieved to find that the floor seemed relatively flat. The path twisted and turned, and soon Arden could see no light either from the cavern, or ahead. He could sense no movement in the air about him, and believed that he was travelling slightly downhill.

He crawled on in total darkness, feeling the way ahead of him with his hands, and pushing with his good leg. The rock beneath him was cool and dry, and was almost smooth in places. That gave Arden hope – had it been worn down by the feet of earlier visitors? His mind conjured up scenes of sinister torchlight processions, of robed figures chanting as they approached the sacred cave. He grinned. *I could do with a torch myself.* The thought helped to dispel his more fearful imaginings.

He began to sing as he moved – ballads that he had been taught by Mallory, bawdy sailor's songs heard in coastal taverns long ago. Although he heard only the faint whispering echo of his voice, the words and the memories they provoked helped keep him going.

Countless hours later, a tiny blur of light ahead renewed his optimism. It turned out to be a slim seam of crystal in the tunnel roof, and would give only temporary respite from the darkness, but Arden was so glad to be able to see anything at all – his own hands, tattered breeches, and the rock about him – that he decided to rest there. Exhaustion reclaimed him as soon as he stopped his relentless movement, and he slept.

When he awoke, his injured leg was in agony. He had apparently twisted it as he slept, and though the movement had awakened him, it was too late to prevent the pain from shooting through his entire body. Gritting his teeth, he tried to recapture his earlier enthusiasm.

166

After all, he argued to himself, this tunnel must lead *somewhere*. The idea that it might still prove a dead end after all his effort was just too dreadful to contemplate.

Arden set off again, singing as he left the meagre light behind. The downhill slope of the tunnel now became more pronounced, much to his dismay, and he swore at the rock, urging it to move upwards. As the hours passed, his vehemently expressed wishes were not granted, and he descended even further into the earth's vaults. To make matters worse, the pain in his leg was now excruciating, and it was only his innate stubbornness that kept him going.

Even that nearly gave way to despair when his probing hands encountered a solid obstruction in his path. It was smooth and cold, and – as Arden quickly discovered – filled the width of the tunnel. It extended upwards higher than he could reach, and he was about to try to stand up when another thought occurred to him. The wall barring his passage was impossibly flat. It could not be natural; the tunnel was blocked deliberately. His fingers moved over the surface again. There was something about it . . . *Metal. Not rock.* This was a new mystery, providing further evidence that Arden was not the first to travel these underground routes. He felt for the join between rock and barricade, sensing where each had been moulded to the side.

Why? he wondered. If this was a well-travelled route, then it made no sense to seal it up. *Unless* . . . Arden ran his hands even more carefully over the metal surface. *Unless it was meant that only some could pass by and come to the sacred cave. And that would mean* . . . His fingers found the tiny seam they were looking for . . . *a door!*

He traced the lower outline with a fingernail. The door fitted perfectly into its frame. It was rectangular, but there was no handle that Arden could reach from the floor, so he began the agonizing process of standing up, bracing his back against the metal wall. Once upright, he explored the surface of the door with expectant fingers, but found nothing except a few irregular shallow indentations near the top. There was no handle.

Arden thumped his fist on the metal in frustration, and, although it boomed hollowly, he heard only a distant echo of the sound.

Cursing the utter darkness, he returned his attention to the markings. They felt as though someone had etched words or illustrations in the metal; perhaps they were instructions on how to open the door. He tried to trace the scratches with his fingertips, hopping awkwardly on his good leg, but could make no sense of them and had to give up when his right leg threatened to buckle under the strain. Before sliding back down to the floor, he hit the door again, pushing at either side with all the strength he could muster. It had no effect.

Arden sat with his back to the metal once more, cursing the darkness, the pain in his leg and the mysterious creators of the obstruction. Angrily, he smashed his fist against the bottom of the door – then stiffened suddenly. Had the metal given a fraction? Had his damaged ears recognized the echo of a sharp click?

He hastily felt along the lower rim of the door, and his heart leapt as he discovered that it *had* shifted a little way. The base of the door was no longer flush with the frame.

It hinges at the top, not at the side, he realized. He began his hammering again, and was rewarded with a tiny increase in the movement of the door. Several blows later, his hands were bruised and aching, but the door had only retreated the depth of one knuckle. At least there was *some* progress.

Arden rested, sweating heavily now despite the chill air, and longing for water with which to slake his raging thirst. *Come on, try again*, he urged himself. *It's got to give soon*. He manoeuvred round, and began raining double-handed blows on the obstinate metal. *One . . .*

two . . . three . . . On the fourth try, the door gave way, and Arden sprawled sideways as light streamed in, temporarily blinding him. When he had recovered both his balance and his sight, he saw that the door did indeed hinge from the top, and that it was now open, but still blocked by small boulders on the other side. A strange green light flooded in from the partial opening, and he rejoiced as he pushed and hammered the door fully open. He crawled through, negotiating the fallen rocks with difficulty, and looked about him.

He was in an immensely long cave, and could see clearly for hundreds of paces. A small stream ran along one side; water dripped from hundreds of stalactites on the ceiling. The whole was bathed in an unnatural luminescence which emanated from the rock itself. The glow was strongest above and on the banks of the stream, and curbed Arden's immediate instinct to go and drink. The green light cast an unhealthy pallor on the water and, after his experiences with the fungi, he was not eager to risk poisoning himself again. He looked upstream, realizing that that was the way he must go. Although it looked wide enough, the rough terrain made it a daunting prospect.

He had just had time to take all this in, when the metal door behind him swung shut, with the muffled boom of absolute finality. Whether he wanted to or not, Arden now had to traverse the green cavern.

He moved slowly, glancing every so often at the water to his right. Eventually he could stand the temptation no longer and moved across to drink sparingly. The water tasted clean enough, but the green light still turned his stomach. Shortly afterwards, a small eyeless fish floated down the stream towards him. It was dead, and Arden felt sick as he watched it pass.

He went on, taking a small measure of comfort in the fact that he was moving upwards, and that every movement took him a little closer to the surface. Then his numb left foot caught between two rocky projections

169

and twisted. Arden screamed in agony, the torment of his broken leg unbearable now. He stopped moving, waiting in vain for the overwhelming waves of pain to subside. Rational thought was impossible, and his head rang with two opposing statements. *I can't go on. I must!*

The solution occurred to him much later, but he hesitated, wondering whether the better course would be to admit defeat now, and just wait to die. In the end, however, he took a segment of fungus from his pocket and slowly, deliberately put it in his mouth. *It took the pain away before. It will again . . . This time I know what to expect, and I can handle it . . . Dreams can't hurt me.* He chewed reluctantly, and swallowed . . .

And knew the madness of complete solitude, buried beneath millions of tons of impervious rock, alone in an endless tunnel of luminous stone, where fish that had no eyes grew larger than a man, and only the crystals breathed. Alone in all the world.

'Gemma!' he cried, not knowing to whom he called, but receiving a jolt of pleasure from the word.

It didn't take long for the monsters to arrive. Only this time, they were real.

CHAPTER TWENTY-ONE

The six creatures were shaped like humans, but this only made their alien appearance more terrifying to Arden. They were tall and thin, and moved gracefully, displaying both agility and strength. Their skin was black and shiny, resembling highly polished leather, and they were completely hairless. Two huge eyes were the only feature on their bulbous heads, the irises startlingly white around massive circular pupils. Three of the monsters carried metal staves in claw-like fists.

They saw Arden from a distance, pointing and gesticulating towards him before advancing quickly. The jagged stone floor did not seem to bother them as they leapt downstream.

Arden could only lie helplessly and watch their approach. He somehow knew that these were not creatures of his imagination, and he waited in fear as they drew close and gathered round him. They towered over his prone body like demons of night, standing perfectly still as they gazed implacably at the man on the ground. Then heads turned as they looked at each other, and Arden realized that some form of communication was taking place. Although he could see that the creatures had no mouths, he fancied he heard the merest hint of muffled speech – then dismissed that as the wanderings of his infected brain.

* * *

D'vor, the leader of the party, was at a loss.

'What shall we do with him?' he asked.

'Leave him to die,' J'vina answered coldly. 'He must be one of them.'

B'van nodded in agreement. 'He looks very ill,' he said. 'If he's been here long, he's already as good as dead.'

'If we take him out, he'll pollute the barriers,' J'vina went on, glancing at D'vor. 'We didn't come here to play nursemaid to the enemy. Let him rot in his own poison.'

'We don't *know* he's one of them,' L'tha put in. 'He could be an ordinary upworlder who strayed in by accident.'

'By accident? Where from? This system's been sealed for a rock-inch!' B'van sounded contemptuous.

'There are still the old chutes,' L'tha defended herself. 'You know yourself that we can't be sure they were all blocked.'

'That's just hearsay!' J'vina snapped. 'We're wasting time here. If we take him, he'll slow us down – and he might infect us too.'

'That's rubbish, and you know it,' D'vor said firmly. He felt that he was losing control of the discussion, and sought to reimpose his authority. 'That's what the barriers were set up for. Once he's within them, his poison will either fade, or he'll die. Either way he's no danger to us.' He cursed the protective bindings that masked all but their eyes and nostrils, making speech a constant effort. He stared at J'vina as if daring her to disagree with him, but she remained grimly silent. D'vor turned to the party's healer.

'What do you think his chances are, C'tis?'

'It depends on how long he's been in here,' she replied, kneeling down to examine the stranger. 'His leg's in a bad way, but could mend. There are no outward signs of the green-poison, but they'd take a while to show anyway. I can't really judge until we get him out of here.' She flexed her taped hands, looking up at D'vor.

'All upworlders are our enemies,' B'van said. 'Haven't events proved that? Leave him to die.'

The sixth member of the group entered the debate.

'He's human, just like us, in spite of his dark skin,' V'dal said. 'Have you no compassion? That's a terrible death for any man.'

'I can make it a quick death for him easily enough,' J'vina put in harshly. 'I'm not as squeamish as some.' The warrior hardness was evident in her voice.

'No,' C'tis said, and turned back to look at the unknown man.

'I will not countenance the murder of someone who may be innocent,' D'vor stated firmly. 'I—'

'Look!' the healer exclaimed, and drew back so the others could see.

* * *

Arden lay silently while the black creatures stood in apparent judgement over him. He expected to die at any moment, and imagined being torn limb from limb and eaten by these hellish monsters. The pain in his leg had subsided, but only at the cost of his sanity. After a while, he realized that they were not going to attack him, and he wondered whether he should try and communicate with them. Then one of the creatures knelt down to examine his leg. It looked into his eyes, while placing a gentle claw on his face, and Arden summoned up his courage, trying to talk. At first his muscles refused to obey him, but when the creature turned back to face him once more, he tried again.

He opened his mouth to speak, not knowing whether to greet them or ask for their help. In the event, he had no need of words. The parting of his lips startled the shining beasts, and they stared first at him, then at each other.

Within moments, four of the creatures knelt down and lifted him up carefully. He made no resistance,

173

confused but reassured by their unexpected gentleness. The party set off upstream, and Arden watched, as if in a dream, as they left the long, green-lit cave.

* * *

The five looked to where C'tis was pointing. Within the stranger's mouth, his tongue moved ineffectually. However, it was not his attempt at speech which held their attention, but the colour of his tongue. It was completely black.

'Raellim!' L'tha breathed. 'He's been eating raellim.'

'A lot of it, too,' C'tis said, her voice awestruck. 'I've never seen anything so dark – not even in the prophets.'

'No wonder he doesn't look too well,' B'van said flippantly.

'Why isn't he dead?' J'vina wondered aloud, her earlier antagonism overpowered by curiosity. 'We couldn't have survived even a tiniest part of what he's taken in.'

'There's more in his pockets,' C'tis said, bringing forth one of the broken pieces of fungi.

D'vor came to a decision.

'Pick him up,' he said. 'We'll get him to the barrier and try to find out more about all this. If he lives, we'll take him to the prophets.'

There were no dissenting voices, so D'vor led them back along the cave, while C'tis kept a careful eye on the stranger.

At the far end of the cavern was a cascade which formed the beginning of the stream. Beside this was another metal screen, which, though smaller than the one Arden had come through, also had a door set into it. D'vor and C'tis placed the metal staves that they carried to either side, then pushed gently. The door swung open on its upper hinges and the other four carried their burden through. They put him down on

174

the floor, then held the door open for their companions to retrieve the staves and step through. Once released, the door closed quickly, and the cavern was sealed once more.

The control party relaxed, knowing they had left the most dangerous area, and had entered the neutral zone between the poisoned caves and the inhabited regions. They called such neutral zones barriers, and it was part of their job to ensure that these barriers remained secure, and to monitor any spread of the deadly pollution which had driven them from their former homes.

Protective bindings were always worn within the barriers, but C'tis knew that she would need all her deftness and skill if she was to save the stranger's life, and so began unwinding the black material from her head and hands. As she did so, the man screamed, his face a picture of fear and revulsion. C'tis looked uncertainly from him to her leader, but D'vor just shrugged. She asked V'dal and B'van to hold the man still in case he further damaged his broken leg, and carried on removing the silkfish tape. The stranger struggled briefly, the look of horror still on his face, then fainted.

'Good,' C'tis said softly, and went to work.

*　　*　　*

Arden's mind was still clouded, but he was aware of passing through the door. It seemed enormous to him, and looked as if it was made of beaten gold, studded with emeralds. The new cavern was dark by comparison, but his vision was aided by a small amount of crystalline light filtering down from above. Arden was placed on the stone floor, and he wondered if the creatures would desert him. Then one of them loomed over him; he tried to focus on its face, but all he could see were impossibly large eyes within a hazy outline.

The creature raised its long talons, and Arden screamed as it began ripping away its own flesh. White blood spilled out as the grisly business continued. Then Arden realized what was happening – the demon was shedding its outer skin, and another evil was emerging from within. For a moment he saw it clearly – pale, almost translucent skin; light brown hair cut short; large, delicate eyes and a tiny mouth and nose. Then the picture wavered and reformed as he recoiled in horror.

'No!' he tried to say. 'You're dead. You're not real!' But his blackened tongue refused to obey him and he began to squirm, desperately trying to get away from this demonic nightmare. Black claws emerged from the darkness to hold his legs and arms, and the demon transformation was completed before his eyes. As his mother stretched out her milk-white hands to strangle him, Arden fainted.

*   *   *

C'tis used her sensitive fingers to probe the stranger's neck and temples, trying to find the best way for her to seek within. The others waited patiently, knowing that this aspect of her talent required much concentration.

'It's difficult,' the healer told them at last. 'There's so much earthwild in his bloodstream that it blurs my sight.'

'Your best guess?' D'vor asked.

'He wasn't in there long enough for the light to be fatal,' she replied, 'but he drank some of the water. It'll kill him if we don't flush it out soon.'

D'vor turned to V'dal. Although they all knew the main routes through the caves, none could match their guide for overall knowledge; his mind was a labyrinth as complex as the cave systems themselves, and his recall was total.

'Where's the nearest safe water?' D'vor asked.

'At the Chiming Steps,' V'dal answered without hesitation. 'I can be there and back in half an hour.'

'Go then,' D'vor said. 'Bring as much as you can – but be quick. We'll wait for you here.'

V'dal disappeared into a shadowy tunnel.

'Can we do anything else for him?' D'vor asked.

'No – I've done everything possible for now,' C'tis replied. 'I've stabilized his heartbeat and made sure that his lungs are clear, but the poison is beyond healing skills.'

The party leader nodded.

'I hope he makes it,' he said quietly. 'I'd like to hear his story.'

C'tis enlisted L'tha's help in splinting and rebandaging the sick man's leg with the small iron rod bound tight with strips of silkfish tape. Although there was some damage she could not reverse, there was every chance that the bone would knit and heal well. The others sat nearby, watching the two women at work. They had all removed the shiny coverings from their lower faces by now.

'The only way he could have got the raellim was to come through Soulskeep,' J'vina said thoughtfully. 'But how did he get in there?'

'He couldn't have come this way,' B'van said. 'That door won't open without the keys.'

'Soulskeep had many entrances once,' L'tha put in. 'For all that we've tried to block them, some may still be open.' She sounded almost resentful.

'The poison was all round Soulskeep,' D'vor reminded her. 'It was better to seal it up than have it destroyed for ever.'

L'tha did not reply.

'Has he any more raellim?' J'vina asked.

A search of Arden's pockets produced several pieces of fungus. L'tha placed them reverently on a nearby ledge.

'More than enough to keep the prophets happy,' B'van said with satisfaction. 'Whoever he is, he's saved us a trip.'

'He's eaten that much himself,' C'tis told them, and they regarded the unconscious Arden with awe.

'He's tougher than he looks,' B'van remarked.

'Apart from the raellim, there was almost nothing else in his stomach,' C'tis went on. 'He was obviously in desperate need of food.'

L'tha gasped, and even J'vina whistled in astonishment.

'He'll be having some pretty impressive dreams,' B'van commented.

'With this much earthwild, it'll go beyond dreams,' C'tis said. 'He'll see things differently even when he's awake. Rael knows what he made of us in this stuff.' She pointed to the discarded silkfish tape.

'He probably thought we were monsters,' J'vina suggested, and they laughed.

'Then he's better off like that for now,' D'vor said, pointing to the stranger's inert form.

'As long as his dreams aren't too bad,' C'tis agreed.

* * *

Arden was not dreaming. He had retreated into the innermost part of his being. The outside world had ceased to exist, and he was alone in an infinite, empty space. No body, no senses, no thought. No visions.

It was his last defence.

CHAPTER TWENTY-TWO

V'dal soon returned, having stored the clean water in a bag improvised from silkfish material. In spite of the need for haste, he had taken time to seal it properly, and not a drop had been wasted. C'tis roused the stranger, who opened blank eyes; he could see, but there was no life behind his stare. C'tis offered him the water, but he did not seem to know what to do with it, so she encouraged him, pouring the liquid into his mouth and touching his throat. He swallowed convulsively, then gulped down the rest. The healer was pleased, but not completely satisfied.

'He'll need more soon,' she declared.

'Let's go then,' D'vor replied. 'We've seen all we need to here. We can take it in turns to carry him until we get to the boats.'

The others rose, glad that the enforced delay was over.

'Strip his clothes off before we go,' J'vina instructed. 'They'll be tainted.' She gave C'tis her knife, a thin, razor-sharp blade, and the healer carefully cut away the tattered remains of the stranger's garments. He watched her without curiosity, his expression unchanging.

'Not much of a specimen,' J'vina remarked, gazing at the naked man.

'Strength need not only be found in muscle,' V'dal rebuked her. 'He has survived experiences that would have killed any of us.'

'True,' the warrior admitted, her expression thoughtful.

'Which way shall we go?' V'dal asked, turning to D'vor.

'To get water first, then we'll take the fastest route to the boats. You lead the first stretch. I'll carry him. L'tha, you take charge of the raellim.'

Their journey was a lengthy one. In this underground world, day and night were defined by action and rest rather than by light and dark, but the time-scale nonetheless corresponded with that of the upworld. There were places where the delicate crystalline light was refracted directly from the surface, and this shone at the same time as the unobserved sunlight.

Travelling first through an interlocking series of caves and tunnels, the group moved easily and confidently, in spite of the near darkness and their unforeseen burden. They passed occasional signs of abandoned habitation, but only V'dal and L'tha, more sensitive to such things than their companions, gave these a second glance.

The stranger remained conscious as he was carried unceremoniously on the shoulders of each of them in turn. Although he never spoke and his expression remained vacant, he turned his head, obviously trying to see as much as he could. This apparent curiosity, combined with his total lack of emotion or reaction, made C'tis's skin crawl. It was unnatural, almost as though he was assimilating information until such time as his mind was able to function capably once more. Nothing in her experience as a healer had prepared her for such a mystery, and she wondered whether her patient's inner self was as calm as his outward appearance. His body still contained an enormous quantity of earthwild, the force produced by eating raellim. Earthwild was part substance, part energy, part dream-image – and wholly enigmatic. Because of its presence within him, most of the healer's normal skills were useless. C'tis hoped that the stranger would recover, so that she could question him on the experience; her greatest fear was that he might have been driven permanently insane.

They reached the water-filled cavern known as the Chiming Steps in good time. B'van laid the stranger down, and as C'tis knelt to examine him, he looked around with unnervingly hollow eyes. The lower end of the cavern was filled with a deep, inviting pool, whose gently rippling waters glimmered in the light from crystal seams above and below its surface. The pool was fed by a waterfall which flowed over a series of steps formed by the uneven erosion of the rock. The splashing of the water created a melodious chiming which was both beautiful and soothing.

'There's no change that I can detect,' C'tis reported, 'but he must eat soon, or he'll grow even weaker.'

'I could do with some food myself,' B'van remarked.

'We all could,' V'dal said. 'We left enough supplies at the boat to satisfy even your enormous appetite, and we could be there by rockdark.'

'As long as you don't get us lost on the way,' the other replied, and the two men grinned at each other.

C'tis made the intruder drink, then set about checking his splint.

'Might as well test the level now that we're here,' D'vor said, and took a small vial from his pocket. Inside the water-filled container was a small green plant, whose tendrils waved gently. D'vor unstoppered the bottle, dipped his finger into the cave pool, and transferred a single drop to the glass tube. He began counting; when he reached eighteen, the plant became agitated, then drooped.

'It's getting worse,' V'dal commented. 'You got to twenty-two last time.'

'We can't hope to prevent all the seepage,' D'vor said, then frowned. 'Even so, four points in one river-turn is faster than I'd expected.'

'It is still safe?' C'tis asked.

'Anything above ten is safe,' D'vor told her. 'As far as *he's* concerned—' He pointed to the stranger '—it will seem like perfectly clear water.'

181

'Good,' C'tis said. 'In that case, I want to wash him.'

'Throw him in the pool,' J'vina suggested. 'You never know, it might wake him up.'

Although the idea had been put forward in jest, C'tis considered it seriously for a moment. Perhaps such a shock might break through the stranger's mental block.

'No,' she said eventually. 'He might drown.'

So they compromised by moving the outsider to the edge of the pool and splashing him liberally all over. He bore the cold assault without flinching, merely watching the process in his usual detached manner.

'That's enough,' D'vor decided. 'Let's get on.'

As they moved off, the musical chiming receded slowly into the distance. They were crossing difficult terrain, but even so, they managed to reach the river-run cavern, where they had left their boats, just as the last light faded from the crystal seams – as V'dal had predicted they would.

D'vor closed the metal door behind them, and they breathed a collective sigh of relief. The barrier was behind them now, and they were in free territory. The constricting silkfish bindings could be removed in comparative safety, and they immediately set about freeing themselves, carefully folding and packing the precious black material. Underneath, they were all as pale-skinned as C'tis, and had the same huge eyes. Although they were a thin race, their muscular frames and limbs displayed the effects of regular exercise. Their hair was cut very short, with no difference in style between the men and women; it varied in colour from V'dal's light grey to J'vina's pale blonde.

Underneath their protective layers, each wore clothes that suited their own particular needs and character. D'vor, B'van and J'vina favoured supple yet tough garments made from treated batskin, while C'tis and L'tha wore the coarse, warm cloth which had been painstakingly woven from the fibres of root crops. V'dal's outfit was made up of an eccentric mixture of all these, plus various skins. They all wore items of metal jewellery.

Having shed their protective outer layers, each member of the group set about their various tasks. V'dal and D'vor checked on the boats and – out of habit – tested the river water, which was clear, much to their relief. J'vina, obeying her warrior instincts even in this remote area, scouted the adjoining tunnels to make sure they were empty. L'tha took great care in packing the broken pieces of raellim into waterproof containers, then she joined B'van, who had lit a fire, and helped him prepare a meal. C'tis gave up trying to learn anything from the stranger, and propped him gently against a boulder, covering him with a blanket. The healer gathered up all the silkfish material, then rinsed it in the lazily flowing water.

'Any fish in there?' B'van called. 'We could do with some variety in our rations.'

'Not that I can see,' she replied.

'There's dimeweed on the far side,' V'dal put in, pointing into the flickering darkness. 'Want some?'

'Better than nothing,' B'van answered, so the guide stripped off his clothes and dived into the water with hardly a splash. He emerged a few moments later, clutching a fistful of straggling white fronds. D'vor helped him out, and gave the dimeweed to their cooks.

'Yum. My favourite,' B'van said, licking his lips. 'All the taste of a lightly boiled stone.'

'Ungrateful oaf,' V'dal complained good-naturedly. J'vina threw him a cloth, and he dried himself vigorously before dressing. 'Besides, just think how nutritious it is.'

'I'm thinking of nothing else,' B'van replied, chopping the dimeweed and adding it to the food he and L'tha had prepared. The coals of the fire were glowing red now, bathing the cavern in a steady, warm light. After a while, the stew began to simmer gently. The group had not eaten for two days, and the steamy aromas awakened their prodigious appetites. When the food was dished out, C'tis was the only one who did not burn her mouth in her haste to eat, and she escaped only because she felt obliged to feed the stranger first. He did not react to heat or taste, or the food's arrival in his empty stomach, but just chewed and swallowed mechanically.

'Obviously not one who appreciates fine cooking,' B'van observed.

'You were the one complaining about tastelessness,' J'vina teased.

'In the hands of a master, even the humblest ingredients can be turned into a feast,' he replied, unruffled.

'He *is* a strange one, though,' L'tha said quietly, and they all turned to look at the unknown man. 'Can't you get *anywhere* with him, C'tis?'

The healer shook her head.

'He's a complete mystery,' she replied. 'The only way we'll ever find out what's going on inside his head will be if he decides to tell us.'

'At least we won't have to carry him for the next stretch,' B'van observed.

'Can't you put some clothes on him?' J'vina asked. 'He's so puny, I feel queasy just looking at him.'

'And there I was thinking you fancied him,' V'dal said drily.

'Hah! I only carried him so much to save you feeble creatures the effort,' she retorted with much indignation. 'I'd treat any piece of baggage the same.'

'He's a human being!' L'tha exclaimed, genuinely shocked.

'He's an upworlder,' J'vina replied derisively. 'They're never anything but trouble.'

'Peace,' D'vor interrupted, a little anxiously. He was beginning to feel the strain of their journey into the remote and dangerous areas of their world, and the subtle balancing act necessary to keep this group operating as a team was beginning to wear his resources thin. 'Trouble or not, he's coming with us. Until we hand him over to the prophets, he is the responsibility of us all. Is that clear?' There were nods of agreement, but no one spoke, and although D'vor was satisfied by his attempt to re-establish his authority, he could not help but wonder why the prophets had chosen *him* as the group's leader. All the others had special skills, and were surely better qualified for the task. But then, one didn't argue with the prophets! He pushed the thought aside.

'This . . . foreigner . . . has distracted us from the job we were sent to do,' he went on, trying to sound businesslike. 'Have we got the information we shall need when we report back?'

'The water counts have all been recorded,' L'tha replied, 'and we can chart them when we get home. There is plenty of raellim, and Soulskeep is still intact.'

'There are only two major rock falls we didn't already know about,' V'dal stated, 'but the water level has changed in a number of places, which means that several new routes will have opened while others have closed.'

'Do you know where?'

'Of course.'

D'vor nodded, then turned to J'vina.

'There's no one else here,' she said. 'Except for him, and he doesn't seem much of a threat, does he? I really don't know where the prophets get their ideas from.'

'You know perfectly well that they gave no time scale,' D'vor rebuked her. 'Perhaps the invasion is still to come.'

'I almost pity any invaders who have to come through *that*,' the warrior responded, jerking a thumb in the direction of the poisoned realms. 'But why do we have to guard this area so carefully? There are more immediate threats in the other direction.'

'The poison *is* an invasion of a sort,' V'dal said

185

quietly, and there was silence for a few moments as they considered his statement.

'Don't you want my report?' B'van asked after a while. 'I know I'm only a menial, but—'

'Go ahead,' D'vor said, glad of the big man's attempt at humour.

'It is my considered opinion,' B'van stated, 'that my cooking is absolutely delicious, as well as life-sustaining, and, what's more, there's a bit left. Who wants some?'

Every bowl was immediately thrust forward.

'Him too,' C'tis said, holding up the stranger's bowl. 'He needs it more than we do.'

'Speak for yourself,' B'van replied, but obediently ladled stew into the proffered vessel.

Once more, the stranger allowed himself to be fed. His expression never changed.

CHAPTER TWENTY-THREE

The images passed before Arden's eyes like those of a silent dream. He could not control or influence them; he could only accept. He felt calm sometimes, and was sometimes troubled by what he saw. On occasion he felt afraid or amused, but through it all ran the thread of pain and confusion. None of this showed outwardly. His body was merely an object in the vision – with as much meaning as a boulder or a pool of water. He had no thoughts, no self. He just watched.

After the strange white beings had discarded their black outer skins, they had performed various tasks, then gathered together to eat a meal. Arden had swallowed his food without tasting it. The creatures had held a conversation which he could neither hear nor interpret, after which they lay down and slept. Arden had watched them until he was sure that nothing else was going to happen, at which point he closed his eyes. He did not sleep, but waited for the light to return.

With the dawning of the underground day, Arden noted incuriously that his body was covered with a sheen of perspiration, and was trembling so much that it was difficult for him to see properly. The gentle creature who had fed him earlier bathed him with water from the river, and placed her hands on the sides of his head. The shaking lessened, and she smiled – somehow Arden knew that she was female – and said something that he could not hear.

Meanwhile, the others were gathering their equipment together, packing it into bundles. Three peculiar vessels were drawn out from a dark corner. Arden did not recognize them as boats until two were placed in the water, secured with ropes, then loaded by three of the strange beings. Each boat was rectangular in shape, shallow and flat-bottomed and – this Arden found most difficult to understand – were made entirely of beaten metal. They looked far too heavy to float, but rode the water easily and the white-skinned creatures were able to lift them without too much effort. The gear was soon stowed away, and Arden was lifted into the third boat. He was joined by two members of the group, while the others manned the remaining vessels. The convoy cast off into the river.

So began a journey that was full of wonder for Arden. Had he been his normal self, the astounding sights of the next few days would have left him bubbling over with excitement. As it was, he remained outwardly impassive, while storing up the amazing images in his memory.

The strange company travelled through halls of stone, where weird pinnacles of rock reached up from the floor and down from the ceiling; through tunnels which were no wider than the river. They crossed a huge, silent lake, propelled across the mirror-still surface by poles thrust to the bottom, and by short, metal oars. At times the river became too turbulent, or too shallow, so they had to leave the water and drag the boats along. One such diversion forced them to carry the boats on to a narrow path which crossed a precipitous cliff face. Water churned far below in a vast chasm filled with spray and grey mist. They passed underneath a waterfall which plunged into the depths far beneath them, and which made their path slippery and treacherous. While Arden was aware of the danger, it meant little to him. He would have accepted a fall into the distant cauldron just as easily as he watched his guardians struggle with their equipment. He could recognize their fear and anger, but they were nothing more to him than abstractions – as were his own emotions.

On yet another occasion, their route took them through a narrow, smooth-sided tunnel which ran downhill. Its base was covered with a thin sheet of fast-moving water, and the boats became sledges, careering along at breakneck speed, and reminding Arden of an earlier, half-forgotten experience. The creatures became visibly excited during this part of the journey; Arden even thought he heard the faraway echoes of their shouts.

The most difficult part of their journey was when they had to climb a cliff that was fully a hundred paces high. A rough set of steps had been hewn out of the rock for most of its height, but the last section would have to be crossed using a free-hanging rope ladder. The group seemed to know what to do. Two of them climbed to the top, and disappeared from sight. Soon afterwards, ropes were lowered from above and the boats, with the equipment secured within by the shiny black tape, were attached, then hauled up by unseen hands. Arden was placed in the remaining vessel, and tied with ropes and more of the strange tape until only his head was left exposed. Two more creatures climbed the cliff face, then Arden felt his boat being steadily lifted into the air. The remaining members of the party steadied the first part of his ascent, then kept pace with his rise on the stairs and later the rope-ladder. It seemed to Arden as if he was being raised by the magic he did not truly believe in, swaying gently as his view of the massive underground dome expanded. The panorama left him no time to think of his precarious situation. Multi-hued crystal seams glinted and reflected off rock and swirling water; deeper shadows promised even greater mysteries and the cliff itself sprouted faces. Animals and other familiar shapes appeared in the strange formations, only to disappear or transform themselves as his point of view changed.

Once the whole party reached the top, and their gear

was rearranged – the pulley system stowed away once more for future travellers – they rested for some time, talking quietly and gazing out over the vast cavern. Then they set off again, travelling through yet more tunnels and caverns in the seemingly endless honeycomb of rock.

Whenever possible, they travelled by water, and these were the easiest times; their strange white faces broke into smiles as they propelled their metal craft, or let the drifting river carry them lazily along. They took a regular period of rest at the end of each day's travelling, and it was then that Arden received most attention; his newly acquired clothes were changed and his body gently examined. This was also the time when the group lit a fire and ate. Arden watched as they supplemented their supplies with fish caught from the river, fronds that reminded him of seaweed, and even some unidentifiable roots which were cut from the roof of one of the caverns. One meal included slices of a dark-coloured fungus which – for reasons he could not understand – made Arden's saliva glands work overtime. When the food came, however, it was as tasteless as the rest, and he felt strangely disappointed. His guardians ate heartily, arguing cheerfully over extra helpings. They talked, though Arden still could not hear them. Although he had forgotten how to use his own tongue, their evident good spirits comforted him.

Sometimes, after these evening meals, Arden found that he was shaking, and his vision was blurred. It was a remote sensation – almost as though it was happening to someone else – and he found it annoying rather than distressing. He wanted to be able to see properly, to continue his study of these strange creatures who treated him so kindly, and whom he was beginning to regard as companions rather than captors.

The final stage of their journey was reached when they crossed yet another wide lake. At first Arden did not think they could continue, because the roof of the cavern swept down and seemed to bar the way. In spite of this, the boats were made ready, while one of the oarsmen lowered his metal pole into the dark water at a specific point, apparently measuring its depth. The boats were heading for what appeared to be a solid wall of rock. As they drew nearer, Arden noticed that the ceiling did not in fact reach the water, but stopped an arm's length above. He still did not see how there could be room for the boats, but he obeyed the motion to lie on his back beside his two companions, and they glided safely beneath the rock. At this point, his fellow travellers raised their legs and propelled the boat along by walking, upside down, on the roof. Wet black stone passed so close that Arden could have touched it from where he lay.

Before long, reflections rippled on the rock, white and red, and Arden realized that it was growing light. As the cavern expanded above them, he was able to sit up and look around.

Fires glowed on the far side of the lake, and a large number of the white-skinned creatures stood watching their arrival. Echoes of welcoming shouts sounded in his head as the boats drew near.

His companions stepped ashore and were greeted warmly, then every pair of eyes turned to Arden, who still sat in the boat. Under such intense scrutiny, something hard in his mind snapped and eased.

He smiled.

CHAPTER TWENTY-FOUR

'Earthdeep!' J'vina exclaimed. 'He *is* alive!'

The smile faded rapidly as the stranger's mouth opened in a soundless scream. He doubled up, clutching at his stomach, and C'tis rushed to his side as pandemonium broke loose all about her. The bystanders had seen his black tongue.

The healer called for water while looking anxiously at her charge. He was shaking, and his eyes were wide with fear and pain. Whatever had enabled him to remain detached and emotionless had also protected him from the pain of his broken leg and the dreadful nausea of the green-light sickness. Now this protection had gone and he was vulnerable once more. C'tis held his trembling hands, talking softly to him while using her own special skills to try to calm him from within and reduce his suffering a little. Their eyes met, and for the first time, understanding passed between them. His mouth moved awkwardly, but the only sound that emerged was a feeble croak.

'Don't try to speak,' she urged. 'Relax.' Over her shoulder she yelled, 'Where's that water?'

B'van handed her a full beaker which she held to the man's lips. He drank eagerly, then grew pale. He lurched to one side and vomited. Groans of disgust came from the watchers on the shore. C'tis took no notice, but held him until his convulsions stopped, cleaned his mouth and face as best she could, then poured lake-water over his head and neck.

D'vor shouldered his way through the crowd.

'What's going on?'

'He's fully conscious again,' the healer told him. 'And he's very sick. Help me get him out of here.'

She and B'van lifted the outsider in their arms and carried him off the boat. D'vor and J'vina cleared a path for them.

'We'll take him to the Whispering Gallery,' C'tis decided, and though the others looked surprised, they did not argue with her.

'I had hoped to keep the colour of his tongue a secret for a while,' D'vor said. He sounded annoyed.

'It can't be helped now,' B'van told him. 'Just keep going.'

The remaining members of the control party had joined them again, and they managed to force their way through the noisy throng. The onlookers all seemed eager to see the mysterious stranger at close quarters.

Pursued by curiosity seekers, the group marched through several of the village caverns, passing the secondary smithy and the cultivation tanks.

'Hey, C'lin!' J'vina called, as they neared their destination. The man she indicated hurried over to them, glancing inquisitively at their burden.

'We're taking him to the Whispering Gallery,' D'vor explained. 'Seal it off for us, will you?'

'Otherwise we'll never be able to help him,' C'tis added anxiously. 'Your timing could have been better!' she muttered to her charge. Another few hours and she would have welcomed the changes in him.

'All right,' C'lin answered, readily enough. 'But your explanation had better be good!'

'It is,' J'vina replied emphatically.

Her fellow warrior nodded, then began yelling orders above the noise of the crowd. Within moments, a group of soldiers held back the unwanted onlookers, so that the members of the control party could enter the narrow tunnel which led to the Whispering Gallery.

The stranger was laid on the floor of the vaulted

cavern and as C'tis knelt beside him, the others stood back to let her work. J'vina returned to the tunnel – the only entrance to the Gallery – both to help guard it, and to give C'lin the explanation he wanted.

After a little while, C'tis looked up at D'vor.

'I know it's unusual,' she said, 'but I'd like to keep him here. Do you think we can get permission?'

'I'll do what I can,' her leader replied firmly, pleased to be entrusted with this extra responsibility. 'But why here?'

'This place is healthy,' C'tis replied, 'and it holds the memories and echoes of countless experiences, just like the dreams he must have endured.'

'That's true. I feel them constantly,' L'tha said, shivering slightly. 'The visions of Rael never really end.'

'I think they'll help him,' C'tis went on. 'But he also needs quiet, rest and plenty of good food. We can't have all and sundry trooping in here to gape at him.'

'I'll go and talk to the prophets now,' D'vor said. 'Will you come with me, L'tha?'

'He's a good man,' B'van commented when D'vor was out of earshot.

'Better than he knows,' V'dal added softly.

'What do you need?' B'van asked, kneeling beside the healer and her patient.

'Fresh clothes, blankets, a lot of water, a constant supply of plain, wholesome food, and the means to make a fire if we need one,' C'tis replied at once. She looked up and grinned. 'Think you can handle that?'

'For you,' he replied, 'anything.'

*　*　*

As D'vor stood before the prophets, he felt inadequate, as he always did in their presence. On this occasion, three had emerged from their inner sanctuary and that made him even more nervous. Normally only one would come to deal with messengers from the people.

194

Two of the prophets, G'lian and T'sin, were men, and one a woman, P'tra. Each of them wore the long black robes of their rank, but their feet and shaven heads were bare. Their eyes were completely black, making it impossible to tell where they were looking.

D'vor presented the report of his control party's journey, then made his unusual request.

'He is in the Whispering Gallery now?' P'tra asked.

'Yes. C'lin has made the entrance secure, on my authority,' D'vor replied. 'I ask for your approval to extend this arrangement until the stranger is recovered.'

'Is this your recommendation, or the healer's?' T'sin wanted to know.

'Both.'

'And is C'tis reliable?'

'She has proved an excellent healer. I would trust her with my life. Indeed, I have already done so.'

G'lian then turned to L'tha.

'Does she have the intuition?' the prophet asked.

'Most definitely,' L'tha replied firmly. As the prophets' representative in the control party, her opinion was all-important. She had no doubts about C'tis.

'Do you feel her course of action to be correct?' P'tra enquired.

'I am not a healer,' L'tha responded, 'so I cannot answer for that aspect, but I trust her, and I know the outsider will benefit from the benevolence of Rael. Until now he has only seen His anger. I stand by the actions of my colleagues.' She had never spoken so forthrightly to her masters before, but knew that on this occasion her daring was justified.

As the prophets drew together for a private debate, D'vor turned and smiled his thanks to L'tha. Her answering smile was almost imperceptible.

T'sin turned back to them and spoke on behalf of his companions.

'The stranger may stay. However, if one of us is called, he must be removed immediately. Please

195

ensure that preparations are made for this eventuality.'

'All will be arranged,' D'vor replied. 'Thank you.'

'Leave the raellim here,' T'sin went on, 'and tell V'dal that we wish to see him when he has finished charting your readings.'

'Of course.'

The prophets withdrew into their secret abode, and D'vor turned to L'tha.

'My thanks for your help,' he said. 'I don't think they would have accepted my word alone.'

'My first allegiance is to Rael, and thus to the prophets,' she replied, 'but you are also worthy of my respect and trust.'

As L'tha strode away to fetch her precious cargo of raellim, D'vor watched her go, surprise and pride mingling in his heart.

* * *

'It's all right,' B'van reported on his return to the Whispering Gallery. 'You've got permission to stay.'

'Good. Are any of the prophets coming to look at him?' C'tis asked.

'If they are, I haven't heard about it,' he told her. 'You know they only come here when they're called. If that happens, we'll have to clear out fast.'

'That's fair enough. Did you get what I asked for?'

B'van had been arranging a number of items, but at her words he stopped, and looked at her with a pained expression.

'I only have one pair of hands,' he said, spreading them wide to demonstrate the fact. 'And every time I leave the gallery, a hundred people approach me with ridiculous questions about our friend here. You've no idea what a stir he's caused.'

'I only hope I'm right, and he comes through all this,' she replied. 'It's only now that I can see just how sick he really is.'

'D'vor and L'tha gave you a glowing testimonial to the prophets. J'vina has threatened to knock the heads off anyone who suggests that you don't know what you're doing, and V'dal is convincing anyone who'll listen that the stranger would never have made it this far without you. C'tis, now is *not* the time to start doubting yourself.' B'van grinned at her astonishment. 'I'm also a big fan of yours,' he added. 'But you know that already.'

'Stop it!' she said. 'You make me feel—'

'Wonderful?' he suggested.

She looked at him uncertainly for a moment, then burst out laughing.

'That's as good a way of putting it as any,' she admitted.

'Then use that feeling,' he told her. 'Use it to help *him*. You're a healer – and the best we have. I've got my own job to do!' With that, he grinned and left. C'tis was alone again with the stranger, who was sound asleep on the hurriedly improvised bed, his breathing deep and steady. After the rigours of the journey, rest would do him more good than anything. C'tis took advantage of the quiet moment, and surveyed their surroundings.

The only entrance to the Whispering Gallery was a narrow twisting tunnel. This meant that it was impossible to see out, but also that nobody could see in. Although the floor was reasonably level, a few boulders of the steel-hard black rock called nightbane jutted forth in places. The walls were irregular and covered with interwoven patterns of dark colours. C'tis looked at these patterns and wondered at the amazing forces which had moulded the earth in such a way. Such power could crush her and all her race with ease, and she shuddered at the thought.

And yet it was the cavern's roof which marked the Whispering Gallery as a unique and awe-inspiring place. This too was multi-faceted, containing many different colours and textures, but its overall shape was so perfect that it seemed almost to have been designed. The cavern was dry, and there were no stalactites here. The roof was oval in shape at its lower levels, but it rose smoothly to a circular apex of diamond-crystal. It was from here that the whisperers occasionally emerged, playful wisps of light which defied the laws of nature and darted about as they pleased, illuminating first this, then that. They changed colour at will as they danced from one point to another. And accompanying their movements would be a faint susurration, a whispering which some claimed to be the language of the stone itself, and which gave the magical lights their name.

The crystal was quiet now, emitting only a pale orange glow. Only the prophets were able to predict the appearances of the whisperers - and even then their displays were rare and short-lived. In all her twenty river-cycles of life, C'tis had only been present at two minor appearances. She had never witnessed a full display; this was usually reserved only for the prophets, and was said to have the power of turning sane men mad. It was also said to be blinding unless you had the protection of the black eyes.

C'tis looked down at her patient, who lay directly beneath the crystal summit of the dome.

'The prophets come here to eat raellim and dream the dreams of calling,' she told him. 'There is healing in those dreams, so I hope you find them too.'

She suddenly realized that she was talking aloud to an unconscious man, and closed her mouth firmly. However, she knew that her decision to bring the stranger here had been prompted by more than the simple need for peace and quiet. It had been an instinctive move, one that had seemed right ever since the idea first occurred to her. It was an acknowledgement that the outsider had experienced – in a more drastic form than usual – the delusions or glories produced by raellim. But there was something deeper that had drawn her into choosing this place, something

198

she had not ever considered to be an important part of her life.

Faith.

*   *   *

His mind set free at last, Arden dreamed. He saw again all the wonders of the underground kingdom, understanding them for the first time. He knew its beauty and terror, and was humbled by its unknown vastness. His journey became a revelation, but with this new knowledge and the freedom it implied came pain and longing, sickness and despair. He was human once again, in all his insignificance and frailty.

And yet he was not alone, his eyes were not the only ones that peered into the gloom. *She* was there . . . and she was joined by many small furry creatures, whose inquisitiveness matched his own. The meyrkats shared his dream.

CHAPTER TWENTY-FIVE

The stranger was to stay in the Whispering Gallery for almost three river-turns, or months as he would have called them. His leg healed completely – although it was very slightly crooked – long before that time was over, but the combined effects of the raellim and the green-light sickness took much longer to wear off. C'tis knew that his leg would be as strong as ever, once he had had the chance to exercise it properly, but at the beginning of her vigil, she could only guess at her patient's overall physical and mental health. The earth-wild still flowed within his veins, making internal exploration difficult and confusing.

The healer stayed with him as much as she could, occasionally even sleeping in the Whispering Gallery. Being in that revered cavern as the diamond crystal darkened then faded into blackness, filled C'tis with an odd mixture of excitement and guilt, almost as if she was a child again, disobeying the instructions of her elders. She constantly expected the whisperers to emerge, and often imagined that she could hear their ghostly voices. Sometimes she would shiver in fear as a strange, inexplicable image appeared in her mind for no apparent reason. These visions were fleeting, and slipped away from her memory like dreams, but their unsettling influence remained. The stranger was also affected at these times; she noted that his eyes moved rapidly beneath their lids, and his muscles twitched. Most of the time, however, the atmosphere in the Whispering Gallery was serene and quiet, and the occasional disturbances seemed worthwhile.

At first, the other members of the control party were frequent visitors, although L'tha never stayed for long, and J'vina lost interest quite quickly. B'van was C'tis's main contact with the world outside the gallery; he brought all their daily necessities, and shared with C'tis the duties of watching over the stranger. The big man was always restless when he returned to the village from an expedition, and these tasks made him feel less at a loose end. C'tis was only too happy to accept his help.

D'vor and V'dal brought them news of the spread of pollution.

'We've collated our charts with those of the other two control groups,' D'vor said, then hesitated.

C'tis raised her eyebrows. 'And?'

'It's bad,' V'dal told her. 'It's moving much faster than we'd anticipated.'

'Just how fast only became clear when we put the three sets of readings together,' D'vor added.

'What do the prophets say?' C'tis asked.

'They've told us to block a few more tunnels, but they know that's only a temporary solution,' V'dal answered.

'They're worried,' D'vor went on. 'Although they won't admit it, there's some thought that we might have to abandon this place.'

'Leave Midholm?' C'tis could not believe this, and the shock showed plainly on her face. *Maybe we are all doomed*, she thought miserably.

* * *

Arden found it difficult to distinguish between his dreams and reality – and was frightened by both.

One good aspect of his dreams was that his vision was better during them. Awake, everything appeared blurred and uncertain, with strange creatures leaning over him, and oddly coloured lights overhead. His head was spinning and he felt sick and weak all the time. His limbs tingled unpleasantly. He was aware of being fed, but had no sense of taste, and did not know what it was that he ate. There were strange sounds too, voices so soft that he could barely hear them, let alone understand what they were saying. His own tongue would not obey him yet – all that emerged when he tried to speak was a hoarse rasping cough. His leg hurt and he could not move it, but compared to the constant nausea and stomach cramps, that seemed only a minor inconvenience.

And yet with all its unpleasantness, Arden preferred being awake to dreaming. He slept a great deal, exhausted in spite of his inactivity. Sometimes his slumber was peaceful and healing, and he awoke on these occasions feeling temporarily refreshed – and relieved that he had not entered the fearful realms produced by some of his dreams.

Some of those images were horrible, while others were terrifying, and all were beyond his comprehension. He saw his own body turn black and crumble into decay; he saw the black-tongued creature from the fungus cave – only this time it was not a drawing but a huge, mesmerizing creature whose eyes burned with fearful power. Bulbous fish floated past him, their swollen bellies bursting to spew forth stinking green ooze. His father's voice plagued him, mocking his impotence and doubling his pain. He floated in cold water, lumps of black ice all around him, and saw the hideous streaks of red within the depths. Most frightening of all were the times when he wandered alone in a huge metal jungle, endlessly treading the same circular path between monstrous structures that throbbed and roared. He crossed and recrossed narrow bridges over metal canyons, climbed steel ladders and slid down mirror-smooth chutes. Each time, his dream ended with a confrontation between his lost self and the men whose faces were encased in metal, blank holes marking their eyes and mouth. Arden woke from these dreams feeling helpless, lost, and terribly alone.

In other dreams he saw creatures with enormous eyes that were entirely black. However, their presence seemed reasonably benign, watchful rather than aggressive. With them came visions of an army on the march, small men remorselessly advancing, filling every space, every tunnel. Their implacable onslaught filled the black-eyed figures with dread, but Arden could not understand the reason for their fear.

A month passed – though he did not know it – before he shared another dream with Gemma. This time, they were not joined by the meyrkats and he was able to sense her confusion and despair. He tried to talk to her but could not, and was unable to see any of her surroundings. She remained a remote, spectral presence that nevertheless awoke all his longing for her. Then the contact was over, and he awoke crying, the flickering lights above him refracted by the tears in his eyes.

He blinked, looking up in wonder.

Something hovered close to the roof of the cave. It was impossible to focus on properly – its movement was fluid, like the reflection of a lamp in moving water. Colours rippled, as though it were made of light. It was beautiful. Arden blinked again, wondering if he was still dreaming, and in that instant the marvellous thing flashed out of existence, leaving him doubly bereft.

'No!' he exclaimed in anger and sorrow. 'Don't leave me!'

* * *

'O! Own eave ee!'

C'tis woke at the sudden sound and was at his side in a moment. It was the loudest utterance he had made, and was the closest to being intelligible. She guessed at his meaning.

203

'I'm here,' she said softly but clearly. 'I won't leave you.'

As they looked at each other in the gentle firelight, she could see the questions in his green eyes, but C'tis was a healer, not a mind-reader.

If it weren't for those ridiculously small, squinty eyes, he'd be handsome enough, she thought. *If only he could talk!*

She offered him some water and he drank gratefully, glancing up at the cavern roof between sips.

'Did you see something up there?' she asked, suddenly curious.

He frowned, then shook his head and pointed to one of his ears.

'Can you hear me at all?'

He leaned closer, and turned his head to one side. C'tis repeated her question, louder than before and was delighted when he responded, holding up forefinger and thumb slightly apart, meaning 'a little'.

They made rapid progress after that; their first conversation was the exchange of each other's name. C'tis found it difficult to talk loudly all the time – her people had sensitive hearing and tended to converse quietly – but she persevered, and Arden, inspired by the gradual return of his own hearing, was strenuous in his efforts to communicate. Over the next few days, they developed a crude sign-language to augment his limited and painful vocabulary. B'van shared in this joint learning process, but no one else was aware of what was happening. Because of his long concealment, curiosity about the stranger had declined; even the rest of the control group visited less often now.

Their early dialogues consisted of a question from Arden, which C'tis would first answer, then expand on, talking for as long as she held his attention. It was in this manner that Arden became aware of the nature of his immediate surroundings. When C'tis told him about the Whispering Gallery, he wanted to tell her in return of the wonderful light he had seen, but his tongue failed him. C'tis knew only that he was excited by what she had told him. She went on to describe the village of Midholm, a group of caves which housed many families in a self-sufficient community. There were three smithies, where various ores were smelted and fashioned into the tools, weapons, boats and other implements on which their society depended. Some people were expert fishermen, while others were soldiers or guides or healers like herself. Others specialized in harvesting the vital root crops and cultured growths which provided the bulk of their diet. B'van, on one of his visits, told Arden that there were many more who were experts in nothing, but who performed less glamorous though nonetheless essential tasks. So saying, he handed them bowls containing his latest contribution. The two men grinned at each other, and the sight warmed the healer's heart.

Arden was often frustrated during the early days of his education, wanting to know so much more than C'tis thought to tell him. Some things were so obvious to her that she did not include them in her teachings and Arden was not yet able to phrase his questions efficiently. He also needed to rest frequently, racked with the aches and discomfort of his sickness. C'tis felt a measure of his frustration, but was too good a healer to allow his thirst for knowledge to delay his recovery. He was improving slowly but surely; the green-light poisoning had not been too severe, and the levels of earthwild lessened all the time. His leg had improved to such an extent that she let him exercise, walking at first cautiously, with her support or B'van's, and later with a metal crutch that the senior smith had been inveigled into providing. Arden was still very weak, and standing made him dizzy and nauseous at first, but his determination was obvious as he struggled to manoeuvre himself between the nightbane. C'tis could tell that he was driven by a powerful force, and she was constantly amazed by his ability to cope with maladies that would have killed even the strongest of her people.

Many days passed before a third dream of Gemma heralded an even more dramatic change in Arden's condition. He still could not communicate with her, though her lips moved silently and a fleeting smile touched her worried face. He clung to the wonderful vision for as long as he was able, but eventually his dream-sight blurred and faded, leaving him alone once more in the darkness.

No. Not darkness.

Shadow-colours played on his eyelids. He opened his eyes and gazed in wonder at the soft, pulsating lights which danced above him.

Like crystals of the moon, he thought.

There were more this time, rainbow-coloured, and they were always moving, always changing, so fast that his imperfect vision could only provide an approximation of their beauty. Arden felt C'tis join him and she too gazed at the roof of the cavern.

'What are they?' he breathed.

'The whisperers,' she replied, her voice full of wonder.

'They're beautiful.'

They watched in rapt silence. Neither of them knew just how long the whisperers stayed, but when they went, flickering out of existence in a single instant, both healer and patient fell into a deep, dreamless sleep. They lay side by side in the centre of the cave until a more conventional light returned to the diamond crystal and spread its subtle glow over the Whispering Gallery.

They woke at the same instant, and looked at each other, with remembrance in their eyes, a little embarrassed to find themselves so close. Then something else occurred to C'tis.

'You can talk!' she exclaimed.

CHAPTER TWENTY-SIX

Just at that moment T'sin entered the chamber, and C'tis jumped to her feet, looking worried. The prophet's black robes rustled softly, and his depthless eyes surveyed the scene before him.

Has he been called? C'tis wondered. *Nobody warned me!*

Her anxiety lessened when the prophet smiled, and faded altogether when he spoke.

'Good day, healer.' He made the title sound like a term of endearment, as though he were speaking to a favourite child. 'Don't worry – my visit is prompted only by curiosity. How is your patient?'

'He is much improved,' C'tis replied, glancing down at the man at her feet.

'Rael is merciful,' T'sin responded, sounding pleased.

'The green-light sickness has left him weak and in much pain,' she went on, 'but it is receding now. The earthwild is down to a manageable level, and his leg should recover almost completely.' She felt nervous, talking directly to one of the prophets for the first time, and took refuge in relating the facts of which she was confident. 'I estimate that he should be fully fit after another river-turn.'

T'sin nodded. 'You chose well when you brought him here,' he told her. 'Your presence has been welcomed.' The prophet glanced up at the ceiling, and C'tis followed his gaze, remembering.

He knows about the whisperers, she thought.

'They are messengers from Rael,' the prophet said,

as if in answer to her thought. 'The smallest signal of his power – bringing dreams within dreams. Your friend here has benefited from their appearances.'

C'tis had hoped that something like this was the case, and rejoiced at T'sin's words, but her jubilation did not blind her to the prophet's choice of words. He had referred earlier to her 'patient'. Now he said 'your friend'. She looked for signs of disapproval, but could find none. T'sin's expression was benign, his black eyes as unreadable as ever.

'I'm glad,' she managed to say.

'You have a rare and valuable talent,' the other went on. 'Your colleagues praise you highly, and we see no reason to disagree with their judgement. Your instincts are good – do not be afraid to trust them.'

C'tis was silent, not sure how to react to such unexpected commendation. T'sin looked at Arden for a few moments, though he did not step any closer.

'Bring him to us when you judge the time to be right,' he said eventually. 'We wish to talk with him.' With that the prophet turned and left.

'Who was *that*?' Arden's voice was a whisper, hoarse and painful, but intelligible nonetheless. At the sound, C'tis remembered their astonishing conversation of the previous night, and she knelt down to help him struggle to a sitting position.

'You can talk properly,' she repeated, smiling.

He nodded, feeling a surge of pleasure at her obvious delight.

'Don't overdo it, though,' she advised quickly. 'Recovery will be a slow process. Would you like a drink?'

He nodded again, and she fetched water. After he had drunk his fill, he said carefully, 'There are so many things I want to ask you. You have no idea how frustrating this has been for me.'

'For me too,' she replied. 'But we can't cover everything all at once. Where do you want to start?'

'By saying thank you,' he replied quietly. 'For all your care. You could have just left me . . .'

'I'm a healer,' she told him smiling. 'It's my job to care for people.'

'Your devotion to duty is impressive, and this benefic-iary is most grateful . . .' His voice cracked then, and he began to cough. C'tis gave him more water, and told him to be quiet. Arden obeyed with obvious reluctance.

'I'll get you some food,' she said, and began rum-maging about in B'van's supplies. Arden looked up when she presented him with his breakfast.

'Thank you,' he whispered, and the expression in his eyes made it plain that he was talking about more than the meal before him.

C'tis smiled, but put a finger to her lips.

'Eat now,' she said. 'We can talk later.'

That morning they established a pattern which was to last for several days. After eating, when Arden's throat was at its easiest, they talked until he showed the first signs of distress. Then C'tis would insist on quiet, in spite of their impatience, and Arden would divide his time between exercising his leg and the rest which, to his intense irritation, his body still demanded. During these rest periods, he watched carefully as C'tis gently probed his body, feeling her awareness of his inner being.

The process fascinated him and, though the pain and nausea had not left him yet, he always felt better for her ministrations. He remembered a mountain village and Gemma's incredible healing of two sick children. Her uncertainty on that occasion contrasted sharply with C'tis's air of quiet competence – yet her results had been just as impressive. *Was it like this, Gemma?* he wondered, longing desperately to be with her, and wishing that she could have been the one to heal him now.

* * *

The subsequent conversations between Arden and C'tis were a source of wonder to them both. C'tis had already told him much about her world, but she had left so much that seemed obvious to her that he made her go back and explain many details. Arden's own life, and the sequence of events which led to his arrival in the underground realm had of course been entirely unknown to C'tis. Even the parts of their stories which overlapped – the journey back to Midholm, the reaction to Arden's arrival and his subsequent convalescence – became fascinating when viewed through each other's eyes.

They became totally engrossed in their discussions, and began to resent any intrusions. Only B'van was always welcome, bringing as he did a constant supply of good humour and the necessities of life. He did this in an unobtrusive manner, choosing his few words with care. He recognized their obsession, and became even more protective towards his charges, discouraging other visitors and acting as their link with the village.

Several of their conversations – especially those where Arden did most of the talking – added little to his knowledge of this strange world, but some made a great impression on him, and he would review these during his quiet times, implanting them firmly in his memory. Almost without exception, they had begun with a question from him.

*   *   *

'Who is the man with the black eyes?'

'T'sin, one of the prophets. You remember, I told you about them. They guide our people.'

'Your leaders?'

'I suppose so.' C'tis thought about this for a moment. The prophets were a fact of life to her, and she had never questioned their position before. 'They're advisors more than anything, I suppose.'

'But all the work is done by people like yourself?' Arden's dislike for most forms of authority was obvious. 'Doesn't that strike you as unfair?'

'Hush! Ideas like that could get me into trouble,' she replied, glancing nervously towards the cavern entrance.

'Some ideas are worth getting into trouble for,' he told her.

C'tis watched him closely for a few moments, wondering just how much of a disruptive influence this strange man was going to be in her life.

'The prophets know many things that we don't,' she said eventually. 'About our past, and about our future. They have never been wrong before, or misled us, and we have every reason to be grateful, and to trust them.' *Even if they are a little eccentric these days,* she added to herself.

'Fair enough,' Arden said, though he sounded less than convinced. 'Where do they get their knowledge from?'

'They are our link with Rael,' she replied. 'He guides them, through dreams and visions—'

'Who is Rael?'

C'tis hesitated. When she spoke again, her words were slow and controlled, as though repeating a lesson from memory.

'He is the god beneath, the spirit of the Earth. His dreams are so strong, so powerful, that they become real to us. This cavern, the rock, you and me, we are all part of His dream. As is all the world.'

Gemma said the same thing, Arden thought, remembering his earlier doubts, *but she called it the Earth-Mind.*

'Do you believe all that?' he asked.

'Of course.' She paused, then added, 'We all do. This didn't just spring into existence, did it?' She gestured at the cavern around them.

'So he's asleep then?' Arden challenged.

211

'What?'

'If Rael's dreaming, then he must be asleep.'

'Not necessarily,' she replied uneasily. 'You don't judge a god by human standards.'

'I suppose not.'

'And, in any case, it's possible to dream without being asleep. Look what happened to you when you ate the raellim.'

Arden shuddered. 'I would hate to live in *those* dreams,' he said. Then something else occurred to him, and he grinned. 'You mean your Rael is a mushroom addict?'

'No!' she exclaimed. 'Nothing like that!' She was genuinely shocked by his sacrilegious attitude, though she could not help but smile at his amusement. '*Please* don't say things like that when you meet the prophets,' she pleaded.

'I'll be on my best behaviour,' he promised. 'It doesn't do to mess about with a god's ambassadors.'

* * *

'Why are their eyes so dark?'

'That happens gradually – the more raellim they eat, the darker their eyes get.'

'Raellim – the fungus I ate?'

'Yes.'

'Will *my* eyes turn black?' Arden seemed rather put out by this idea.

'I doubt it. They eat the raellim regularly, but only in tiny quantities, and the change occurs slowly, over several river-cycles.'

'Mine was a bit of an overdose, then?' he asked flippantly.

'It should have killed you many times over,' C'tis replied soberly. 'I still don't know why it didn't.'

'Oh, I'm tougher than most,' he said, with the bravado she was coming to recognize. It was obvious that her statement had shaken him, however, and his next question was more subdued.

'Why do they risk eating it then?'

'Because it opens their minds to Rael, and allows them to accept His messages and instructions.'

'That was a picture of Rael in the cave – what did you call it?'

'Soulskeep.'

'A picture of the god?'

'A representation, yes.'

'Did my tongue look like that?' he asked, grinning.

'Much worse,' she replied, returning his smile.

'No wonder I caused such a stir when I opened my mouth,' he commented. 'I didn't need to say a word!'

'I presume that's how you usually get into trouble,' C'tis said. 'By talking too much.'

Arden ignored her gentle joke, and returned to an earlier point.

'I hope what I saw weren't messages or instructions from Rael,' he said. 'If they were, he's a very sick god indeed.'

'Not sick,' she replied. 'But I think he might be angry with us.'

* * *

'How many of you are there?'

'In Midholm?'

'No. In the whole of this Lightless Kingdom.'

'What?' C'tis was puzzled by the way he described her world. 'We have light! And we *don't* have a king!'

'Poetic licence,' he explained. 'You must make allowances for my ill-health.'

'You're getting better all the time!' she exclaimed.

'Thanks to you,' he replied, unabashed. 'Now, will you answer my question?'

C'tis did some mental calculations. There was Midholm and Riverholm and Deepling, and all the smaller outlying villages, not to mention the temporary sites and single dwellings. And the travellers, of course.

'About three thousand,' she decided.

'What!' Arden was staggered by her answer.

'It used to be more,' she said defensively, misunderstanding the reason for his amazement.

'Gods, how big *is* this place?' It was an expression of surprise rather than a question, but C'tis took it literally.

'The Lightless Kingdom?' she replied. 'It's vast – you can travel for many days in any direction. You've only seen a tiny part of it.' She rather enjoyed seeing him so nonplussed.

* * *

'How do I get out of here?'

'You don't.'

Arden looked at her sharply.

'At least, not for some time,' she went on. 'You're getting much better, but you've still some way to go before I'll let you make *that* journey.'

'But there are ways?'

'Of course. They haven't been used for ages, but they should still be passable. V'dal will know. I'll ask him. Though why you want to go back upworld is a mystery to me.'

'It's *my* world, C'tis.'

'And it's full of poison,' she stated flatly.

'It may be poisonous to you, but to me it's home,' he replied in his most maudlin voice, placing a hand over his heart.

'Are you *ever* serious – about *anything*?' she asked.

'He'll take my food seriously, if he has any sense,' B'van put in, as he entered with an armful of fresh provisions.

'Now there speaks a man after my own heart,' Arden said.

'Where are the entrances?'

'You mean the exits.'

'If you like,' Arden agreed. 'The routes to the upworld.'

'Most cave systems have them,' she told him. 'Some are a bit less complicated than others. V'dal's checking on the nearest for you.'

'No, I meant where are they *above* ground? Where will I come out? In the mountains? The desert? The coastal plain?'

'Now how do you expect us to know that?' C'tis responded, sounding almost cross. 'You'll just have to take your chances. Whichever it is, you'll be stuck there. You won't be able to get back in.'

'Why not?'

'Because we'll seal the exit after you've gone.'

'Why?'

'Are you really this stupid?' she retorted, angry now. 'Because we can't risk your bringing upworlders down here to attack us. We're already under enough pressure.'

Arden was shocked and hurt.

'I would never do that!' he exclaimed. 'You've been wonderful to me, and—'

C'tis cut him short.

'You and I may know that, but as a race, we just can't take the risk. You're an upworlder, and in most people's eyes that in itself makes you our enemy.'

'But—'

'Leave it, Arden,' she said, her voice gentle again.

'There must be *something* I can do to prove my worth,' he pleaded.

C'tis shook her head sadly and was about to speak when D'vor came in and stood hesitantly in the entrance.

'Hello,' he began. 'How's the patient?' Their continued silence made him nervous. 'Have I come at a bad time?' he asked.

215

C'tis roused herself. 'Of course not. I was just explaining a few facts of life to Arden.' She told her control party leader the gist of their conversation, and much to Arden's dismay, D'vor confirmed her diagnosis. By this time, Arden's voice was giving out and he had neither the strength nor the will to argue further. D'vor left with a sympathetic smile for C'tis, and a thoughtful look in his large eyes.

*　　*　　*

'How long have you been down here?'

'What do you mean?'

'You're human, aren't you?'

'Nice of you to notice.' C'tis bowed, mocking him gently, but Arden pressed on.

'So you must have come from the upworld. Human beings don't live underground.' He stopped, realizing how tactless he had been, but C'tis was still smiling.

'That is upworlder arrogance at its worst,' she remarked. 'We've always been down here, as you put it. Just because there are more of you shrunken-eyed, dark-skinned creatures doesn't make you the true measure of humanity. Perhaps we're your ancestors!'

'I'm sorry,' he said quietly. 'I just find it so hard to believe that this incredible society exists beneath my own – and that nobody knows about it.'

'Oh, some people know,' she replied, bitterness creeping into her voice, 'but they think we're just animals.'

*　　*　　*

'Aren't you ever curious about the upworld?'

'No. We have legends about those who were, ages ago, but apparently they soon saw the error of their ways.' She grinned. 'Those are tales used to frighten young children.'

'There *are* good things up there,' he protested.

'Not as far as we're concerned,' C'tis stated with finality.

216

CHAPTER TWENTY-SEVEN

The one subject that Arden had been reluctant to discuss with C'tis was the exact nature and cause of his illness. Just thinking about the green-lit cavern and the dead fish within its stream made him feel sick. However, as he was slowly restored to health, there came a time when his curiosity outstripped his repugnance. C'tis had noted and understood his avoidance of the subject, and was glad when he finally mentioned it. It was yet another sign of his continued recovery.

'I'm no expert,' she told him. 'V'dal will explain it far better than I could. I'll get him.'

She returned a little while later with the guide and D'vor, who had decided to join them. After exchanging greetings, Arden thanked them for all they had done. He had not had a chance to do so coherently before. Then V'dal told him of the encroaching pollution which had totally changed his people's way of life.

'It began four river-cycles ago,' he said. 'Or, as you would say, four years ago. The river patterns altered drastically then, changing from their normal ebb and flow.'

Arden sat bolt upright. 'That was four years ago?'

'Yes.'

'Tell me,' the upworlder went on eagerly. 'Before then, was there a river which flowed one year but not the next?'

'It is *all* one river to us,' V'dal replied, puzzled by Arden's sudden eagerness. 'But there *was* a section which acted in the way you describe.'

'How long had it been running in alternate years?'

'Since The Shaking. How do you say it? The Levelling.'

'But it stopped four years ago?'

'Yes. And it led to our having to abandon three villages.'

Arden sat back, nodding to himself. Now he knew why he had named this underground realm the Lightless Kingdom. Shanti's diary had called it that. *It's the other half of the equation*, he thought. *The valley would get the water one year, and this place the next. The evil which deprived one also deprived the other.*

'You look as though you know more about that than we do,' D'vor commented. Up until now, Arden had given C'tis only brief details of the valley and his search for the source of the river. Now he elaborated on that, omitting only the more incredible aspects, and concentrating on the strange metal dam whose destruction he had witnessed. After a while, his throat began to protest, and he asked that they continue their own story.

'The change caused us a few problems, as I've said,' V'dal went on. 'We depend on the river for so much. But even that was a mere inconvenience to what happened later. The first thing we noticed was a rise in the temperature of some of the caves. This caused all sorts of abnormalities in the growth patterns of fish and plants. Then we noticed that the light in certain places was also increasing, for no apparent reason. Our source of light had always been the crystal refractions, but now there was also this strange green glow.'

'At first, we welcomed the extra light,' D'vor put in. 'Together with the added warmth, it meant that there was a remarkable increase in the growth of our crops.'

'But then the sickness began,' C'tis said, her eyes hollow at the memory.

'Whatever was causing the green light also made our people nauseous and weak. After prolonged exposure, this led to blurred vision and internal bleeding.'

218

V'dal paused, noticing the expression on Arden's face.

'It sounds familiar,' the upworlder said.

'Many died before we could work out what was happening,' V'dal went on.

'And it's only through the brave efforts of healers like C'tis that so many of us are still alive,' D'vor added.

Arden glanced at his friend, who tried to brush the comment aside.

'The centre of the pollution was near Soulskeep, and we've been forced further back all the time. We haven't been able to find out where it was coming from,' V'dal said disgustedly, as if he counted this as a personal failure.

'Our retreat gradually became more orderly,' D'vor went on, taking up the tale again. 'We blocked some tunnels with rockfalls, and sealed others with metal doors in an attempt to slow the spread – and it's worked to some extent. But we need the river, so we couldn't just shut ourselves away.'

'It's a hopeless situation,' V'dal said. 'We are doomed without the river, yet with it comes pollution. If we can't find a way to stop it, it'll only be a matter of time before our world is destroyed.'

'This village was once in the centre of our realm,' C'tis put in. 'Now it's near the edge of the sealed lands, the region that's a barrier between us and the bad places.'

'You were very lucky to be found,' D'vor told Arden. 'We don't often go that far now. It's too dangerous.'

'What were you doing?' Arden asked hoarsely.

'Monitoring the progress of the pollution,' V'dal replied. 'And trying to collect raellim for the prophets.'

'You saved us the trouble,' C'tis said with a grin.

'And is the situation still getting worse?'

V'dal nodded. 'We're being pushed further and further north,' he said. 'And that brings its own set of problems.'

Arden looked at him questioningly. D'vor said, 'There are men in the northern caves. Upworlders.'

There was an awkward silence.

'I take it,' Arden rasped, 'that they are not exactly friendly.'

'They think we're animals,' C'tis said angrily. 'And they kill us on sight.'

'We attempted to negotiate with them,' D'vor went on, 'though we'd much rather remain separate and unseen, but how can you talk to people who won't listen?'

'We've had to fight them,' V'dal said. 'We're not very good at it but we're learning all the time.'

'We're having to,' D'vor agreed grimly.

'Do these upworlders wear grey clothes?' Arden whispered.

D'vor nodded, surprised. 'Do you know them?'

'I know *of* them,' he replied.

'We can talk about this another time,' C'tis advised. 'You need to rest.'

Arden submitted to her ministrations with some relief. He felt exhausted, and now had even more to think about.

* * *

'Why don't you try to live above ground?' Arden asked. 'And escape the pollution *that* way. Not all upworlders are as mad as the Grey Raiders.' He had told them about the fanatical grey-clad soldiers and of the rumours he had heard of them using caves beneath the desert as hiding places.

'Sky-light will kill us,' C'tis replied. 'It is foolish of you to ask such a question.'

Arden looked at her huge light eyes and delicate skin, and knew that she was right. For those who had lived generations underground, sunlight would be deadly. C'tis placed her hand next to his.

220

'See how it has burnt you,' she said.

They smiled ruefully at each other, knowing that their worlds were separated by more than just layers of rock.

'Do you feel ready for this visit to the prophets?' she asked, becoming the efficient healer once more. 'We won't go if you're not up to it.'

'I'd like to go,' he replied firmly. 'It's about time I saw something of your world.'

C'tis nodded, and helped him to rise. She tried to hand him his crutch, but he waved it away.

'I want to try and walk unaided.'

Is this pride? she wondered. *Or is he really so much stronger?*

'All right,' she said. 'But I'll bring it just in case.'

'Have we far to go?'

'No, but you must be prepared to attract considerable attention – even in a short distance. Most people have lost interest while you've been out of sight, but when they see you again—'

'They'll be stunned by my good looks?' he asked innocently.

'Hardly!' she replied. *You are feeling better.* 'They'll be curious to see my tame madman.'

Arden stared at her, trying to decide whether she was joking or not.

'And *please*, don't poke your tongue out at them,' she ordered. 'It's still discoloured, and they may think you're going to become a prophet.'

'Perhaps I am,' he responded, grinning.

It was C'tis's turn to be puzzled.

'Come on,' she said eventually. 'It doesn't do to keep them waiting.'

Arden arrived in the outer sanctuary after a short journey which had been made uncomfortable by the number of eyes avidly following his progress. J'vina had joined them at the entrance to the Whispering Gallery, and she discouraged anyone from approaching too closely, but the silent curiosity had been almost too much for Arden.

Three prophets were waiting for him, and T'sin introduced his companions, P'tra and G'lian, then bade Arden sit. It was clear that they were expecting to talk for some time – and so it proved. Arden repeated his story, then answered many questions. In turn he made a few enquiries of his own, mainly about the conflict with the Grey Raiders.

'You will return to the upworld when you are strong enough.' G'lian's words were a statement rather than a question.

Arden nodded.

'You understand the necessity of our blocking the exit once you have gone?' P'tra added. 'It will be useless for you to attempt to find it again.'

Arden took a deep breath.

'I wish that were not the case,' he said, as firmly as his weary voice would allow. 'I owe you all – C'tis especially – a great debt. You have been incredibly kind, and while I realize that we must part, I wish that it could be on terms of mutual regard and trust.'

'We appreciate your feelings, and thank you for your openness during this discussion,' P'tra replied, 'but you must surely see the danger your knowledge of us represents. We are already sorely pressed.'

'Is there no way I could prove myself worthy of your trust?' Arden pleaded. 'I am willing to do anything within my capabilities.'

'D'vor has already made this suggestion on your behalf,' T'sin said. Arden was taken aback, and he glanced at C'tis, but she admitted her ignorance with a shrug.

'He proposed that you use your knowledge of upworld ways to help us in our fight against these Grey Raiders, as you call them,' P'tra said.

'I'll do that gladly,' Arden responded.

'But we have decided that we would not ultimately gain much by this,' G'lian continued. 'And – forgive me – it would present further opportunities for treachery.'

C'tis almost spoke then, but Arden waved her into silence.

'Besides,' T'sin concluded, 'the Grey Raiders have one advantage that no man can withstand.'

Arden looked puzzled.

'Demons,' T'sin stated. 'They send these terrifying creatures forth to frighten and disorganize our soldiers. The demons move faster than mortal creatures, and they change shape at will. There is no way to stand against them.'

'Elementals?' Arden asked.

The cavern grew very still.

'You know of them?' P'tra asked quietly.

'In their own shape, they are like blue flames,' Arden replied, and saw the prophets exchange glances.

'Tell us what you can.'

Arden related the little that he knew about elementals, while six black eyes watched him intently.

'They're not harmful in themselves,' he concluded. 'Although they cause a great deal of trouble to many travellers, they don't attack anyone directly. I don't think they *can*.'

There was a pause, as though the prophets were conferring silently.

'Would you be willing to test this theory personally?' T'sin asked eventually.

'Yes,' Arden replied promptly.

'Prove the demons harmless, and we will have no doubts about your friendship for us,' the prophet told him. Then he turned to C'tis. 'When you judge him to be well enough, healer, let him be guided to our soldiers in the north. We will rely on you to pick a suitable escort for the journey.' He smiled and C'tis nodded quickly, to cover her conflicting emotions.

'Thank you,' Arden said, a broad smile on his face. 'I *will* prove worthy of you.' He was looking at T'sin as he spoke, but C'tis had the feeling that his words were addressed to her.

'I have no doubt of that,' the prophet replied. 'Our trust is not lightly bestowed, but once won, it is as strong as iron.'

The walk back to the Whispering Gallery took rather a long time. Many people had gathered to see Arden, the news of his visit to the prophets having spread far and wide. This time he was able to smile in response to their stares and frank curiosity. He was happy in the knowledge that he would have a chance to repay a little of what he owed to this remarkable race. He wished that he could talk to more of them, but his voice had failed now, after the long session with the prophets, so he contented himself with a few half-formed words of greeting.

One brave youngster ran right up to him and extended a white hand in friendship. Arden took it gently in his own brown fingers and the boy smiled, then ran off to boast of his daring to his friends. After that, Arden was besieged by children, but he enjoyed their attention after his long period of isolation. Eventually C'tis put an end to these attentions, telling the children that her patient needed to rest.

As she and Arden walked on, they passed a woman carefully folding and storing the strange black material that Arden had first seen wrapped round the members of the control party.

'What is that stuff?' he whispered.

'Silkfish tape,' she replied. 'It's very precious. The silkfish expel it from their mouths to build nests for their roe. Then they abandon the nests when the eggs are hatched, and we collect it. It's strong and waterproof, and it will stick to itself if you know how to seal it properly. It's also proof against extremes of cold and heat – and it gives some protection against the greenlight. That's why we wear it in the barriers and beyond. The smiths even cover their eyes with it when their fires grow too bright.'

Precious stuff, indeed, Arden thought.

By now they had reached the entrance to the Whispering Gallery and, once within, their privacy was respected as before. Arden lay down, for once glad to go to sleep.

* * *

The night before he was due to go north, Arden lay asleep in the cavern that he had come to regard as his home. He was alone, but as he dreamed, C'tis and L'tha entered silently, bending over him to check that all was well.

'The night is full of echoes,' L'tha said, glancing up at the diamond crystal. 'Do you feel them?'

'A little,' the healer replied. 'Perhaps.' Arden stirred in his sleep. 'We should leave him alone now. He is as well as I can make him.' The two women withdrew; as they left, tiny flickerings marked the arrival of the whisperers.

Arden dreamed that he was searching for something, someone who was very dear to him, but who remained remote and invisible. Then his vision became a mirror-image. Now it was he who was being hunted, by a confused but relentless spirit. He desperately wanted to be found, but the searcher could not locate him, and he could not call out. His lips were sealed, and his tongue was frozen to the roof of his mouth.

I love you.

Gemma! His eyes snapped open, awake within the dream. Her dream. It was Gemma who was searching for him. But where was she?

Can you hear me?

He looked about wildly, totally confused. Pain throbbed in his leg and his head.

I love you.

Then she was gone, and Arden was left alone. He looked up at the mesmerizing sight of the whisperers at play, but this time did not appreciate their beauty or their wonder. All he could feel was his loss.

CHAPTER TWENTY-EIGHT

C'tis had – quite naturally – chosen the members of her own control group to act as Arden's escorts. Although they were less familiar with the northern regions than with the dangerous caves and tunnels of the south, they were a team; their recent experiences had drawn them even closer together, and their regard for each other had risen even higher. Declaring their support for one another publicly and to the prophets had cemented their mutual respect, and they treated Arden now as one of their number. He was delighted by this.

B'van had been itching to travel again for some time, so he was pleased when C'tis announced her plan. He immediately began making preparations. J'vina was also keen on the expedition, though for a different reason. She was looking forward to what she called 'real fighting, not just looking for phantoms'. Even the discouraging reports from the north could not dampen her enthusiasm. No one questioned L'tha's right to travel with them as the prophets' representative. Her reactions to the elementals would be very important. D'vor and V'dal approached the task more soberly, but both were determined to share in the enterprise, and felt a measure of responsibility for Arden and C'tis. They also looked forward to the possible benefits, should their efforts succeed. Since the prophets had granted Arden's request, he had had several discussions with D'vor and V'dal about the bad relations between their world and his own. One of these conversations had made him even more aware of the implications of the task ahead, and had added much to his understanding of the Lightless Kingdom.

* * *

'I can see why you have such a poor opinion of us upworlders,' he said. 'After all, the Grey Raiders are disliked enough by my people . . .'

'They *are* your people,' V'dal interrupted, his voice soft.

'Only in the broadest sense,' Arden replied. 'There are so many more of us up there – hundreds of thousands.'

'Which makes *us* all the more vulnerable,' V'dal commented.

'But our society is fragmented, and people like me want nothing to do with groups like the raiders,' Arden went on. 'Of course there are madmen and all manner of evils, but there is much that is good – you've only come into contact with the worst of it.'

'We have only your word for that,' D'vor replied. 'I believe you – I *want* to believe you – but just think how it appears to us. Apart from the men who kill us without compunction, treating us as if we were vermin, only fit for extermination, the only thing your world has given us is poison.'

'That might just be through ignorance,' Arden said, but his heart was not in the words. 'No one knows that you're here.'

'Poisons do not just disappear when they're hidden underground,' V'dal answered. 'This is your earth too.'

'Whatever the reason,' D'vor said, 'it doesn't exactly endear your world to us.'

'I can see that,' Arden muttered. 'Do you believe there's no hope of our two peoples co-operating then?'

'There is always hope,' V'dal replied.

'I know of many who would gladly help in your fight

against the Grey Raiders,' Arden said, regaining a little of his optimism. 'They are a blight on the upworld too. And perhaps we can find a way to stop the pollution. It must be worth trying.'

'Maybe.' D'vor's tone was non-committal, but Arden saw – or hoped he saw – a glint of encouragement in the alien eyes.

'You have so much that could benefit my people,' he went on eagerly. 'Your metalwork alone is revolutionary.' It was true. Arden now wore a metal brace on his injured leg which was comfortable and strong, but so light that he often forgot it was there. He knew of no metal like it above ground. 'If only we could establish a link between our worlds, we could all gain so much.'

'The possibility has been discussed frequently,' V'dal said, smiling at Arden's enthusiasm. 'But to many it would be anathema, a last act of desperation. All the evidence we have . . .' He shrugged eloquently.

'Our isolation has suited us for countless river cycles,' D'vor went on. 'And it is difficult now for us to even consider a merging with the upworld. Perhaps it is time that we did. Although we have always rejected the idea before, there is just a chance that you could be the bridge between us.'

*   *   *

As Arden travelled north with his six companions, he was more determined than ever to earn their trust and help them in their bitter fight for survival. He saw this journey as the first step in the reconciliation between the two worlds, and he longed for the process to begin. In his mind, the Lightless Kingdom was now akin to the valley; both had taken him in and helped him in spite of any initial reservations; both were places afflicted by evils imposed upon them from outside. His sense of justice, as well as his personal feelings of gratitude, made him long to be their champion.

This train of thought led him naturally to wonder about how the valley was faring. He had no doubt that the river would have returned, and he imagined the land rich and fertile once more. He gazed at the rock over his head, and wondered where he was in relation to his sometime home. He couldn't wait to see it again, to greet his friends and share in their joy. And surely Gemma would be there too. *She's a survivor*, he told himself, pushing aside any doubts. *Where else would she go?* His last words to her before they had parted were, 'Remember our destiny.' 'I will,' she had replied. Arden would normally have laughed at such sentiments, but now he found himself silently repeating the phrase, as though it were a vow, and believing in it totally. They *would* be together again.

During the journey's first rest period, Arden took the opportunity to ask about something that had been bothering him.

'As you see the upworld as being so vile,' he began hesitantly, 'why did you rescue me?'

The members of the control party all looked at C'tis, and she answered for them.

'I'm a healer,' she said, 'and as such, I have responsibilities towards *anyone* who is sick.'

'But there must be more to it than that,' Arden persisted. 'Weren't you suspicious about how I came to be there?'

'Of course,' J'vina replied. 'I would have left you to die.' There was no hint of apology in her statement, and although Arden was taken aback, he appreciated her honesty. 'And that shows why I am a soldier, not a patrol leader,' J'vina went on, equally honest in her judgement of herself. 'Leaving you would have been a mistake.'

'Why?'

'Because we're here now,' she responded simply. *Because of what you might be able to do for us*, her tone implied.

'We were curious, too,' V'dal said. 'You were a mystery.'

'Especially when we found out that you'd been eating raellim,' D'vor added. L'tha nodded in agreement, though she did not speak. 'We've learnt a lot from you – about the tunnels around Soulskeep, and the river's flow—'

'And the Grey Raiders and the elementals,' B'van put in.

'Also, you're a medical phenomenon,' C'tis said, grinning. 'And they're always interesting! You survived what should have been a fatal illness, and because of what I've learnt from you, I have lots of ideas that I want to try out on my own people.'

'Besides, we're not *all* as ruthless as J'vina.' V'dal's comment was not made as a criticism, and was not taken as such.

'There is always hope,' Arden quoted.

'Exactly,' V'dal replied.

Now I must turn that hope into reality, Arden thought.

* * *

The journey north lasted several days, and Arden began to appreciate just how vast this strange underground realm was. They progressed mostly on foot; the river was too fragmented or wild in this area to make travelling by boat possible. Unlike the previous trek, Arden was in full possession of all his senses, and he marvelled at the endless variety of scenery offered by the Lightless Kingdom.

He also came to see that, in spite of its size, the cave and tunnel system offered relatively few sites suitable for habitation. Any place that could supply adequate space, light, water and food was already fully exploited. On two occasions, the group stayed in villages overnight, once in Deepling, a settlement almost as big as Midholm, and once in a much smaller community known as White Falls. The latter was named after the nearby rapids, where a section of the river plunged through a twisting series of passages and gullies, producing a constant roar that underscored life in the village.

Arden was the subject of intense curiosity in both places, even experiencing animosity from some until his companions explained their joint purpose. After that, his presence was accepted gladly. Everyone was afraid of the demons, and when they learnt that Arden was willing to face them, he became doubly fascinating. These visits also allowed him to see further evidence of the crafts of his hosts. Metal work was a major concern, and furnished raw material for almost all their tools, but the way in which the meagre plant and animal life provided not only food, but cloth, leather, rope and many other essentials, was just as remarkable. The village people all worked hard, and most of them specialized in a necessary field; mining, fishing, cultivation, and so on. But they also managed to find time for less vital pursuits. Story-telling was common, and they were musical too – though to Arden's ears the predominantly percussion-based instruments sounded very strange. One of the smiths in Deepling produced sculptures, exquisitely detailed figures, so lifelike that their eyes seemed to follow the observer. With each new discovery, Arden's regard for the people of the Lightless Kingdom rose ever higher.

At White Falls, J'vina and V'dal consulted the local guides and soldiers, and before they left, warned the others that they would soon be moving into territory that was considered unsafe. The Grey Raiders had never actually penetrated as far as the village, but there had been fighting not too far away. All except L'tha carried weapons now – Arden had been presented with a sword by the best smith in Midholm – and J'vina looked quite pleased when she informed them that their weapons would almost certainly be put to use soon.

Although Arden was no stranger to violence, he had never used a sword in anger, and felt uncomfortable at the prospect. J'vina, as though reading his mind, promptly offered him lessons.

'She just wants a chance to show off,' B'van commented.

'Jealousy is so unbecoming in cooks, don't you think?' the warrior retorted. B'van just grinned at her.

So J'vina showed Arden some basic moves; how to use the point and the cutting edges; how to balance and grip; and how to brace oneself in order to fend off an opponent's blow. At first, he felt foolish and inept, especially in front of interested spectators, but eventually some of her teaching sank in.

'And this is the most important lesson,' J'vina told her now breathless pupil. 'What would you do if faced with two or more armed opponents at once?'

'Run away?' Arden suggested.

'Right!' she laughed. 'You've too much sense to make a good soldier.'

If the 'opponents' are elementals, Arden thought, I must stand my ground. And this sword won't be any use at all.

*   *   *

After leaving White Falls, V'dal led them into a labyrinth of interconnecting tunnels. There were few caverns of any size here, and Arden marvelled at V'dal's confidence in his route. Arden was sure that, had he been alone, he would have wandered in endless circles. The terrain was difficult, and their progress slow. In some places, it was so dark that D'vor took the unusual step of lighting a glow-lamp; the dim red radiance made it possible for Arden to continue unaided.

They set up camp that night in a small, crystal-lit cavern which had several tunnels leading from it. As preparations were being made for their meal, J'vina and

V'dal scoured the surrounding area, reporting back that there was no sign of either friends or foes. While eating, Arden became aware of the unusual cross-currents of air in the cave. He had already noticed various underground winds on the journey, and had noted the use people made of them – in siting their smithies and cooking fires – but this was different. The movement was inconsistent, arbitrary, bringing with it a soundless vibration. Arden felt uneasy, and glanced at his companions, but they did not appear to sense anything out of the ordinary.

Before long, however, the vibrations became audible, and Arden stopped eating to listen. Each note flowed into the next, dividing and blending, rising and falling, in a melancholy liquid song which reminded him at first of the brothers' chants in praise of the gods. Then he realized that this music was of the earth itself.

'The singing sands,' he whispered, mesmerized by the perverse beauty of the sound. 'It sounds so different down here.'

The others observed his preoccupation with interest.

'It is beautiful, isn't it,' L'tha agreed quietly.

'It's just the wind,' J'vina told him.

But Arden did not hear them; his mind was occupied partly with the hypnotic music and partly by speculating on the fact that they must now be underneath some part of the Diamond Desert. *Of course!* he remembered. *The caves under the north of the desert, by the coastal road – that's where Gemma was first attacked by the Grey Raiders.* He looked up at the ceiling, wondering, not for the first time, what was above him.

The song died down, becoming softer, less insistent.

'It's not *just* the wind,' V'dal said. 'Some of the vibrations are set up by river water.'

J'vina stiffened, then stood up suddenly, her sword hissing from its scabbard.

'Someone's coming,' she whispered. 'Over there.' She

233

pointed to one of the tunnel entrances, and the others slowly got to their feet, hands on the hilts of their weapons.

As the music died away, another song became audible. This one sounded just as odd, but was smaller somehow, more personal. Its high-pitched intonation echoed around the cavern. It seemed to Arden as if he recognized it, but, before his mind could make the connection, another sound was heard. Scratching, shuffling footsteps came from the tunnel they were all facing so defensively.

They drew their swords quietly, hearts beating fast. Shadows moved in the cavern's entrance, and the singing stopped abruptly.

Several meyrkats emerged, standing up on their hind legs and regarding the astonished humans with solemn, black-rimmed eyes.

For several moments nobody moved, then Arden laid down his sword and stepped forward. The meyrkats peeped happily at the sight of him, glancing back and forth with interest.

Arden began to laugh.

CHAPTER TWENTY-NINE

Arden's bewildered companions were more confused than ever when he sat down and stuck one leg out in front of him. After a moment's hesitation, the strange little creatures began jumping over the outstretched limb, to the accompaniment of Arden's laughter and their own piping calls.

'I know them,' the upworlder explained. 'We played this game in the desert.' He glanced round and saw the incredulous expressions on his companions' faces for the first time.

'Stop laughing and *explain*!' J'vina shouted, although she was close to laughter herself.

Arden gradually regained his composure, and explained as much about the meyrkats as he was able.

'What are they doing down here?' D'vor asked. 'We've never seen their like before.'

'Who knows?' Arden replied. 'I can't talk to them – only Gemma could do that. Perhaps they're exploring. Or looking for me.' He turned back to the clan with a new eagerness in his eyes. 'Is Gemma with you? Can you take me to her?'

The meyrkats, who were now ranged along one wall of the cavern, did not react to his words. *If only I could communicate with them*, he thought ruefully.

'I should like to meet this Gemma,' V'dal said. 'The more we hear about her, the more remarkable she seems.' Arden made no reply, lost in thoughts of hope and longing.

The tunnels were quiet again, and the members of

235

the control party relaxed, though they still glanced frequently at the animals, who were now huddled together, showing every sign of going to sleep. Leaving J'vina on guard, the humans followed their example.

* * *

When Arden and his party set off the next morning, the meyrkats went with them, scampering ahead and investigating all the side passages along the way. Their insatiable curiosity was amusing to watch, but J'vina did not enjoy their antics.

'We may as well light lamps, or sing to announce our progress,' she complained. 'With that lot clattering around, the enemy will hear us coming without any problem.'

Arden saw her point, but could do nothing to help.

'I'm sorry,' he said quietly. 'I can't control them.'

'We could always frighten them away,' she muttered, but neither she nor the others made any attempt to do so. Somehow, the presence of these lively little creatures made the purpose of their journey seem a bit less grim.

Towards the end of the day, they made contact with one of the eight-person military patrols in that area. They made camp together and exchanged information, learning that the Grey Raiders and elementals had been close by the day before. A number of guards remained on duty during the rest period.

The meyrkats were the subject of much bemused comment, but they were relatively subdued now, and merely watched the proceedings, huddled together for warmth.

Some of the soldiers had seen elementals during their recent scouting trips, and Arden questioned them closely.

'They're always changing shape,' one told him, 'and they move so fast you can lose them as soon as blink.'

'I've seen them catch a man and cover him in an instant,' another said, shuddering. 'It looked like he was being burnt in a blue fire.'

'I've seen that too,' a female soldier commented. 'The poor bastard was screaming and thrashing about, but he couldn't get away. It was as if he was being eaten alive.'

'Were they harmed by this?' Arden asked.

'Not physically,' the woman replied, 'but their minds were gone. They'd no stomach for fighting after that – and no wonder.'

'The upworlders . . . begging your pardon, the Grey Raiders, often follow up, and cut them down while they're defenceless,' the second man said. 'But even when they don't, a soldier's no good after an experience like that.'

After some discussion about the nearby territory, it was decided that they would go to the huge cavern known as the Hall of Winds, where elementals were often seen. This site would give Arden the advantage of being able to advance a considerable distance into the open while still remaining within sight of his colleagues at the cavern's southern entrance. From there, they would be able to watch his encounter with the elementals in relative safety, but would still be able to go quickly to his aid should he be threatened by Grey Raiders.

'What happens if *they* go with you?' B'van asked, nodding towards the sleeping meyrkats.

'I won't be trying to hide,' Arden replied, 'so the noise won't matter. And I'd welcome their company.'

'Are you sure you want to go in on your own?' D'vor asked.

'Yes. It's the only way.'

'Then you're a brave man, after what we've heard this evening,' V'dal remarked.

'Brave or insane,' Arden said. 'Take your pick.' He grinned, but was in fact beginning to feel distinctly nervous. He had never heard of elementals behaving in the way that the soldiers had described. *Maybe they're not what I think they are*, he worried, then dismissed this as pure speculation. He dreamt of the whisperers that night, and awoke wondering if that was an omen – and if so, of what.

* * *

For some reason, the Hall of Winds reminded Arden of the ruined abbey – it had the same quality of tranquillity and other-worldliness. The main cavern was fully two hundred paces in length, and half that distance across at its widest point. The floor was uneven, with many strange rock formations reaching up to the convoluted roof, but there were several well-defined pathways which would make access reasonably easy.

'Stay near the central walkway,' J'vina ordered. 'That way we can reach you in a hurry if need be.' Arden nodded. 'And good luck,' she added.

Arden stepped forward as confidently as he was able. The meyrkats stayed close behind him, darting back and forth as busily as ever. He ignored them as best he could, and kept a sharp eye on the far end of the cavern. He knew that there were several entrances there, but in the dim crystal-light he could not make out the individual tunnels. It was only when he reached the centre of the Hall that he noticed the faint blue glow in one dark corner.

Arden stood quite still, watching the light increase in intensity. The meyrkats stopped their explorations, and stood up on their hind legs, sniffing the air and glancing about nervously.

Two flame-like beings darted into the cavern, their radiance almost unbearably bright after the endless twilight of this underground realm. Arden shaded his eyes, his heart thumping, and forced himself to push fear aside. The elementals hovered by the entrance, as if uncertain of their purpose there, and Arden was glad to see that they were not accompanied by any grey-clad warriors. He swallowed and cleared his throat.

'Greetings!' he called. 'I am your friend.' His words echoed in the stillness of the cavern, and he suddenly felt very foolish.

At first, the elementals did not react, but when they did, just a few moments later, the result was breathtaking. They transformed themselves so swiftly that the amazed onlookers could only take in a fraction of the images. Arden saw flashes of Lightless Kingdom soldiers, first dressed in leather, then wound about with silkfish tape. Their arms were flailing, their eyes wild. He saw Grey Raiders with arms outstretched and pointing, mouths open as if shouting; he saw rock and water and fire, and other things he could not name; all in the blinking of an eye.

Then the blue flames moved again, so fast that it was as though they had not travelled, but had been instantaneously transported from one place to another, leaving only the memory of shadows as evidence of their flight.

The meyrkats began to sing, their strange, discordant voices unmistakably reverent, but sounding so out of place that Arden could not help but smile. All his fear left him.

'Your friend!' he shouted again, and was enveloped in an instant.

The world sparkled as his body became weightless; in a moment of pure wonder, Arden realized that for the first time, he could understand what the meyrkats were singing!

> The burrow-gods bring shadows to our clan,
> The roarers and the whisperers bind us.

Though the words made little sense, they were clear and unmistakable – and obviously joyful. Arden felt

239

this fill him too, and received in return a wave of friendliness from the elemental being that surrounded him. It was a sensation unlike any he had ever known.

He turned, though he was not conscious of the action of moving, and found that some of his companions – J'vina and C'tis foremost among them – had advanced into the cavern, swords in their hands. Their expressions were horrified, and he realized that a terrible misunderstanding had drawn them from their hiding places. He must put them right.

'No!' he cried, holding up his hands to forestall their threatening advance. 'They are not demons!'

His friends stopped at his words, and Arden smiled – then the elemental disappeared, and he was left feeling suddenly weary, but jubilant nonetheless.

'They will not harm you!' he told the others. 'If you will only accept them, they will be your friends.' J'vina and the others did not look any less grim. 'There's no reason for you to be afraid,' he insisted, then realized that his audience were no longer paying him any attention. Instead they were looking towards the far end of the cavern.

Arden spun round.

And saw the twenty or so Grey Raiders who were standing silently beside the tunnel entrances. Crystal light glittered coldly on their drawn swords.

CHAPTER THIRTY

The air was suddenly thick with the sound of running feet. Arden stood quite still, acutely aware of his exposed position but unable to decide whether to retreat or stand his ground. As his friends hurried to his aid, he drew his sword and turned to face the raiders.

The two sides collided moments later, with a clash of steel and screams of hatred. Arden had no time to see how his friends were faring, because he was too busy coping with a grey-robed fanatic swinging wildly with a two-handed sword. Arden's own blade was shorter and much lighter, and he put his superior mobility to good use. Dodging the first clumsy blow, he twisted behind a stalagmite just as his opponent's weapon smashed into the bulbous formation. Arden attacked swiftly before the raider had time to recover. Darting round the rock, he drove his blade upwards beneath the man's ribs, then pulled away, leaving him for dead.

A quick glance around showed him that the battle had divided into several small engagements; there had been casualties on both sides, but, as yet, neither had the upper hand. The raiders' greater numbers were counter-acted by their opponents' agility and eyesight more suited to the environment. It was an even match. There was no sign of the meyrkats.

Two more raiders bore down upon Arden, but hesitated as they drew close.

'Why do you fight with these *animals*?' one of them growled. 'You're one of us.'

241

'He's demon-spawn!' the other spat. 'Let's take him.'

Arden smiled grimly, remembering J'vina's advice about being faced with two opponents. *Not this time,* he thought. *I have a few scores to settle.* He set himself, his sword held as J'vina had taught him, then leapt forward, taking his adversaries by surprise. They recovered quickly, and Arden was soon forced back. Then another figure hurtled past, landing a crunching blow which demolished the shoulder of one of his opponents. B'van had come to Arden's rescue, but paid a heavy price for his wild attack; his sword stuck, and the second raider chopped down savagely with his own blade. B'van's neck was almost severed, and a second spray of blood flew into the air.

Arden was gripped with fury; he dived forward over the body of his fallen friend, lashing out at the enemy. He had the satisfaction of feeling his blow strike home – then someone hit him on the back of his head and he fell senseless to the ground.

* * *

When Arden awoke, it was pitch black, and his head ached abominably. He tried to assess his injuries, and instantly regretted the attempt at movement. Apart from the large lump on the back of his skull, his entire body felt as if it had been pummelled black and blue. He was in dreadful pain – far more than could have been caused by his fall. His face felt puffy and sore, and his mouth was dry. He lay quite still, letting the waves of agony wash over him until he could bring them under control and try to think.

He recalled B'van's death with sickening clarity, but nothing since. *What's happened to my friends?*

Light flared suddenly. He winced, and saw that he was imprisoned in a tiny, bare cave whose entrance was barred by a solid wooden door. A lamp flickered outside, casting red beams through the bars of the window.

Arden heard somebody mutter outside his cell, then the sound of bolts being withdrawn. The door opened and a man came in carrying a burning torch. Arden did not move.

'I know you're awake,' the newcomer said. 'And I think it's time we had a little talk.' He set the torch in a wall bracket, then sat down on the step, folding his grey robes carefully about him. When he spoke again there was a cruel humour in his voice. 'Actually, you owe me a debt of gratitude. Your situation could have been much worse.'

Arden opened one eye and looked at his gaoler, who smiled.

'Had I not intervened,' the raider went on, 'my men would undoubtedly have killed you. As it was, I'm afraid I could not prevent them from venting their frustration on you – just a little. After all, you did kill two of their comrades.'

That explains it, Arden thought. And then, *What does he want?* He opened both eyes, and looked properly at the man for the first time. He had a sharp-featured face, with small shrewd eyes; although he looked thin and wiry, much of his body was hidden beneath bulky robes.

Arden remained still and silent, waiting.

'I'm sure you'd like a drink,' the other said eventually. 'Shall we make a trade? I'll give you some water if you answer some simple questions. Does that suit you, Arden?'

Arden started at the sound of his name.

'I thought it was you,' the raider said smugly. 'My name is Aric. Now that we've been introduced, do you want that water or not?'

'Yes,' Arden whispered through swollen lips.

'Good.' Aric shouted an order through the door, then sat in silence, his arms folded. Arden managed to twist himself into a sitting position, then became still once more, breathing slowly and shallowly as he waited for

243

the pain to subside. A soldier brought in a pitcher of water, handed it to him, then left. Arden drank gratefully

'Now,' Aric began. 'Tell me how you came to be down here.'

Arden said nothing.

'Come now! What harm can it do to tell me that?' Aric's eyes narrowed menacingly. 'My troops are only too willing to help you talk, and their methods are usually less civilized than mine.'

'I fell,' Arden said shortly.

'From where?'

'The mountains.'

'Don't lie to me! That's leagues away!'

Arden stared sullenly at his inquisitor, but made no reply.

'How long have you been down here?'

'Months.'

'Really! This is getting us nowhere!' Aric exclaimed in exasperation.

'It's true. I've been ill, and I'd broken my leg.'

'And those animals looked after you, no doubt?' The raider's voice was thick with sarcasm.

'They're not animals. They're as human as you or I.'

'They're vermin. What else can you call creatures that scurry round in the dark? Why were you fighting on their side?'

Again, Arden did not reply. Aric's anger subsided, and he abruptly changed tack.

'What did you do to the elemental?'

'Nothing.'

The raider scowled. 'We heard you shouting – was it a spell?' Arden smiled crookedly. If Aric wanted to believe him capable of casting spells over elementals, then who was he to disabuse him?

'Where does your power come from?'

'I have no power,' Arden replied disgustedly. 'If I had, do you think I'd have let myself be kicked about like this?'

244

'If you insist on deliberately misunderstanding my questions, it will be the worse for you in the end,' Aric remarked. His tone was light, but held an unmistakable threat.

They were silent for a while. Arden sipped some more water, then choked when Aric asked suddenly, 'How's Gemma?'

When Arden stopped spluttering, he stared at his interrogator, accusation in his eyes.

'The witch *was* your companion, was she not? Have you had a falling out?' Aric smiled maliciously.

'I haven't seen her for months.'

'Mmm.'

'What's that supposed to mean?'

'When you learn to answer my questions, I will answer yours,' Aric replied, then rose, collected the torch, and left the dungeon.

Arden sat in total darkness once more. He soon abandoned the hopelessly confused speculation prompted by Aric's words, and lay down on the hard floor, trying to sleep.

*   *   *

When he next awoke, another man stood silhouetted in the doorway, hands on his hips. He tensed as Arden stirred.

'So it's alive,' the raider remarked. 'I thought our boots might have finished it off.'

'Water,' Arden croaked.

'And it can talk!' the man exclaimed in mock astonishment. He moved further into the cave, and Arden saw the fanatical glint in his eyes. Compared to this man, Aric had seemed only mildly threatening.

'You're lucky – some *very* important people want to talk to you. Otherwise . . .'

'That's the second time today I've been told how lucky I am,' Arden responded quietly.

245

'If I had my way, I'd have skinned you alive by now. Any man who fights with those demon-spawn deserves at least that.'

Arden made no comment.

'And you wrecked the elemental bond!' the man ranted on. 'They were useless after that. What did you do to them?' When no reply was forthcoming, he leaned forward and grabbed the front of Arden's shirt. 'What did you do to them?' he yelled, so loudly that Arden's ears rang.

'I told them I was a friend,' he replied truthfully.

The raider's face contorted with fury, and his hands tightened their grip.

'I ought to cut your lying tongue out,' he snarled.

'Some very important people might not like that,' Arden whispered back.

Then he was shoved away so fiercely that he fell against the rock wall.

'I may not be able to touch you yet, but sooner or later they'll tell me to get some answers out of you – any way I choose. I shall look forward to that.'

He left, slamming the door shut. In the darkness, Arden tried to survey the damage to his body. His head felt marginally better, but his ribs and stomach still ached badly. Movement was slightly easier. He was very thirsty – and hungry. How long have I been here? he wondered.

Aric returned some hours later, and Arden regarded him suspiciously.

'I trust you slept well,' the raider said pleasantly.

'Until your friend arrived,' Arden replied.

'I'm afraid Wray does get worked up rather easily, especially where the elementals are concerned,' Aric said. 'You should try not to annoy him.'

'How long are you going to keep me here?'

'Why?' Aric was amused. 'Are you in a hurry to leave? Do you have an appointment elsewhere?'

'What do you want from me?'

'Just the answers to a few questions. Would you like something to eat?'

And so began a pattern which continued for some days, though Arden had no real way of measuring the passing of time. The two raiders visited him alternately, between long periods of total isolation. Aric was outwardly all concern, offering food and drink, and speaking gently – although the menace beneath his words was abundantly clear. Wray, on the other hand, would shout and threaten, always on the edge of violence, but drawing back at the last moment. Both quizzed Arden incessantly about his links with the Lightless Kingdom, with the elementals, and with Gemma. They demanded details of the cave systems he had seen, the rivers and tunnels, and they also tried to get him to reveal the exact location of the valley. He was shaken by the amount they already knew about him, and responded with a judicious mixture of truth and lies. They caught him out many times, but this was all part of the game.

And it *was* a game. They all knew it. The real confrontation would come when the *very* important someone arrived – or sent instructions. In the meantime, Arden fenced with words, occasionally managing to make a feeble thrust of his own. After a while, he grew confused, unable to remember what he had told them and what he must keep hidden, and he began to dread the idea that he was being broken. He would soon have no reserves left, and would then tell them everything he knew. *Not that that's much*, he thought bitterly.

What made the situation worse was that neither of his cross-examiners answered, or even pretended to answer, Arden's own questions. They gave no sign of knowing whether Gemma was alive, or where she might be. The fate of his friends from the Lightless Kingdom was also a mystery. Arden knew that B'van was dead, but could glean no news of the others. It was

247

obvious that Wray could influence the elementals in some way – a fact which Arden found immensely disturbing – but the nature of this power remained obscure. His only reassurance lay in the fact that the Grey Raiders obviously had no idea where the valley was. That was one piece of information Arden would not reveal unless the relentless, two-pronged attack destroyed him utterly. But he felt that this could only be a matter of time.

*   *   *

After several days, a new player entered the game, by which time Arden's physical condition had improved considerably, even as his mental state had deteriorated. He was standing when the shutters were drawn back from the grille in the door, and a young man looked in.

'Come to the door – quickly. I don't know how long I've got.' The whispered words were urgent.

Arden did as instructed, then asked. 'Who are you?'

'Don't talk so loudly,' the other hissed. 'Just listen. My name is Dacey, and I'm a friend of Jordan's.' Arden's eyes widened but the young man motioned him to remain silent. 'I'm sorry I couldn't come sooner, but I'm going to try to get you out of here.' Dacey went on to explain how Jordan had for some time wanted to contact the cave-dwellers, believing that he could help them, and get their help in return.

'Until now,' the young man went on, 'no one from the surface has been able to get even close, but you could do it. Will you help us?'

Arden cast aside any worries that this might be a trick, and nodded vigorously. 'There's nothing I'd like better,' he whispered. 'There are some people underground who want the same thing.'

'That's good news,' Dacey said. 'I have to go now – but don't give up hope. You've held them off so far, and I know just how ruthless those two can be. Don't worry!'

'Thank you,' Arden breathed.

Then noises sounded in the tunnel outside, and with a final wave, Dacey closed the shutter. Arden sat down, his heart thumping, as the beginning of hope swelled within him.

CHAPTER THIRTY-ONE

Dacey's next visit came – as far as Arden could judge – two days later. It was brief.

The young man smiled when Arden came to the door.

'There's going to be fighting soon,' he told him. 'We're on alert now. The cave-dwellers have never been this close before, so with luck, there'll be a lot of confusion. I'll try and get you away as soon as it starts.' Arden nodded. 'When this door opens, follow me. If anything happens to me, follow the yellow triangles marked on the rock. They'll get you to the surface – after that, you're on your own. Understand?'

'Yes.'

'See you soon. Be ready!'

Dacey closed the shutter and left without waiting for a response.

I'll be ready, Arden thought. He crouched down beside the door, listening intently for any sounds of movement outside. He did not have long to wait.

Running footsteps were closely followed by shouts and the clash of weapons. Arden tensed; obviously the fighting had come even closer than Dacey had foreseen. Being able to hear but not know for sure what was going on was intensely frustrating. He wondered whether he should call out – if Dacey was not able to free him, perhaps his friends from the Lightless Kingdom could.

The noise outside grew louder for a time, then paused, and in the lull Arden heard a familiar voice.

'Where is he?'

'Over there,' came the half-strangled reply. A crunching sound and a gurgling rattle followed, and Arden shivered. Moments later the bolts were drawn back, the door opened, and J'vina glanced inside. The warrior held a blood-stained sword in each hand, and was breathing heavily. When she saw Arden, she smiled, and handed him one of the weapons.

'Come on!' With that, she turned on her heels.

Arden emerged, blinking in the sudden light, and followed his rescuer. Several bodies lay in the cavern and the stench of blood was almost overpowering. Three more Lightless Kingdom soldiers stood guarding the entrances. Like J'vina, they were wrapped in the sinister-looking silkfish tape.

'I've got him!' J'vina yelled. 'Let's go!'

As they moved off, three Grey Raiders burst into the cavern. One had a crossbow and J'vina lost one of her men to a bolt through his chest before anyone had time to react. Hand-to-hand fighting followed, vicious and bloody. When it was over, all three raiders lay dead, but Arden was left with only J'vina, bleeding from cuts on her arm and cheek, and one other for company.

'Where are the rest?' J'vina asked.

'I don't know,' C'lin replied. 'We'd better go.' He swung round to one of the tunnel entrances just as Dacey emerged from it, carrying a sword. He made no move to attack, his face a mixture of surprise and bewilderment, but C'lin struck like lightning.

'No!' Arden screamed. 'Not him!'

But it was too late. Dacey fell to the ground, his eyes already sightless, as the last of his life gushed forth from the gaping wound in his stomach. C'lin turned to look at Arden uncertainly as the upworlder swore viciously.

'No time for that now,' J'vina told them urgently. She shoved Arden in front of her, and the three of them stumbled out of the cavern, stepping over Dacey's body. The sounds of fighting came from further down the tunnel.

'They're working round behind us, trying to cut off our retreat,' C'lin said, looking back over his shoulder.

'Go on!' J'vina urged. 'There's no choice. If we can't go round, we'll just have to go *through* them.'

So they went on, emerging into a honeycomb maze of tunnels, through which a deadly game of hide-and-seek was being played. Torches flared and fell, steel screeched and voices roared; moments of silence intervened, then the fragmented battle began again. J'vina raised her voice in a strange hooting wail which echoed and reechoed in the labyrinth.

'Now they know we've got you, and they're to fall back,' she explained briefly, then led them on again. By now, Arden was revolted by the bloodshed he had witnessed, and hopelessly confused, but he eventually caught the implication of her words.

'All this was for *me*?' he exclaimed.

But J'vina had no time to answer. Just at that moment two raiders appeared to bar their path. She faked a lunge at one, then at the last moment turned her attack on the other, catching them both on the wrong foot. Her blade sliced along the rib-cage of the second man, but failed to disable him. Her own side was exposed now. Arden saw the first raider raise his sword for a killing blow and reacted instinctively, fury rising within him. Crashing forward, his clumsy attack put the raider off long enough for J'vina to recover. She engaged her man while Arden thrashed at the other. As C'lin shoved past him, entering the fray, Arden overbalanced, catching his leg on a jut of rock and twisting it horribly. He cried out in pain as his shin was held fast by the metal splint, while the rest of his body fell. The bone shattered, and he gasped in agony.

J'vina and C'lin overcame their respective opponents, and came to kneel beside him.

'Looks like you'll be needing our healer's services again,' J'vina remarked, grimacing as she looked at the bloody, twisted leg. 'Can you carry him, C'lin?'

The soldier sheathed his sword, then hoisted Arden on to his shoulder. Although he was as gentle as he could be, the pain was so bad that Arden fainted.

When he came to, he was lying in a crystal-lit cavern with C'tis bending over him. He lay still, listening to the gentle sounds of running water and the murmur of conversation. His leg was a red ball of fire, but he could tell that it had faded from the earlier torment; it even seemed possible now that there was more in the world than his agony.

C'tis saw his eyes open, and smiled worriedly.

'How do you feel?' she asked.

'Better for seeing you,' he replied truthfully.

'That was a stupid thing to do, after all my hard work,' she reprimanded him, though her anger was not convincing.

'I'll try not to do it again.'

'You do, and you may never walk again,' the healer told him. 'Some things are beyond even my skill. As it is, you'll be on your back for some time.'

Another person came into Arden's field of vision.

'How's the demon-tamer?' D'vor asked.

'Better,' C'tis replied. 'And very contrite.'

'What did you call me?' Arden asked.

'That's your title now,' D'vor replied with a grin. 'It was quite a show you put on.'

'What . . . what about the others?' Arden asked quietly.

'B'van and L'tha are dead, killed in the fight after you met the demon . . . the elemental.' D'vor's voice was sad but resigned. 'V'dal's still out there somewhere.' He jerked a thumb to the north. 'Bringing home the stragglers.'

'I'm not worth all this,' Arden said helplessly.

'We'd have to fight the raiders sooner or later,' D'vor responded. 'And we've already done far better since you proved that we didn't have to be afraid of the elementals.'

'It was stupid of us to allow you to be captured in the first place,' C'tis said. She stood up, and Arden noticed for the first time that her right leg was heavily bandaged.

'You're hurt!'

'It's just a scratch. They wouldn't let me fight much – I'm a better healer than I am a warrior.'

Arden looked at D'vor, but the control group leader said nothing.

'Is J'vina all right?' Arden asked after a pause.

'She's had a few nasty gashes, and she'll need to rest – but try telling her that,' C'tis replied.

Arden looked around as best he could. Several groups of soldiers sat around the cave, talking in low voices; every so often they were joined by another.

'What happened to the meyrkats?' Arden asked, seeing no sign of the small creatures.

'They disappeared into one of the tunnels during that first fight,' D'vor told him. 'We haven't seen them since. And we can't wait around for them to turn up – we'll have to move on soon. Although we're safe enough here for the moment, the raiders may decide on revenge. We're almost all back now, so we can move to safer territory.'

'It's going to be a painful journey for you, I'm afraid,' C'tis told Arden. 'I've already done what I can.' Arden nodded, gritting his teeth in anticipation.

'What happened to you in there?' D'vor asked, as if wanting to delay the painful journey.

'They beat me up a bit, then asked a lot of questions, most of which I didn't answer. They told me they were keeping me alive for someone else – someone important they said – but I never found out who that was.' Arden paused as he remembered Dacey.

'I also met someone who wanted to enter into an alliance with you,' he added.

'What?' His listeners were astonished.

'He was pretending to be one of the raiders, but

254

was really working for an organization called the Underground. I know them – they're good people. They want your help, and in return will help you with your problems. He was going to help me escape, but then you made that unnecessary. I don't know what else he managed to do.'

'Why not? Where is he?'

'He was killed as we escaped,' Arden told them sadly.

'Oh,' D'vor said, and his face fell.

CHAPTER THIRTY-TWO

Arden was carried back to White Falls on a stretcher. Although several others in the party had been injured, they were all able to travel under their own steam; this left Arden feeling like a fraud. However, a visit from J'vina raised his spirits.

She said nothing about the way he had intervened in the fight, but looked at him with a new and friendly regard. In her eyes at least, he had proved his worth.

When they reached the village, C'tis and the other healers worked tirelessly to help the wounded soldiers, while stories of the rescue were told to an eager audience. Arden was treated with respect – tinged with awe – and, although he remained immobile, he soon began to feel much better. As the 'demon-tamer', he was also much in demand by the leaders of the community. D'vor, V'dal and several citizens of White Falls spent a considerable time discussing the implications of Arden's imprisonment and inquisition, the approach by Dacey, and that young man's unfortunate death. Arden told them all he could about the Underground, adding that he believed its leaders to be honest. His friends from the control party were eager to accept the possibility of an alliance, but others were understandably sceptical. V'dal was sent to Midholm to give the prophets all the facts, so that they could decide on a course of action. C'tis refused to allow Arden to travel with him, and he was glad to be able to rest.

After a few days, however, his enforced inactivity

began to chafe at his nerves – in spite of the friendly company – and it was a considerable relief to him when V'dal returned with news.

'You've stirred them up good and proper,' he announced. 'They want to talk to you personally.'

'I'll go,' Arden said determinedly, looking at C'tis.

'There's no need,' V'dal told him. 'They're coming here. All of them.'

The others were amazed. Such a thing was unheard of.

'All the prophets? Here?' one of the village elders exclaimed in disbelief. 'The most we've ever had before is two!'

'*All* of them,' V'dal repeated. 'And they're in a hurry. They should be here around rockdark tomorrow.'

This statement caused further panic among their hosts. An influx of such eminent guests would involve much organization, and the whole cave system was soon buzzing with activity. The cavern in which Arden lay was left as a haven of relative quiet, and he was able to discuss events with V'dal, D'vor and C'tis. They were all desperately keen for the attempt to be made to contact the Underground, and they began planning the best way to present their case. V'dal reported that there had already been several heated arguments over this issue – it was even rumoured that the prophets were divided over the matter.

'Your performance with the elemental made quite an impression,' their guide remarked. 'Although L'tha's death was a double blow, because the prophets are therefore not able to get an eye-witness account from one of their own people.'

'Fortunately,' D'vor added, 'there were plenty of others whose stories were clear enough. The fact that you dealt with the elementals *and* fought with us is pretty hard to ignore.'

'I was more of a liability than anything else,' Arden said.

'Don't belittle yourself,' D'vor replied. 'I was there, remember.'

'But what's really thrown them was the contact with Dacey,' V'dal went on. 'You'd never mentioned the Underground to us before, and it seemed to some to be an amazing coincidence that you should discover this supposedly friendly organization—' He held up a hand to forestall Arden's protest, '—among the very people who have proved our worst enemies.'

'There was no reason to tell you about them,' Arden burst out. 'I hadn't thought about them since I'd been down here – and I certainly had no idea that they were even aware of your existence, let alone were looking for an alliance.'

'We know that,' D'vor said gravely, 'but we have to convince the prophets.'

'No one here understands the upworld,' C'tis put in. 'Before you came, the only way we could judge it was from the actions of the raiders. Why should the Underground be any better than them?'

'That's why they need to talk to you personally,' V'dal went on. 'And you're the only one who can hope to convince them.'

Arden swallowed as he felt the weight of responsibility being lowered on to his shoulders.

'I'll do my best,' he promised.

* * *

The party from Midholm entered White Falls in a long and stately procession. All eyes were on the prophets. There were twenty-two of them, their black cloaks tied back for ease of travel, their dark eyes unreadable. Formal greetings were exchanged, then two prophets came to see Arden. He found their presence unnerving, and had to stop himself from blurting out all his arguments there and then. It was arranged that Arden would meet with the whole council – and as many of the soldiers and villagers as possible – in White Falls' largest cavern the following day. The prophets confessed to weariness after their long and arduous journey; they would be glad of the night's rest. Arden could do nothing but agree, though he guessed, correctly, that he would find it difficult to sleep.

* * *

The crystal dawn found him nervous and bleary-eyed, but as he was carried to the meeting, his brain began to function properly and he ran over all the points he had rehearsed with C'tis and the others, recalling his answers to any likely objections. However, as he was borne into the hall and he saw the massed ranks of people all around, his mind went a complete blank.

The prophets sat together, a solid mass of midnight black, each impassive face turned to watch his entrance. The crowd had left only a small area in the centre of the cave free, and it was here that Arden's stretcher was set down. C'tis helped him to sit up, smiled warmly at him, then withdrew. Her footsteps sounded loudly in the otherwise silent hall.

One of the prophets rose, signalling the beginning of the debate. He faced Arden directly.

'Your actions have silenced many doubts, but others remain, and more have been added. Will you help us in attempting to find an answer?'

'With all my heart,' Arden replied.

And so the debate began.

Arden was told to give a first-hand account of his encounter with the elemental and, though the details must have already been familiar to his listeners, his words were heeded with intense interest. Then he was quizzed about his emotional reactions to the blue-flame beings, the feelings of friendliness and warmth, and about the change in the elementals' behaviour. Others who had been present were called upon to describe

259

what they had seen, then two soldiers, who Arden did not recognize, were brought forward. These two, it appeared, had volunteered to attempt to duplicate Arden's feat. They had both survived an encounter with an elemental, and, though they had been too nervous to encourage reciprocal warmth from those mysterious creatures, they had not felt any antagonism. They stated that they would be willing to repeat the experiment, and expressed the hope that – if given this chance – they would improve their level of communication, thus enabling others to learn to do the same.

All this was new to Arden, and he was buoyed up by the unexpected support.

Next came a close examination of the fight in the Hall of Winds, and the manner in which Arden had been captured. He took little part in this section of the debate; he had been unconscious for much of the time, so most of it was described by others. He heard of the deaths of L'tha and several others, and of the fact that his companions had been pushed back, and forced to abandon him.

Then the debate's attention switched back to Arden; he was subjected to endless questions about his imprisonment, the raiders, and the attempts of Aric and Wray to prise information from him. He answered as best he could, but at times his memory wavered, and this led to some of the questioning becoming rather aggressive.

After that came the subject that Arden and everyone else had been waiting for. He described his two brief conversations with Dacey, wherever possible recalling the exact words used.

' "Jordan has wanted for some time to contact the cave-dwellers, believing that he can help them, and get their help in return," ' he quoted.

'What does this Jordan want from us?' a prophet asked.

'I can only guess,' Arden replied. 'Dacey was not given the chance to be more specific.' He described what he knew of the Underground and its purpose. This took a long time, as his audience was mystified by the details of upworld politics. 'My belief is that Jordan hopes either that you can help them in their struggle, or that you will be able to speed up the recovery process after the Revolution,' he concluded. 'But I don't know how.'

More questions followed – some betraying deep suspicion about Dacey's role as a spy within the Grey Raiders, about Jordan and his aims, and about other aspects of the Underground's organization.

'And how could they hope to help us?' another prophet asked.

'By protecting you from the raiders,' Arden responded immediately. 'If the Revolution is successful, there would be ample opportunity for upworlders to seek out the source of the pollution which is destroying your home.'

Whispers filled the air.

'Why should that be so?' The question was posed by a prophet whom Arden recognized.

'I can give no guarantees, T'sin,' he answered. 'I believe in Jordan and his people. I am sure that in return for your help he would promise to aid you. He is an honourable man, and keeps his word.'

Muttered arguments took place within the ranks of the prophets, and Arden watched anxiously, occasionally glancing round in search of a friendly face. C'tis and V'dal smiled encouragingly, but he could see the doubts in their eyes.

The disagreements among the prophets grew more agitated and vocal, but calm was eventually restored, and T'sin spoke again.

'There are many practical difficulties raised by what you have told us. If we are to make contact with these people, are you willing to act as our messenger?'

'Gladly,' Arden replied eagerly. 'I could go to him as soon as my leg heals sufficiently.'

The prophets returned to their discussions, and the onlookers began to murmur again. One single voice rose above the hubbub.

'This whole matter rests on the truth of his picture of Jordan,' a prophet stated loudly. 'All else is mere trivia. How else can we make our judgement?' She paused, and looked round at her colleagues. After she had received their nods of agreement, she turned back to Arden.

'Is what you have told us of this man true?' she asked.

'Yes.'

'Then you have nothing to fear.' Black eyes stared, like those of an eagle assessing its prey. 'You are willing to prove these assertions to the whisperers?'

'Yes.' Arden had no idea what this would entail, but now was not the time for backing down. The cavern grew very still.

'Good.' The prophet motioned to P'tra, who stepped forward, carrying a silkfish bag.

Now what? Arden wondered, his heart thumping.

P'tra unsealed the bag and took out a clear, multi-faceted crystal the size of her hand. What little light there was in the cavern flickered and darted to the crystal, which gathered all luminescence to itself, and left the rest of the cavern dark. Arden was mesmerized, and heard neither the murmurs of the onlookers, nor their sudden intake of breath.

Diamond crystal.

P'tra held the shimmering stone in front of Arden, then closed her eyes. For a few moments nothing happened, then a blue-green vapour writhed up from the depths of the crystal and hung in the air like a cool flame. It was joined by other colours, which weaved in and out of each other, producing a spectacle of breathtaking beauty.

T'sin's voice floated out of the dark space beyond the stone.

'Place your hands upon the crystal. Show us Jordan.'

Arden did as she bade him, moving as though in a trance. His fingers felt nothing strange when they came into contact with the cool, hard surface of the rock, but the coloured flames reacted immediately. Images, confused and horrific, flashed briefly within.

'Show us Jordan.'

A remote part of Arden's mind grasped the idea; he thought of the Underground's leader, deliberately picturing the tall, broad-shouldered body, the black skin and dark, tightly curled hair. He pictured his smile and expressive hands, the voice he could adapt to suit his audience, and his ready humour. Arden closed his eyes, recalling Jordan's words, his hopes and fears.

From somewhere far away, he heard exclamations of wonder and surprise. Arden opened his eyes.

Jordan stood before him, floating above the crystal. Arden watched in utter astonishment as the image crumpled, shrinking back into the multi-hued flame that sparkled before him.

A faint, inhuman whispering reached his ears.

'Enough!'

P'trạ opened her eyes, and the crystal slept.

*　　*　　*

'They can judge just from that?' Arden was struggling to understand what had happened. 'But it wasn't the real Jordan.'

'Of course not,' C'tis replied patiently, 'but it was your true knowledge of him. You cannot lie to the whisperers.'

'Why not?'

'Because anyone who tries loses their mind,' she told him. 'Completely.'

Arden stared at her. It took him a few moments to recover his composure.

'So now they have to believe me,' he said.

'If you summoned a true picture of his inner character

263

as well as you did his outward appearance,' she answered, 'then yes.'

'How can they tell?'

'I don't know,' C'tis said with a shrug. 'Nor do I know how P'tra summons the whisperers from the crystal, but she does.'

'When will they decide?'

'When they're ready to,' came the matter-of-fact reply. 'For now, you need to rest.'

'How can you expect—' he began, then saw her smile, and grinned in return. 'I'm not a very good patient, am I.'

'Awful.'

The hours passed agonizingly slowly until D'vor at last brought the prophets' decision.

'Hurry up and get well,' he ordered. 'You have a job to do. You're our ambassador to the upworld!'

* * *

Arden grew increasingly fretful as the days passed. His leg was healing well, and, with C'tis's regular attentions, remarkably quickly. But it just wasn't fast enough for him. He insisted on exercising as soon as he was able, in spite of the pain, and his determination increased with every step he took. A new and stronger metal splint was attached to his leg, and – at last! – C'tis agreed that his journey could begin.

He travelled north and west with a strong guard; the four surviving members of the control party were among the group, and they accompanied him on the final upward stretch.

'We can't go any further,' D'vor stated. 'The surface is very near.'

'Note the exit well,' V'dal told Arden. 'Don't mark it in any way, but remember the location – you'll never get back in unless you do.'

J'vina wished him luck, while C'tis, ever the healer, warned him to take care of his leg.

'It's not back to full strength yet,' she told him. She looked as though she wanted to say more, but thought better of it.

'Thank you, all of you,' Arden said, embracing each of them in turn. 'I'll be back soon.'

'We'll be waiting,' D'vor replied.

A little while later, Arden stepped out into the blinding light of the moon.

CHAPTER THIRTY-THREE

Arden stood blinking in the silvery radiance of the moon and stars, wondering why he had ever considered travelling at night to be impractical. Far from there being too little light, there was too much! The thought of the sun's rising filled him with dread, and he realized for the first time how the people of the Lightless Kingdom must feel about entering the upworld. He had been underground for only a few months; they had lived in the semi-darkness all their lives.

The small, boulder-strewn vale into which he had emerged was unknown to him, but the silhouetted skyline to the west looked familiar. He set off in that direction, taking careful note of his surroundings. Warm desert winds blew around him, and he was soon sweating profusely. Sunrise was now a doubly ominous prospect.

However, his misgivings turned to joy when he crested the tree-lined ridge. He knew this place! The Abbey was within a few hours' walk over gently rolling hills, and Arden knew that with luck he could be there by daybreak. The ancient buildings and the hospitality of the brothers would provide him with an excellent place to readjust and to rest. What was more, it was only eight leagues from Great Newport. His friends had hoped to deliver him as far to the west as possible, but this was beyond even his wildest hopes. He strode on in high spirits, ignoring the niggling pain in his leg. Indeed, his only disquiet stemmed from the blue glow which stretched along the western horizon. Clearly visible to his newly sensitive eyes, it was a light where no light should be, but, as always, Arden dismissed the inexplicable phenomenon, concentrating only on practical matters.

He reached the Abbey shortly before dawn. The gradual lightening of the sky had already made his eyes hurt. As he felt the day's heat on his back, he was glad of the prospect of rest within the Abbey's quiet and shady confines. The men who made up this remote religious community had always treated him as a welcome guest, and this occasion was no exception. He entered their hall, the only ancient building not in ruins, and was shown to one of the cell-like guest rooms. The brothers' day had already begun, with singing and prayer in praise of the gods, but when they realized that Arden had been walking all night, they left him to sleep.

He awoke late in the afternoon; the little sunlight streaming through his tiny window almost blinded him. The sound of voices drifted down the corridor from the communal eating hall. That in itself was unusual. Apart from their communications with the gods, the brothers led their lives in silence – only speaking to outsiders when necessary. But what brought Arden stumbling from his room was a voice he thought he knew. If he was right then this was an amazingly fortunate coincidence.

Turning the corner, he saw Jordan in conversation with one of the more elderly brothers. The black man turned as Arden came in, and they stared at each other in mutual astonishment. Jordan was the first to recover.

'We thought you were lost for good!' he exclaimed, then smiled and stood up. The brother, realizing that the two men knew each other, left them alone.

Arden sat down opposite the leader of the Underground.

'This is incredible,' he breathed. 'What are you doing here?'

'I could ask you the same question,' Jordan replied.

'Mine is a long story,' Arden answered, laughing.

'Then you'd better eat first,' the other responded, indicating the remains of a meal on the table, 'and I'll tell you why I'm here.' The sight of bread, cheese and fruit was especially enticing after months of unfamiliar food, and Arden began to eat.

'I often come here,' Jordan began. 'The brothers are remarkably well-informed for men who travel only in the spiritual sense, and I learn a lot from them. And this is a wonderful place – you must feel the tranquillity of it here.' Arden nodded, his mouth full. 'Even I have to get out of Newport sometimes,' Jordan went on, grinning. 'However, this time I am here for a specific reason, or I could not have spared the time. The city is close to boiling point now, and I can't spend too long away.'

Arden swallowed and asked, 'What specific reason?'

'A few days ago I had an unnerving experience,' Jordan replied. 'That's not unusual these days, but this was unlike anything I'd known before. It was as if I had been transported outside my body, and was looking down on myself. I was in some sort of cave or hall, surrounded by people who were staring at me as if to judge me.'

Arden, his eyes wide, gave up all thoughts of food.

'Then Paule was bending over me, telling me that I'd fainted.'

'Was it dark in the cave?' Arden managed to ask.

'Yes, but there was an odd flickering light I couldn't place,' Jordan answered. 'Why?'

Arden ignored the question and posed another of his own. 'The people judging you, did you see what they looked like?'

'No. I sensed them rather than saw them.'

'And why did you think the brothers could help you?'

'Well, they've often told me of similar experiences,' Jordan said. 'They believe it to be a communication from the gods. I'd always dismissed it as nonsense, but that started me wondering. It felt as though someone was stealing my soul. I couldn't talk about it to my practical colleagues – they'd have thought I was cracking up.' He grinned. 'It seems that you might know something about it.'

Arden told him.

* * *

By the time he finished his story, it was almost dusk. Jordan had listened intently, both fascinated and inspired by the people of the Lightless Kingdom, and had been astounded by Arden's description of his own spectral appearance from the diamond crystal.

'That must have been . . .' His voice trailed away into awed silence.

'They *did* judge you,' Arden told him quietly. 'And you were not found wanting. I've been sent to find you, and see if you will agree to an alliance.'

Jordan was silent for a while.

'This has been a dream of mine ever since I first heard of the underground world,' he said eventually. 'A whole new civilization.' He shook his head in wonderment, then frowned. 'But the timing's going to be difficult – the Revolution is only days away.'

'We can reach them in a few hours,' Arden put in eagerly. 'It's not far—'

'I can't go,' Jordan interrupted. 'I *have* to get back to Newport. I can send someone else—'

'No! You're the *only* one who can go,' Arden insisted. 'Don't you see? They've already met you! They won't trust anyone else.'

'But there will be so much to discuss,' Jordan protested. 'And that will take time. I have no way of letting my colleagues know where I've gone.'

'Can't the brothers send a message?'

'They could, but that would be tantamount to telling

269

the whole world where I was. Their spiritual distance from the world can make them rather indiscriminate in who they divulge information to. I can't risk it. I'll have to go back to Newport first.' It was clear from the tone of his voice that he was reluctant to do this. The Lightless Kingdom obviously attracted him strongly, and Arden made a further attempt to persuade him.

'If we go now,' he said, 'and ride there, we could be at the entrance before midnight. Then you can make the initial contacts and be back in Newport before the day's out.' He paused, then tried another tack. 'If you go back to the city now, you may never get this chance again. Have you thought how valuable they could be in any fighting in the tunnels? And once you've won . . . they have so much to offer.'

'*If* we win,' Jordan replied, but his thoughts were far away, weighing the alternatives. Arden waited expectantly, knowing that if Jordan chose to go back to Newport now, it was unlikely that his ambassadorial efforts would ever bear fruit. Once the Revolution began, it would be too late.

'You don't have a horse, do you,' the black man said, his voice suddenly purposeful. 'We can double up on mine. Come on. If we're going to travel by night, then we haven't got all day.' He stood up and strode off in search of his mount. Arden followed, grinning broadly.

* * *

The horse plodded steadily through the night.

'I take it you've had no news of Gemma?' Arden said without much hope.

'Only that she survived the desert, was captured by Grey Raiders, and escaped with a tribe of meyrkats,' Jordan replied. 'After that, nothing.'

Arden was dumbfounded. 'Explain!' he ordered.

When Jordan finished his tale, he added, 'We've been

270

looking for her, of course. Hewe's searching now, but so far no one's seen her.'

'She's gone back to the valley!' Arden exclaimed, filled with relief and joy.

'We thought so too,' Jordan replied. 'Unfortunately, we can't find that either.'

But I can, Arden rejoiced silently. *I can!*

They rode on, each mulling over their recently acquired knowledge.

'I'm sorry about Dacey,' Arden said eventually.

'These things happen.'

'It was poor repayment for his efforts on behalf of me and Gemma.'

'He was a good man. We've lost a lot of good men.' Jordan was uncharacteristically solemn.

They talked then about the Underground's plans for wresting control from the Guild, and about the various roles of the raiders, the elementals, and now the people of the Lightless Kingdom.

'The raiders believe the underground people are demons; they in turn think that the *elementals* are demons—' Arden said.

'And the elementals mimic the underground people so that travellers on the coast road think *they* are demons,' Jordan added.

'Altogether too many demons,' Arden remarked.

'And none of them real,' Jordan agreed.

They emerged from a copse then, and looked out over the rock-filled vale. Arden's excitement rose another notch.

'We're here,' he said.

CHAPTER THIRTY-FOUR

Even with the details etched into his memory, Arden had difficulty finding the entrance. This was so well concealed that Jordan thought he must be mistaken, but Arden eventually led the way between two large boulders, squeezing through a low opening, until, much to his astonishment, Jordan found himself in a downward sloping tunnel. The darkness closed about them as they walked slowly onwards.

'It's hard to believe this isn't man-made,' Jordan commented. 'It's so like the tunnels under Newport.'

'Wait until you see the rest of it,' Arden replied. They walked on slowly, feeling their way in the deepening gloom. Eventually their eyes adjusted and the crystal light began to glow, as above them the sun rose.

'Hallo!' Arden called, sending echoes rumbling into the labyrinth. 'They won't have expected me back so soon,' he told Jordan, 'but I should have thought they'd leave someone on watch.' He halted, uncertainty showing for the first time. 'They must have,' he added.

'If they haven't, we're going to be lost pretty soon,' Jordan finished for him. 'This maze looks impossible.'

Arden took another few paces forward, and shouted again. Both men tensed as a rustling came from ahead, and a bat swooped past, so close that they felt the movement of the air.

'Only a—' Arden began, then stopped abruptly when one of the shadows moved. He found one arm pinned behind his back, and a knife at his throat. The sudden movement and the silence from behind him showed that Jordan had met with a similar fate. He held his breath, not daring to speak.

He was spun round, and found himself face to face with J'vina. Her huge eyes grew wide with disbelief. 'Arden? What are you doing back here?'

'If you take that knife away, I'll tell you,' he replied; the blade's point was almost touching his skin. J'vina withdrew it hurriedly, then glanced at Arden's companion.

'Who's this?'

'Look at him,' he told her. 'You've seen him before.'

'Jordan?' she exclaimed.

'The same,' the black man responded calmly.

'How . . . ? Let him go, C'lin.'

The soldier obeyed, and the newcomer was studied curiously.

'And I thought you were burnt,' J'vina remarked to Arden. 'I thought he must be wearing silkfish tape.'

'Black skin does have certain advantages when one lives underground,' Jordan said wryly, watching the pale faces of the strangers.

'You are welcome,' C'lin said, recovering from his surprise. 'I apologize for the nature of our greeting, but your arrival was unexpected.'

'I understand.'

'Are you willing to help us?' J'vina asked suddenly.

'Yes. If I can.'

'Come with us,' C'lin said. 'All is not ready, but we can at least offer you some hospitality.'

'Thank you,' Arden said. 'We've ridden all night to get here.'

'Ridden?'

Arden then found himself having to describe the function and appearance of horses. By the time J'vina and C'lin understood, they were entering a large cavern. Crystal light reflected off the convoluted rock surfaces, illuminating the group of people within. D'vor, V'dal and C'tis rose to greet Arden joyously,

273

puzzled but delighted by his early reappearance. They became even more excited once they realized who his companion was. Before their story could be told, the sixth member of the reconstituted control party was introduced. Her name was T'via, and she had replaced L'tha as the representative of the prophets. For some time, she took no part in the ensuing conversation, but watched carefully, her solemn grey eyes missing nothing.

*   *   *

'Your finding Jordan so soon is an amazing piece of luck,' D'vor said as Arden ended his tale, 'but it also presents us with a problem.'

'Why?'

'The prophets have already returned to Midholm – and that's several days' travel from here.'

'I can't stay that long,' Jordan put in quickly. 'Events in my world are moving too fast. Can't any of you take a message to them?'

'No. The prophets must speak with you directly,' T'via said. Although her voice was soft, almost timid, she was sure of what she said.

Jordan frowned at Arden, but he could only shrug.

'It is unfortunate. They might take your refusal to make the journey as an insult,' V'dal said thoughtfully, 'and this would not be a good start to the relationship.'

'But this is absurd!' Jordan exclaimed in exasperation. 'You don't understand. I *have* to get back to Newport.'

J'vina spoke now – and there was steel in her voice.

'Perhaps it is *you* who does not understand. I doubt if even Arden could find his way to the surface from here. *You* would be lost in moments. So, you already need *our* help – would you deny us yours?'

'I'm not used to being threatened,' Jordan replied, dangerously quiet.

'I'm not threatening you. Merely pointing out a few facts.'

'Please,' D'vor intervened. 'If we are to be allies, then talk like this is harmful. Jordan is free to leave at any time, as is his right. If necessary, we will *all* assist him.' He paused, and when no objections were forthcoming, he went on.

'I feel bound to point out, however, that the prophets may decide that they would be unwilling to arrange another meeting, should you refuse this one.' He glanced at T'via, and she nodded her agreement. 'This may be your only chance.'

'Our only chance, too,' C'tis added quietly.

Jordan was silent for a long time.

'If I agree to come,' he said eventually, 'will you guarantee to take me to Midholm as quickly as possible, and return me to this entrance as soon as our discussions are completed?'

'Yes,' D'vor answered for them all.

'Whatever their outcome?'

'Of course.'

There was another pause, then T'via spoke.

'My mistress, P'tra, was the one who summoned you from the crystal,' she said quietly. 'She knows that this meeting will benefit both our peoples. I have seen now that your reality matches her judgement. In her name, I ask you to come with us. If you refuse, I will have failed.'

Her mention of the strange events which had brought Jordan to the Abbey in the first place clearly affected him.

'You have not failed,' he reassured her. 'I should like to meet P'tra.' He turned to D'vor. 'I'll come,' he said, then glanced at Arden. 'If this turns out to be a big mistake, I'll know who to blame.' He smiled as Arden spread his hands wide as if to say, 'Who, me?'

'Thank you,' D'vor said.

'But before I go *anywhere*,' Jordan added, 'I must rest

for a while.' He turned back to Arden. 'What shall I do about the horse?'

'I'll take him,' Arden replied, and faced the dismayed expressions of his underworld friends with stubborn resolve.

'Aren't you coming with us?' C'tis asked.

'No. I have other things to do.'

'Can't it wait?'

'No.' And Arden turned to Jordan in mute appeal.

'Bring her back safely,' the black man said. 'We'll need her help as well as yours.'

Arden smiled with relief, grateful for the understanding.

So J'vina led Arden back to the surface. He was in the grip of a kind of fever, and knew that he must act now. Although he felt guilty about abandoning Jordan, he had been assured that the revolutionary leader would be well looked after, and Arden had no desire either to accompany him on another underground trek, or to return to Newport in Jordan's place. His whole being yearned to get back to the valley, to find Gemma again. Ever since Jordan had told him what little he knew of her story, Arden's longing to see her had become more acute than ever. Now it was overwhelming.

'I hope you know what you're doing,' J'vina said, as they parted.

'Jordan doesn't need me,' he replied. 'And we'll all meet again soon. I know it.'

'Good luck then,' she responded. 'I hope you find what you're looking for.'

She turned back and Arden went on, shading his eyes from the bright sun as he emerged. He toiled up to where Jordan had tethered his horse, then rested in the shade for a few moments, letting his eyesight adjust.

Jordan's horse was a sleek and powerful animal but had an easy temperament and recognized Arden, readily accepting her new rider. They set off in a north-eastward direction, skirting the desert: Arden had to

276

prevent himself from urging his mount to a suicidal gallop.

Just after he left, a group of small brown creatures came rushing out of the entrance to the Lightless Kingdom, and threaded their way between the boulders and up the slope. The meyrkats gathered at the spot where the horse had grazed, milling around, seemingly without purpose, as if the direction Arden had taken had confused them. Eventually they made up their collective mind, and headed off westward.

* * *

When Arden rode into the valley eight days later, it was hard to tell who was more exhausted – the horse or its rider. It was dusk when he half fell from the saddle at Mallory's kitchen door. She and Kragen came running.

'Arden!' Mallory exclaimed. 'I don't believe it!'

'We thought you were dead,' Kragen said, open-mouthed.

'You don't get rid of me that easily,' he replied weakly, smiling at their amazed – and delighted – expressions.

They hurried to his side and helped him indoors, Kragen yelling for the boys to attend to the horse.

'Is Gemma here?' Arden asked as he flopped into a chair.

'She *was*,' Mallory replied, 'but she left about . . .' she did a rapid mental calculation, '. . . about eighteen days ago.'

Arden swore softly.

'Somebody called Hewe came from Great Newport to ask for her help,' Kragen told him.

'They should be back there by now,' Mallory concluded.

Arden groaned.

* * *

277

At first, he felt that he would never sleep, his dejection was too deep, his frustration too fierce. But once in bed he had surrendered to exhaustion and was dead to the world for fifteen hours.

When he finally awoke, Mallory was sitting at his bedside. She brought him food and drink, then demanded his story.

'We thought you were dead,' she explained. 'After all this time, we'd just about given up hope. Gemma hadn't, though. Bless the girl for being right! Where have you *been*?'

He told her his tale, and she in turn related Gemma's experiences as best she could. Each account filled the other with wonder.

'What will you do now?' Mallory asked.

'Go back to Newport,' he replied. 'To think that we were so close!' He grimaced, and shook his head.

Voices were raised downstairs.

'I think you have a visitor,' Mallory remarked, smiling.

Arden climbed out of bed and dressed, feeling stiff and sore, then made his way to the kitchen.

The visitor was Kris, who filled the room with his usual joyful warmth. Mallory and her family watched as Arden approached the misshapen man.

As Arden looked at the crooked face and unnerving yellow eyes, Kris smiled and beckoned to him, holding out a fragile hand. Arden took it, remembering, a little fearfully, the first time he had met Kris. Then, the deformed man had looked into Arden's mind and examined his past, his present, maybe even his future. It had been a test of sorts, and one which, even now, Arden did not know how he had passed. This time, the sensation was different, but after a few moments Arden heard an unknown voice say, 'Just relax, and let us all help you.'

The room about him disappeared, and he found himself facing a pulsing blue screen of power. It was cold, and he was frightened, but something – or someone – was opposing the strange force. A fountain of light burst forth, and he heard Gemma say, 'By will-power alone.' She sounded triumphant, and as a door opened in the screen, its edges crackling with opposing forces, he followed her into the marble room beyond.

She walked forward a few steps, then stopped as a man turned to look at her from the far end of the hall. He spoke, but Arden did not hear his words, for he was screaming in terror. This was an image from his worst nightmare. The man's face was covered with a mask of shining metal; his eyes and mouth were black, empty holes.

Arden pulled away, appalled at the image and sick with fear at Gemma's predicament. As his hand lost contact with Kris, he was suddenly back in Mallory's homely kitchen. But nothing could dispel the quaking horror of the scene he had just witnessed.

The echoes of his own scream reverberated in the room as the onlookers watched him, their faces shocked and fearful.

Arden looked at Kris, whose face was as stricken as the others. For once, his presence gave no comfort.

Somehow, that was the most terrifying thing of all.

Part Three

THE CIRCLES OF MAGIC

CHAPTER THIRTY-FIVE

'Who *are* you?'

Gemma stared in horror at the man with the metal face.

'Dear girl, don't you recognize me?' His voice was amused, soft and confident, and Gemma suddenly knew who he was. The chill realization showed on her face, and prompted him to speak again.

'Ah, I see you have remembered.' He obviously took pleasure in this fact. 'Of course, I do look a little different from when we last met. Because of certain . . . shall we say *impulsive* . . . actions on your part, my treatment had to be speeded up. I must say, I have found it *most* beneficial.'

Gemma remembered that silky, persuasive voice from the auction where this man had been in the process of selling her as a slave. She had disrupted the disgusting events of that night, discovering in astounding fashion the magical power within her. She had hoped that the auctioneer had died in the resulting fire, but it was clear that this was not the case.

'Mendle,' she breathed.

He bowed, mocking her fear, then straightened up and took a step forward, beckoning with his hand. Gemma retreated.

'Come, my dear. You have nothing to fear from me.' He paused, studying the disbelief on her face. 'Your antics caused me some pain at the time,' he admitted, 'and the fire seriously damaged my business. But that is all in the past now. As you can see, I have a new face, my vision is once again perfect, needing no lenses, and my . . . business . . . is more prosperous than ever. I have returned in a position of far greater strength, and am now *Overlord* of this fair city.' He pronounced the title in dramatic tones, underlining the bitter, amused irony of his words. 'It is just as I had always intended. Your intervention merely speeded up the process.'

He paused again, and for the first time, Gemma caught a cruel glint of life within those soulless eye-sockets. She still could not speak.

'I see that you are not convinced,' Mendle went on. 'I will try to explain.' He turned his back on her, and began to walk away, making it plain that he considered her no threat. Gemma turned to look at the dancing blue light of the elemental wall. She tested her will against its power, and knew herself to be helpless. The door she had opened was closed forever; she was beyond the aid of her friends. When she looked back, Mendle was watching her from the table at the far end of the room.

'Your friends can't help you now,' he remarked, echoing her thoughts. 'Won't you join me?'

Gemma did not move.

'I confess that for a time I harboured thoughts of revenge,' Mendle told her conversationally. 'I had the power and the means to inflict more pain upon you than I had suffered. But that would have been petty. Men of vision such as myself must not allow the actions of others to divert them from the course of destiny. I saw that you were meant to play a greater role in my triumph than that of a pathetic, blood-soaked victim.' His iron face did not move, but Gemma sensed the malevolent smile behind the mask. She shuddered.

'So I have another part for you to play,' Mendle continued, 'which can begin now that you have made your entrance. For one who knows how to use . . . and abuse it, you have much to offer.'

'What could *I* offer *you*?' she whispered.

'Power,' he replied. 'You've heeded its call, as I have. We are much alike.'

'No!' It was a denial pulled from her innermost core.

Mendle just laughed; it was a sinister, unnatural sound that issued from those unmoving metal lips.

'But I have proof,' he said. 'Come and see for yourself.'

* * *

'What's happened?' Ashlin's voice was shrill with fear. 'Did you see anything?'

Hewe stared at the opaque blue barrier through which Gemma had passed.

'There was a man in there,' he said hesitantly. 'I think.'

'Nothing else?'

'I couldn't see – it happened too quickly.' Hewe turned to his other companion, but Paule only shrugged, his eyes never moving from the pulsing elemental screen.

'We must do something!' Ashlin exclaimed. 'We can't just stand here.'

'What would you suggest?' Hewe asked, but his apparent calm only made Ashlin more frantic.

'She's in danger, I know it.'

'Gemma knew the risks,' Paule said quietly. 'Don't forget – she opened that door. None of us could even get near it. Her power is considerable.'

'If she could open it once, then she can do it again,' Hewe added, hoping that his confidence was not misplaced. The door had snapped shut the instant after Gemma had stepped through, and that seemed ominous. 'She'll be more than a match for anything in there,' he concluded. *And we must find out what it is*, he added to himself.

But nothing could ease Ashlin's desperate anxiety. With a final glance at the two men, he made a dash towards the shimmering blue wall, as though he would attack it with his bare fists. He moved before they could stop him, but his frenzied attack soon came to an abrupt halt. Before he was within an arm's length of the barrier, he was seized by an invisible force and hurled backwards with tremendous power; skidding to the far side of the dark chamber, he lay sprawled on the stone floor. He was unconscious for a few moments, and was speechless with shock when he came to.

'The faster you approach it, the more violently it repels you,' Paule explained. 'One of our men tried it and told me it was like running into an invisible wall.'

'*Now* do you believe us about Gemma's power?' Hewe enquired. 'That was brave but stupid. Don't try it again!'

Wide-eyed and white-faced, Ashlin shook his head in agreement. He coughed feebly, grimacing, then all three resumed their observation of the elemental wall.

Half an hour passed and nothing happened.

'Isn't there anyone else we could get through?' Hewe asked quietly.

'We've many with talent, all right,' Paule replied, 'but none who could touch this. Those who've seen it were terrified.'

'Great!' Hewe muttered savagely. They waited again – there was nothing else to do.

Footsteps sounded in the dark corridor and a breathless Egan emerged.

'Guild soldiers,' he gasped. 'Lots of them – headed this way.'

Hewe swore.

'Our men?' Paule asked.

'Falling back,' Egan told him. 'We can't match them down here.'

'We'll have to go,' Paule decided.

'No!' Ashlin grabbed his arm. 'We can't abandon Gemma!'

'She's beyond our help,' Paule said, steel-eyed. 'Don't be so stupid.'

Glaring, Ashlin withdrew his hand.

'We could make a fight of it,' Hewe suggested.

'Not in the tunnels,' Paule replied with certainty. 'I've already explained that to you. We wouldn't even get as far as exchanging blows. They'd just pick us off like rabbits in a cage.' He paused. 'Besides, if we stay, they'll know something's going on inside there.' He jerked a thumb at the blue screen. 'Gemma would not thank us for that.'

Hewe hesitated, feeling Ashlin's eyes upon him.

'Let's go,' he agreed eventually.

Egan led the way. Each cast an anxious glance back at Gemma's prison as they left.

They moved stealthily down dimly lit corridors; in some places Egan's torch provided the only light. A crash sounded close behind them, then a scream, shouting, and the thud of a body falling.

'Damnation!' Paule looked at Egan. 'Get them out of here,' he ordered. 'We can make it on our own now.'

His lieutenant moved off without a word, and Paule led them on, muttering to himself. He took them through a series of convoluted passageways, and up some stairs, then rapped out a signal on an overhead trap-door and waited until those above let them out.

The three men were soon sitting in Jordan's underground haven beneath the vast rubbish tip. Hewe and Paule were deep in thought, while Ashlin was slumped in despondency.

'We can send patrols back to spy it out every so often,' Paule said, 'but now that the Guild's men have been alerted, our options are limited.'

'The underground has always been our province,' Hewe remarked, shaking his head. 'What's changed?'

'I don't know. Suddenly, it's as if they can see in the dark. They don't carry torches, and make a point of dousing ours. They seem to prefer fighting when it's pitch black.'

'And they've new weapons,' Hewe said.

'Yes, and deadly accurate too – though the gods

287

know how, in those conditions,' Paule confirmed. 'Tiny metal arrows only so long.' He held up a thumb and forefinger spread wide. 'It's impossible to see how they can fly so straight. And another thing – the Guild soldiers are wearing outlandish helmets.' Paule spread his hands, admitting his confusion. 'All I know for sure is that we can't fight them down there.'

Then Ashlin spoke for the first time since their return. 'So even if Gemma gets out, we can't help her,' he said, his face a mask of anguish.

*   *   *

'What proof?' Gemma whispered.

'Your co-operation with me is fully described,' Mendle replied, waving a hand towards the large book which stood open on the marble table. 'Come and see.'

Gemma did not move. She summoned up her last vestiges of confidence, and spoke defiantly.

'You could do *nothing* that would make me help you!'

'Ah, but that's the beauty of it, my dear,' he answered smoothly. 'I don't have to *do* anything. You're already past the point of no return.'

'You're insane!'

Mendle laughed. 'That's what they say of all great innovators,' he remarked. 'It doesn't change anything. Your part in the script – mine too – was written long ago. You can't change anything now. Even your initial disbelief was predicted.'

The confidence with which he spoke filled Gemma with dread. *Is he right? Am I only a helpless tool in his hands? No! I would kill myself first.* Her hand went to the knife in her belt, but she hesitated, unable to believe that this last resort was her only alternative. She drew the blade nonetheless, taking comfort in the weapon's solidity.

'Shouldn't you be afraid of me?' she asked, as boldly as she could. 'After all, I burnt you once. What's to stop me from *killing* you this time?' She took a few steps forward, but Mendle did not shift from his relaxed pose.

'I'm disappointed,' he commented. 'I had credited you with greater intelligence.'

Gemma waited, forcing herself to continue her advance.

'I have no reason to be afraid of you,' Mendle went on. 'My face is not the only thing that has changed, and this is my territory. Here you can do nothing against my will.'

She rushed at him then, panic filling her mind, but Mendle held up a hand and her legs became suddenly leaden. Terror overwhelmed her as she realized that, once again, she was a puppet – and he the puppet-master. She stood rooted to the spot, her mind in turmoil.

I would kill myself first.

She brought the knife-point up to rest at the side of her throat while she pleaded for the strength to make a bloody end to this vile mockery. Mendle did not even try to stop her, just turned his back. His absolute contempt for her actions was clear and, after a few frozen moments, the knife fell from Gemma's nerveless fingers, clattering on to the marble floor.

'Come here.' All reasonableness had left his voice. This was an order.

Gemma's legs were granted life once more, and she walked slowly to Mendle's side. Though she gazed at the open pages of the book, the letters danced before her eyes. She did not want to know what was written there.

'Read it!'

Gemma obeyed.

' "The signal marking the beginning of the change was the return of the Bringer of Destruction to the Apex City, and his accession to its highest power. Although the actions of his associates achieved nothing except an orgy of bloodletting, he was nonetheless able to build a secure, impregnable fortress of steel. From there, he maintained absolute rule over the city and its associated territories, and set in motion the experiments and processes which would lead to the new age.

' "Only one power could have opposed his progress, but because of their ignorance, and their insistence on clinging to outmoded ideals, the Servants of the Earth were defeated. Their end was made certain when the Key to the Dream became entombed in the steel fortress, and her power used to destroy not only her former allies, but also the last vestiges of magic itself.

' "That was only the beginning, but thereafter progress was inevitable, and the old order was completely destroyed.

' "The Age of Chaos began." '

Gemma could no longer pretend that the words had no meaning.

'That's just a book – it doesn't *prove* anything,' she protested feebly, her lack of conviction obvious. Mendle ignored her.

'Fanciful titles of course,' he remarked lightly, 'but I rather like mine. "The Bringer of Destruction".'

'Just because something is prophesied, it doesn't make it true!' Gemma exclaimed desperately.

Mendle turned to look at her. Behind his mask, evil power glinted in whatever now took the place of eyes.

'But this isn't prophecy,' he replied, amused. 'It's *history*.'

'That's impossible!' she retorted, but knew that he could be right; she herself had read the alternative futures of Cleve while trapped in the floating city.

'This book has always existed,' Mendle went on patiently, as though explaining something to a child. 'Even those fools in the blue-flame sect have known about it for years. Of course they never found it, but there were numerous references to it in other, more accessible volumes. You're the Key to the Dream,' he added sarcastically. 'Surely you can see that this

290

book is ancient – timeless in fact. Just look at it!'

'It could be a fake,' Gemma replied, not believing her own words. 'You could have written it yourself.'

Mendle laughed at the idea.

'I'm not such a poetic soul,' he said. 'Besides, how could I have known about this?' He turned the pages back to a point marked by a silk ribbon.

Unable to stop herself, Gemma read the book's description of the early life of the Key to the Dream. The first sentences horrified her – but she could not look away. The words ran on, her eyes following them helplessly.

It was the story of her own childhood.

The names were different, but it was accurate in every other detail. Her relationships with her royal parents and the wizards on the islands of Heald and Ark were reported in depth. The violent overthrow of her home and the magical war that ensued were fully described, and the rite that she had witnessed which brought the war to an end was also there. Everything matched her earliest memories, bringing back the joys and horrors of that momentous time with vivid clarity.

She stepped back from the book, breathing hard, feeling as if she had been damned. Mendle stood watching her.

'Recognize anything?' he asked, cruel humour in his tone.

Gemma was speechless, struggling with the manifest certainty of her fate. *To destroy not only her former allies, but also the last vestiges of magic itself.* The ironic horror of her role crashed in upon her, and she wilted visibly.

'I see that you are facing the truth at last,' Mendle stated with satisfaction. 'Come. You will be the privileged witness to my first great experiment.'

CHAPTER THIRTY-SIX

That night and the following morning, rumours flew thick and fast in Great Newport. The nameless Overlord had always been secretive, communicating his direct orders through written messages and an endless stream of underlings, but now it was said that he had cut himself off entirely. He was, so gossip went, sealed within the site of his great tower, behind metal doors and screens of arcane power. Construction still went on however, though no sign of the tower could yet be seen.

Even the members of the Guild, for whom the new Overlord's reign had been so profitable, were concerned by the situation. A number of them tried to contact their governor, but did not succeed. There was absolutely no response. Their nervousness led to the Guild soldiers' being deployed on the streets; the city simmered on the edge of violence.

While rumour and speculation came quickly to the ears of the Underground, Hewe and Paule were reluctant to commit their organization to any drastic action. They had no news of Gemma, and Jordan was still missing. They had to face up to the fact that their leader might not return. If they attempted to fight the Guild now, with that organization's troops on full alert, they would stand no chance at all. And so they waited, listening to reports as they came in, and trying to reassure each other. Ashlin was coughing frequently now, and, although he would not admit it, was clearly in considerable pain. He had tried to go with each scouting party as they went to check on the scene of

Gemma's disappearance, but had been dissuaded each time, and now sat huddled miserably in a chair in the underground room.

Then came news that made all the previous rumours seem unimportant. It was a young lad named Spratt who brought the message; he arrived out of breath and bursting with pride at being allowed into the inner sanctum.

'Something's happening at the site,' he gasped. 'The ground is shaking, and there's people running in all directions!'

'We'd better see this for ourselves,' Hewe said. 'Let's go.'

'The chamber where Gemma's trapped is directly below the site,' Ashlin said as he struggled to his feet. 'Maybe she's—' He broke off in a fit of coughing. Nobody else spoke as they followed Spratt out into the corridor.

When they arrived at their observation post in a building near the site, the whole world seemed to be vibrating, and the air was filled with a low humming. Clouds of dust rose into the sky, and cracks appeared in the walls of several buildings. It was impossible to see clearly into the site, but from the noise and the few glimpses which their location afforded, it was obvious that the construction work was in chaos. In places, the surrounding wall had fallen, and terrified men and women were running for their lives. The guards on the gates darted back and forth, clearly unsure of their duties, and obviously very frightened. The grinding sounds of the collapse of immense metal structures, and the screams of those trapped within, echoed around the city. Flames sparked and flared, and lights flashed – so brightly that they made the noonday sun seem dim by comparison.

'Gods,' Hewe breathed. 'What a mess!'

'What's going on?' Ashlin asked, hobbling in after his companions.

'I wish I knew,' Paule replied.

Then all conversation was silenced by a tremendous crunching noise, and the boards beneath their feet shook even more. They all watched, open-mouthed, as stunned as any of the hundreds of citizens of Great Newport who were witnessing the impossible.

Before their amazed eyes, the Overlord's tower began to build itself.

A gleaming metal cylinder, several rooms wide, rose from the ground. The structures around it were toppled like matchwood, thus completing the earlier devastation. The tower moved slowly but inexorably up towards the sky, until it dominated all about it. And still it grew, a bright column of steel, seeming almost to touch the clouds.

It was almost featureless for much of its height, with only a few indentations varying the smooth curved surface. But before its unnatural growth was complete, a marking appeared, and the tower looked even more sinister. It was the design of the unbalanced scales, etched in black lines, and so large that it was several times the height of a tall man.

At last the tower stopped; in the ensuing silence no one dared move or speak. The whole city watched to see what would happen next. They did not have long to wait.

Orange flames spurted forth from several of the lower indentations. The fire covered the entire site, turning everything within – be it metal, stone, earth or wood – into a uniform black sludge, and incinerating anyone unfortunate enough to still be inside. In some places, those outside the walls were badly burnt as clothing and hair burst into flame, and smoke and fumes scorched their lungs.

Hewe and his companions sheltered behind the stone walls of their hide-out, but even there the wave of heat left them gasping.

When the smoke and stench had cleared, the tower

stood in the centre of a circle of utter devastation. All shape and character had been erased from the land around it, which was now nothing more than a black stain on the face of the city.

As they took their first cautious glances from their window, they could see soldiers emerging from an unseen door at the base of the tower. Each wore a strange helmet which covered his entire head, but otherwise they appeared to be dressed in normal Guild uniform. Only closer inspection showed that the device on their chests was no longer the even scales of justice that had been the Guild's singularly inappropriate marking. Instead it was the unbalanced scales of the tower itself.

These soldiers took up positions around the base of the tower, but made no further move.

It was a long time before anyone could find their voice.

'Seems quite keen on his privacy,' Hewe remarked, desperately trying to sound flippant but unable to keep the awe from his voice.

* * *

For the rest of that day and the following night, Great Newport curled into itself in a state of shock, whispering quietly. The great metal tower, which some reckoned was forty storeys high, stood silent and aloof, mocking the thought of any attempt to approach its mystery. The guards at its base remained on duty, but no one even thought of approaching them. Throughout the night, the whispers multiplied and grew in strength. A storm was brewing and it was only a question of where the lightning would strike first. Some of the more astute members of the Guild made hasty arrangements to leave the city. They had been abandoned by their leader, and knew it was time to cut their losses. The clandestine movements of people and property fuelled the fires of rumour, giving support to those of the Underground who wanted to strike now, while the Guild was in such disarray. Egan expressed it most succinctly in one of his periodic reports to Hewe and Paule, now back in their underground retreat.

'We can take the Guild now!' he said eagerly. 'It's breaking up into factions again, and their guards are in a shambles. Everyone's in a state of shock, but the people are beginning to blame the Guild for the tower. After all, they were the ones who agreed to the building of it. If we attack now, we'll have greater support than we could have hoped for, and a weaker enemy.'

'I don't think the Guild is the enemy any more,' Hewe said softly.

'They're *always* the enemy – and it would be better than doing nothing,' Egan replied. He hesitated. 'In any case, I don't think you could stop it now if you tried. Feelings are running too high. Perhaps if Jordan were here . . .' His voice died away.

'Do *you* want to strike now?' Paule asked him. 'Risk everything we've planned for all these years on a rush of blood?'

'Face facts!' Egan shot back. 'The uprising's coming – whether the Underground supports it or not. The least we can do is make sure the right side wins.' He paused, looking from one impassive face to the other. 'If the Guild is thrown out, and we haven't helped, then we'll have no hope of establishing any worthwhile form of government afterwards. It'll be complete anarchy. We *must* be involved.'

'We've no time to co-ordinate our movements,' Paule objected. 'Without a coherent strategy, it'll be nothing but a bloodbath.'

'Send the signal,' Egan urged. 'We'll work out the rest as we go along.'

'No. Not yet.'

Egan groaned in disgust. 'You're wrong. There's no way to stop it, and many of our people have already made plans. I tell you frankly – there's no way I can hold them back.'

For a few moments the only sound in the room was Ashlin's persistent coughing.

'What about you?' Paule asked quietly.

'I'm stupid enough to want it to be unanimous,' Egan replied angrily. He turned to leave. 'I'll keep you informed,' he added over his shoulder.

'Do you think he's right?' Paule asked as the door closed.

'Probably.'

'Gods! Why isn't Jordan here? I never wanted to be in this position.'

'I'm going out to talk to a few people,' Hewe said. 'I'll stay in touch.' The bear-like man went out, leaving Paule to receive the reports of growing unrest.

Dawn proved Egan's predictions correct. Fighting had broken out in several parts of the city, and mobs had overrun the homes of many of the Guild members, killing everyone within, smashing and burning the contents of the dwellings. Some mansions were found to be empty – this enraged the crowds still further, and they grew hungry for further prey.

Elsewhere, sections of the Underground had attacked Guild strongholds in various government buildings and trading warehouses. Guild soldiers were hunted down and overwhelmed; those who resisted were better armed and trained than their attackers, but were undermined by the loss of authority, and by the sheer weight of numbers.

At first, Paule and the few like-minded leaders of the Underground tried to stem the tide of violence, but by mid-morning even they realized it was hopeless. The resentment that had brewed during decades of oppression was being released in one blood-soaked orgy of revenge, and the best that they could hope for now was to bring some sort of reason and hope to the city once it was over.

297

'Light the beacons,' Paule ordered, giving the signal which would spread the revolution along the coast to Altonbridge and Clevemouth. 'At least we can try to bring some sort of order to this mess.'

The fighting continued, leaving no sector of the city untouched. Smoke rose from many buildings; in some streets the gutters ran red, and looting was common-place. The Underground, now with the official sanction of their leaders, tried to ensure that the only targets of the violence were those forces who had bled the city dry for so long, but the Revolution was being used by many to settle old scores. The participants rarely knew what was going on outside their immediate area, and it was impossible to get an overall picture of the situation.

Paule and Hewe travelled as widely as they could, seeing for themselves the carnage which had littered Colosseum Square with bodies. Many people were maimed or left homeless. With the help of some of their calmer colleagues, they began the lengthy process of restoring some semblance of discipline. Food and water supplies would inevitably become precious, and sentries were organized to help protect stores and ensure that everyone in need received a share. The head-quarters of every government department had been ransacked, but they too were saved from further destruction. Whatever form of government finally emerged from the chaos would have need of them.

Some of the heaviest fighting took place in and around the city walls. Many of the Guild's soldiers had their barracks there, and for a while they made the most of their secure defensive positions. However, they were assailed from inside the city by mobs of hysterical citizens, and from outside by the inhabitants of the sordid shanty town which grew like a mould around the perimeter of the city. The people there had seen, at last, a chance to exact retribution from the forces who had refused them entry to the opportunities of the city, and had kept them in squalor in the filthy huts and tents at the base of the city walls.

The Underground also played a part in this battle. Many of its members lived in these same huts, and now they showed their people the secret ways into the city. As a result, many of the Guild's defenders were overwhelmed by surprise attacks. Many hundreds of people were nonetheless slaughtered by soldiers during less well-organized assaults.

The violence raged for two days and two nights, and then the tireless efforts of a few began to have an effect. Exhaustion also took its toll, and the fighting grew more sporadic.

One of the last major conflicts took place just before dawn on the third day. A group of Guards near the metal tower had been flushed out of hiding, and were being chased towards the Overlord's lair. In desperation, they had run onto the blackened area, appealing for help to their oddly garbed colleagues, who still stood at the tower's base. The response had been a levelling of the strange metal weapons and a lethal shower of small arrows. The fleeing Guards were cut to pieces, falling dead or dying in a nauseating splatter of blood and severed limbs. The pursuing throng watched them die in silence, then melted away into the last of the night.

*　　*　　*

Paule slumped in a chair in the Underground's headquarters. He and Hewe had not slept for two nights, and they were both completely exhausted. They had witnessed appalling scenes which had left them numb, and they were unable to share in the rejoicing that was going on in some quarters. The enemy that they had wanted to overthrow for so long was indeed vanquished, but at a cost that was impossible to stomach. The Guild was no more, but they now faced the arduous task of ensuring that what replaced it would not be worse.

Over and above all this stood the tower. The Guild might have been destroyed, but the nameless Overlord was still there, and he no longer needed the protection of Newport's men of power or their soldiers.

'It's too late,' Paule said dejectedly. 'Whatever we do now, there can be no answer to that.'

Hewe did not need to ask what he was referring to. The tower loomed over all their thoughts.

'The real enemy,' Hewe muttered in agreement.

'I must sleep,' Paule breathed.

'Me too.'

The two men stretched out on the floor, and within moments the only sound in the room came from their snoring.

Three hours later they were woken at the same instant, convinced that the world was about to end.

CHAPTER THIRTY-SEVEN

Arden had left the valley within a few hours of his vision of Gemma and the man in the horrifying mask. Mallory and Kragen tried to persuade him to stay a little longer, to rest and regain his strength, but he had been insistent. The conviction that Gemma was in serious danger, and his own frustration at having already wasted so much time made him all the more determined to get back to Great Newport as fast as was humanly possible.

Kris had departed after explaining – through his sign language – that he had merely accepted the vision that he and Arden had shared. He did not know where it had come from, or what it meant. For the first time ever, he left Mallory's household less happy than when he arrived. The small, crooked man seemed utterly confused by this turn of events – and that in turn worried everyone else.

Arden's horse was still too exhausted to travel, so Kragen lent him two of his own animals.

'I can borrow others if need be,' he explained, so Arden accepted them thankfully. The second mount would speed his progress considerably.

'I wish I could go with you,' Mallory said as he prepared to leave, 'but—' She patted her belly, which was already showing a noticeable swelling. 'Be sure to remind Hewe of his promise to get Gemma back here for the birth of her namesake.'

'I'll bring her myself,' he replied; though he smiled at his friend, his voice was full of grim determination.

Four days later, Arden was still riding at a steady pace, the sturdy horses carrying him ever closer to his goal. The early morning sun was already warm on his back as he skirted the north-eastern border of the Diamond Desert. He would soon be able to join the great coast road, and after that the progress would be easier. A more direct route would have been to travel straight across the desert, but this time Arden had neither the equipment nor the stores to make such a journey possible. In other circumstances he would have preferred the solitude and savage nature of the desert, but speed was all that mattered now. He drove the willing horses hard, switching mounts regularly, but made sure they had enough fodder and water, and took sufficient rest to keep them from exhaustion.

Arden did not spare himself, and sometimes fell asleep in the saddle for a few moments. However, he was wide awake this morning, having allowed himself four precious hours of sleep the night before. Even so, he blinked and rubbed his eyes, sure that he must still be dreaming, when a white bank of fog appeared directly in his path. It was dazzling in the sunlight, but Arden nonetheless doubted its existence. It was clearly unnatural, and an absurd anomaly in the desert landscape, but the horses did not seem nervous. They cantered onwards as if the road ahead were perfectly clear.

Oh no! A sudden, alarming thought struck Arden and in that instant he saw – or thought he saw – faint flickers of blue within the cloud. He turned the horses to the right, urging them into a gallop, but the mist flowed in front of them, easily outdistancing them. Arden halted, and the fog rolled closer. There was no escape.

Arden dismounted and stood waiting, furious but resigned to his fate. The mist swallowed him up, and blue lights flashed past at dizzying speed. Then the fog disappeared abruptly, and he found himself standing in the hall of a mansion that he recognized only too clearly. The floating city had claimed him once again.

On the previous occasion, he had been accompanied by Gemma and Mallory. He had not liked it then, and he liked it even less now. Rage bubbled within him, but there was no one on whom he could vent his anger; the hall was empty.

To either side were several doors, each with a different emblem carved into the wood. Beyond these doors were libraries. Thousands and thousands of books, for which Arden had no use. Each library represented an alternative history – or future. Arden was still unsure of exactly how that worked. In front of him was a wide staircase curving up to a railed balcony. More doors led off from that, but Arden did not know what lay behind them – and he did not want to know. All he wanted was to get out.

He stood quite still, trying to calm himself, and thinking hard. From his previous experience he knew that time did not pass in this place. In theory, all he had to do was wait and he would eventually be deposited back in his own world, with no time lost. The horses would not notice his absence even if – for him – hours or even days had passed. He knew this in theory. In practice, he found it impossible to believe that he was not 'wasting' time, and he bitterly resented the seeming delay.

Arden decided that he would not leave the house. That was one mistake he was in no hurry to repeat. He hated the mansion; it removed the solid ground from beneath his feet and left all his close-held notions of reality in tatters. Yet he hated the barren, inhuman city outside even more. He shuddered at the memory of that featureless maze.

In any case, he reasoned, it had been in one of these many libraries that Gemma had found the answer to the riddle of the rocking stone, and had thus been able to save the valley. Arden may not like the house, but he remembered its usefulness on that occasion. Perhaps he could learn something useful now. In which case, there was no point in standing there like a statue.

Arden took a deep breath, remembering the mansion's eccentric inhabitants; the idea of facing their anger again was one he dreaded. Yet what choice did he have? So he filled his lungs and summoned up all his courage.

'Wynut! Shanti!' he roared. 'Where are you?'

In an instant, two figures appeared before him, materializing out of the air on the other side of the hallway. Their arrival was so sudden that Arden jumped violently. Although he had seen the two wizards vanish on previous occasions, they had always arrived in more orthodox fashion.

'Where are the others?' one of them asked.

'Where is the Key?' the other demanded.

Arden stared at them, feeling rather sick. He had never seen them before.

'Who are you?' he asked hesitantly. He remembered Wynut and Shanti distinctly. The former had been dwarf-height, reaching just above Arden's waist, while the other had been more than a head taller than any man Arden had ever seen. These two were the same height, slightly shorter than himself. And yet in all other respects, they matched his memories exactly. Each wore shapeless brown robes and a voluminous leather hat. Beneath the rims, deep-set eyes sparkled; their noses were long and pointed, their beards white and unruly.

Can there be more of them? Arden thought. His bewilderment was completed when a stray image entered his mind – of an infinite number of peculiar wizards, varying in size from that of a young child to a giant.

'You called us, didn't you?' one of them snapped irritably. 'Who did you expect us to be?'

'I am Wynut,' the other answered in calmer tones. 'This is Shanti.'

304

'But . . .' Arden looked at them in amazement. 'You've grown . . . er . . . shrunk.'

'No matter,' Wynut said quietly. 'We are who we are. And we've been looking for you and your companions. Where are they?'

'Looking for us?'

'Of course,' Shanti replied. 'Don't restate the obvious! We most certainly would not have come to this confounded region without good reason. Too many interfering people,' he added with a scowl. 'Now, where are they?'

'I don't know – or rather I do—'

'Talk sense!'

'They're not with me. I'm alone,' Arden went on, his voice gaining strength. 'Gemma's in Newport, and Mallory's back in the valley.'

'This changes everything,' Shanti said, turning to look at his identical twin. 'I was prepared for her, the adept. She proved herself worthy of the knowledge we allowed her, but *this* one—' He jerked a thumb at Arden. 'He doesn't even know about the Key.'

'How could he?' Wynut replied calmly. 'If they've parted?'

'How can we trust him?' Shanti shouted, pointing at Arden with a long, bony finger. 'This meddling will have serious consequences, you mark my words.'

'This *meddling* may save us!' Wynut retorted, angry himself now. 'You think I haven't weighed the risks?'

There was a moment's silence. Throughout the exchange, neither wizard had looked at Arden, ignoring him completely. When he spoke, they turned sharply to stare at him.

'What are you talking about? What is this key?'

Neither answered for a moment, then Wynut reached a decision.

'Come with us,' he ordered, taking no notice of Arden's questions. Turning on his heels, he shuffled towards one of the doors. After a moment's hesitation, Shanti joined him.

Arden followed slowly, wondering what was coming next. He went through the door after them, noticing that the emblem carved upon it was that of the unbalanced scales.

Inside the library, Wynut was already seated in a large armchair, while Shanti sat behind an imposing wooden desk at the far end. Many of the shelves that lined the walls were empty, and they gave the room a rather forlorn air. Even so, there were still hundreds of books, standing in dusty rows. Shanti held an open volume in his hands, and seemed absorbed in his reading, though he could have sat down only a moment before. He appeared oblivious to Arden's entry.

'Sit down,' Wynut said, indicating a chair.

Arden obeyed.

'We have certain things to tell you,' Wynut began. 'They are important and we may not have much time, so you must listen carefully. And please do not interrupt.'

'Or ask questions,' Shanti added, without looking up from his book. 'I hope you know what you're doing, Wynut.'

'He's the only chance we have,' the other replied. 'If she is already in the Apex City, then we cannot contact her directly. And the Valley of Knowing is forever beyond our reach.'

'I'm aware of that,' Shanti retorted, but there was an undertone of sadness in his words.

'This man is not mentioned in our sources,' Wynut went on, 'but my calculations brought us here. Which is significant, don't you think?'

'He was her companion, yes,' Shanti replied, 'but it was not he who restored the stone spell.'

'Granted, but I do sense power within him. Perhaps not his own . . .' Wynut lapsed into silence, looked at Arden curiously. Arden bit his tongue, wavering between anger and frustrated curiosity.

306

'What did you think of the Lightless Kingdom?' Wynut asked.

'What! He's been there?' Shanti's exclamation stopped Arden from answering the question. As both wizards stared at him intensely, he had the uncanny feeling that they were probing his mind, uncovering his past, his secrets. He felt naked and afraid.

What seemed like an eternity passed in silence. Eventually Arden could stand it no longer.

'You were going to tell me—' he began.

'Don't speak,' Wynut ordered, holding up a restraining hand. 'It harms our perception and could hurt your friends.'

Shanti scowled at Arden's obvious puzzlement.

'Just tell him,' he said shortly. 'The sooner we can move on the better. These regions make me nervous.'

Make you nervous? Arden thought incredulously.

'Very well then,' Wynut began, glad to have obtained his colleague's agreement at last. His eyes twinkled with enthusiasm beneath the gloomy folds of his absurd hat. 'Since we last met, I have been doing a little research.'

Shanti snorted. 'A little?' he exclaimed. 'You've been locked away with your books for at least two decades.'

Wynut silenced him with a glance.

'It is not our place to change the events of the world,' he continued. 'The dangers of that are manifold.'

'And obvious,' Shanti put in, then turned back to his reading.

'However, we have chosen to take a certain amount of risk in the hope that you and your companions will prove worthy of our trust.' Wynut paused. 'You will be wondering why we should make such a choice.'

Arden nodded but remained silent. That was far from being the most pressing question currently on his mind, but he did not say so.

'He doesn't need to know that!' Shanti snapped.

'We take this chance in order to save magic,' Wynut went on, ignoring the interruption. 'Magic is our life,

307

we embody it as it encompasses us. When it died, we, and all this about us,' he waved his hand around him, as if indicating the mansion and the city outside it, 'became an anomaly in all times. The Dream does not allow such a thing, so we were cast adrift, isolated and meaningless. That is a hard fate to accept.'

'What did you *think* set this city afloat,' Shanti added sarcastically. 'The wind?'

But Gemma's sure that magic hasn't died, Arden thought. He felt too confused to question the point.

'What do you want us to do?' he asked quietly, speaking at last out of utter necessity.

'Restore us to the world,' Wynut replied promptly, 'by saving magic.'

CHAPTER THIRTY-EIGHT

'You're asking *me* to—' Arden began.

'Be silent!' Shanti's peremptory command cut his astonished words short.

'I realize that you are sceptical,' Wynut said levelly. 'But surely you have seen more than enough to make you at least consider the idea. Your companions are central to this. The one you call Gemma personifies what little magic there is left in your world. She is the present key, the point through which all lines run. The other, Mallory, represents the future. The two are crucial, that much is clear.'

'But their influence can be either for good or ill,' Shanti put in.

'There is nothing evil in them,' Arden protested.

'Quiet!' Shanti roared. 'Did I say that? Do you listen to *nothing*?' He had risen from his seat and was shaking with anger.

'It seems a little unreasonable to be asking our guest questions while instructing him not to answer them,' Wynut commented mildly.

Shanti subsided into his chair.

'The branches of time are infinite,' Wynut said, turning back to Arden. 'Within them, all things are possible. All things.' He paused, letting Arden consider that notion.

'Get to the point,' Shanti said wearily, and, for once Arden agreed with him.

'The branches are infinite,' Wynut continued, 'but certain points on the path have special significance.

"The turning points of history", as our more pompous chroniclers would have it. Anyway, as I explained, I've been doing some research, and the time you live in is approaching one of these points. There is a fork in the road ahead, and the future of the world depends upon whether you turn right or left.'

Shanti surprised the others by bursting out laughing. 'You've been reading too many of those political speeches from the Sigalurian Empire. All poetry and images and no substance.'

'They *are* an art form in themselves,' Wynut replied good-humouredly. 'They refined pointlessness to dazzling effect.'

Get on with it! Arden urged silently, appalled by the wizards' indifference to his agony of anticipation.

'It will be decided very soon now,' Wynut went on, serious again. 'Within the Apex City, which you call Great Newport, events are unfolding which will signal the beginning of the Age of Chaos – unless we can do something to prevent it.' His words meant little to Arden but they sent a chill through his heart nonetheless. 'Of all the possible outcomes, there is only one factor which I have been able to identify which we may be able to influence now that Gemma is already in Newport.'

'My smallest friends,' Shanti murmured. 'It hardly seems possible.'

Arden glanced at him, wondering why these enigmatic words sounded so familiar.

'The guardians of the stone have become wanderers,' Wynut said. 'And it is they who may tip the balance.'

Guardians of the stone? Arden wondered, then understood suddenly. *The meyrkats!* He grinned, remembering the arrival of the small furry creatures in the Lightless Kingdom. But then his expression changed to a puzzled frown. *How could the meyrkats possibly be a deciding factor? What was going on in Newport – had Jordan begun the overthrow of the Guild?*

310

Who was the man in the metal mask? Questions multiplied in his head until he thought it would burst.

'I see you recognize the creatures we refer to,' Wynut said, watching Arden closely. 'You must ensure that they enter Great Newport.'

'But how?'

'Please, your questions endanger us all.'

Arden tried to push aside his angry frustration.

'Their presence in the city is a necessary but not sufficient condition of success. It guarantees nothing, but their absence means certain doom.'

'We had hoped that the Key, Gemma, would lead them. After all, she can communicate with them,' Shanti took up the tale, 'but that is impossible now. You will have to do it.'

Forbidden to talk, Arden threw his hands wide in mute question.

'They are waiting outside the city now,' Wynut stated. 'They cannot enter alone.'

At last Arden had a solid image to grasp. *I'll do it if I can*, he promised silently. He did not understand why the meyrkats were so important – on the face of it, the idea seemed ridiculous – but there was much he did not understand. The wizards' advice had been instrumental in saving the valley. Perhaps now they could help save far more. Including one very special person. The question burned in his brain and would admit no other thought until at last it forced the captive tongue to give it voice.

'Does Gemma survive?' he asked, afraid both of the possible answer and of their refusal to reply.

'We can't answer that,' Shanti said with unexpected gentleness.

'Not because we don't want to,' Wynut added, 'but because we don't know.'

The next few moments passed in silence, with Arden listening to the thumping of his heart.

'We're already breaking the rules by telling you this

311

much,' Shanti said quietly. 'You must ask no more questions. They serve no purpose and may even do us harm.'

'They could harm Gemma too,' Wynut added.

Arden shook his head helplessly. Nothing made any sense. He clutched at the one single recognizable goal and held on to it firmly. He would find the meyrkats and take them into the city.

'It must be done quickly,' Wynut told him. 'As soon as we leave you.'

'But I have at least four days' riding before I get to—'

Arden felt shattered as he saw the dismay on the wizards' faces.

'Four days!' Shanti exclaimed. 'It can't wait that long.'

'Too late,' Wynut agreed.

The pair looked at each other, apparently lost in thought. Arden was aware that some arcane form of conversation was taking place, and remained quiet.

'Do you think we can?' Shanti asked eventually.

'The thaumaturgical drain will be immense,' Wynut replied, immersed in his calculations.

'But it is possible?'

'Yes. In theory.'

'Can you think of a better reason for putting theory into practice?' Shanti sounded almost gleeful.

'There may be . . . complications . . . later,' Wynut said slowly, as if he was still working it out.

'We'll worry about that later, or earlier if necessary,' Shanti replied forcefully. He turned to Arden. 'Go into the hall,' he ordered. 'You won't have long to wait.'

'But—'

'Just go!' Wynut commanded, in a voice which brooked no argument.

Arden turned reluctantly; as he walked out of the library, the door closed quietly behind him of its own accord.

What now?

He was answered by a long drawn-out miaow, a

312

piercing wail which came from the large, fat tortoise-shell cat he remembered from his earlier visit.

Oh no!

As his memories of the animal came flooding back, Arden waited apprehensively for the sound to become intelligible. Instead of dying away like any natural noise, the cat's cry echoed and reverberated, growing in intensity and modulation. Although Arden knew that it would eventually form human speech, the message still came as something of a shock.

'Now is the time for you to become a wizard,' the cat remarked. 'And then again, perhaps you always were one.'

CHAPTER THIRTY-NINE

'I thought *those* two were mad,' Arden said, 'but you—' His words came to an abrupt halt. *I'm talking to a cat!* He felt ridiculous, and stared at the animal in disbelief. Then his anger and confusion boiled over.

'At least I *can* talk to you!' he exclaimed. 'They wouldn't let me get a word in edgeways!'

The cat nodded sagely, as if it sympathized with his problems, then licked a paw and began to wash its face.

'*You*, I suppose, would let me ask questions, and give me some answers,' Arden said bitterly, 'but as all your statements are nonsensical riddles, that wouldn't be much use, would it?' He advanced a few paces, his fists clenched.

The cat paused in its grooming, looked up at Arden with piercing green eyes, and miaowed again.

Arden halted. 'Stop doing that!' he cried, but the sound would not go away. Like it or not, Arden could not help but listen.

'Questions reveal more about the asker than about the subject. And then again, ignorance is most profound in those who know only a little.'

Arden glowered, but the cat was unconcerned. It delicately licked another paw.

'You can talk,' Arden said venomously, '*and then again*, you're only a cat. I might just decide to wring your fat neck.'

The tortoiseshell rose to its feet, uttered a long, ear-splitting yowl, then ran to the foot of the stairs. It moved with amazing speed for one so large, and the feline grace with which it flew up the steps would have impressed many a watcher. Arden just snarled.

'Good riddance,' he muttered, as the sounds of the cat's legacy echoed around him.

'You could try to catch me.' The words were filled with condescension. 'And then again, a wizard's time is never his own.'

'I am *not* a wizard!' Arden shouted angrily.

Then felt momentarily sick, swaying on his feet and experiencing an instant of disorientation so severe that he almost blacked out.

He was standing in the middle of a grassy field; a few paces away, several sheep gazed at him curiously.

'What are you staring at!' Arden yelled, and the sheep fled, bleating nervously.

Arden swung round - and glimpsed the walls of Great Newport a mere two hundred paces away; however, his attention was held by a peculiar bank of fog drifting rapidly towards the sea.

'So *that*'s what they meant,' he breathed, and turned back to look at the city. His jaw dropped. The early-morning sunlight glinted off a huge metal tower which rose from within the walls of Great Newport. Arden stared at it in disbelief. It was unlike any construction he had ever seen, and it reminded him uncomfortably of one of his nightmares; it also gave him an unpleasant feeling of inadequacy.

He finally tore his eyes away, and looked around. The sheep had moved to a safe distance from him, and had resumed their placid munching. There were no other animals in sight.

Where are the meyrkats?

For a moment, Arden resented the fact that Wynut had not arranged to drop him off in the midst of the clan, then realized how absurd that was. If in fact no time had passed since the beginning of his encounter with the floating city, then the wizard had transported him the distance of four days' journey by horse in an

315

instant, and that was impressive enough. His return to his own world had been abrupt and unpleasant, unlike the seamless transition he had experienced on that earlier occasion, and he assumed that this was due to his displacement in space. Arden, as usual, was made distinctly uncomfortable by the manifestation of things magical, so after wondering briefly what the 'complications' Wynut had mentioned might be, he abandoned idle speculation. He was determined to make good use of the time the wizards had bequeathed him.

He tried to remember as much as possible about the meyrkats. If they *were* waiting outside the city, where would they be? In caves? Arden knew of none in the immediate vicinity. The old river bed? That was a possibility. Where else?

His thoughts were interrupted by a sudden flash of light. An impossibly bright orange beam was shining forth from an indentation in the metal tower, and was focused on one of the gate-towers of the city wall. Arden watched with mounting horror as the stone began to glow, then crumbled. Ancient fortifications, which had withstood even The Levelling, collapsed, as if the very structure of the rock itself was being destroyed. Then came a dull thump, which shook the ground upon which he stood, and in a roar of flame and fire, an entire section of the city wall was flung into the air. Arden threw himself to the ground as stones and boulders flew past, raining onto the ground like an insane hailstorm.

When it was over, Arden was miraculously unharmed. A huge pall of smoke hung over the silent city, and he looked again at the metal tower, his sense of dread now almost overwhelming.

*   *   *

'These are merely toys, of course,' Mendle said dismissively. 'They may prove valuable at some time in the future, but for now we have more important matters to consider.'

Gemma looked out from their eyrie high in the metal tower, and surveyed the appalling destruction she had just witnessed. The explosion had ripped away an entire section of the city wall, shattering it into a million pieces and flinging them into the sky. And this had been achieved by the simple act of pressing a single button, one among many in the incredible room in which she now stood.

The room was circular; large sections of its curving walls were transparent, affording spectacular views of the city and the land beyond. Beneath and between these windows was a mass of complicated panels, whose buttons, switches, pulsing lights and other instruments Gemma could not even begin to understand. In the centre of the smooth floor was a large metal column, also circular. Mendle and Gemma had emerged from this, after entering from a small room far below which, against all the laws of nature, moved up inside the tower. Mendle had called it an elevator.

At last, Gemma found her tongue.

'Why?' she whispered. 'Why destroy the wall?' *And everybody who lived down there?*

'It is of no consequence,' her captor replied. 'It was a useful test of my equipment, and will help my minions realize just what I could do to them if they choose to displease me.'

The utter callousness of his words sickened Gemma, and she raged inwardly at her impotence, imagining the various gruesome fates she would like to arrange for him. She had been his prisoner for some days now; she could not tell exactly how long, because she had been locked up in a windowless room for much of the time. Nor did she know why he had brought her here to witness this 'test'. Perhaps he was merely demonstrating his power – though Gemma needed no reminder of that. Or he was showing off, and she was

317

the only audience available. As far as Gemma could tell, she was the only other living creature within the gigantic tower.

'I think it's time we had a little talk,' Mendle said, sounding almost jovial. 'My preparations are almost complete, and when they are, I shall require your co-operation.'

Gemma said nothing, but bristled with resentment. She wanted to deny him, oppose him with every last fraction of her spirit, but knew it was useless. Her mind was her own, but not her will. She would respond to Mendle's orders, unable to resist; her magical power lay dormant, beyond her reach. Ever since she had entered his domain, Gemma had been groping for the light within the dark, magic-filled regions of her mind, but to no avail. She sensed the presence of her power, but could not reach it. Adria's advice was useless now and her friends could help her no longer. In her hour of greatest need, she was truly alone. And in the thrall of an evil madman.

'I know that you've been wondering about your role since your arrival here,' Mendle went on.

Gemma could not deny it – she had had the opportunity to do little else.

'It is important that you understand what is going to happen. Of course, you won't like it – you'll even oppose it. That is all part of the script, and will make no difference in the end.' He was gloating now, making no attempt to hide the fact.

'When you first came to this land, I did not realize how important you were. This was a failing on my part, but your own ignorance was your best protection. Since then, you have learnt a little, but, my dear, you haven't learnt *everything*.' Mendle paused as though expecting a response, but none came, so he continued.

'You are, as you know, what our unknown chronicler called "the Key to the Dream". Why you should have been chosen for this part is still something of a mystery,

318

but you probably have more ideas about that than I. The fact remains that you exist as the focus of what is called magic. You have already worked out that magic these days depends upon more than one mind, needing groups of minds to be able to function. It was not always so, but the reason for that belongs to another story.

'What you may not realize is that as the Key you are a part of every group.'

Gemma could not keep the astonishment from her expression; although Mendle's metal face could not smile, his voice gave a clear indication of his amusement.

'Think of it as a number of overlapping circles,' he explained condescendingly, 'each passing through one point. That's you. They intersect elsewhere of course, but only two at a time. There is only one main focus of power.'

Why are you telling me all this? Gemma asked silently. *Why am I so important?*

'You have experienced contact with some of the circles,' Mendle went on, 'but not all, I suspect. It must have been rather confusing for you.'

Pieces of the jigsaw began to fall into place in Gemma's mind. She understood now why she responded to the joint entities of linked minds: the people of the valley, the meyrkats, Cai's bees. Then – *Cai himself!* *What circle does he belong to?* she wondered. *Who else is in it?* Her thoughts were disrupted as Mendle continued.

'I have isolated you from them all in here,' he reminded her, 'but I will soon allow you to contact them again.'

'Won't that make me rather powerful?' Gemma asked quietly, a last desperate hope allowing her to find her voice.

'The more powerful the better,' Mendle replied confidently. 'Your magic is merely a force of nature, one of many. I have found stronger ones, as you see.' He gestured at the machinery about them.

'They're hardly natural,' Gemma commented.

'They are instruments which *harness* the natural power,' Mendle replied. 'Do not mistake appearance for substance. That's the trouble with magic – it is wild and uncontrollable, especially when in the wrong hands. My sources of power are malleable; I can use them exactly as I wish. That is not possible with magic. It cannot be moulded, therefore it must be destroyed. You and I will achieve that together.'

'No!'

'Be realistic, my dear,' Mendle smirked. 'I allow you certain freedom of thought, but your actions are mine to control. If I asked you to jump from that window, you would obey without hesitation.' He paused, waiting for the truth of his words to sink in.

'Let me explain just what will happen. This tower has been designed as a receptacle of power. Within its steel shell, I can control anything. When I open the screens about you, you will draw power from your circles of magic, and I will immediately take it from you.'

'Why should I draw on the power, knowing I will lose it to you?' Gemma asked.

'Because you will be unable to refuse,' Mendle replied. 'The arrogance of magic itself will insist upon its superiority, and its ability to overcome all things, and it will come to your aid. Your friends will *insist* that you accept their power – and when they find that what they have given you still leaves you weak, they will insist on giving you more – and more. As they do, so I will syphon it off, accelerating the process until it becomes unstoppable – and irreversible.

'You will drain each circle of all its energy. They will be left powerless and vulnerable. But the best part of it is that they will be prevented from ever rebuilding any appreciable power again – by the memory of your betrayal. A much more subtle form of revenge for your fire, don't you agree?'

*　　*　　*

The meyrkats emerged from their hiding place when the dreadful shaking stopped. They looked up fearfully at the huge column of smoke and dust which rose above the city.

Earth-dark, Ul commented, but the clan knew that this was no ordinary sand-storm.

Tall-ones-shed-skins destroy their own burrow, Ox said incredulously.

They had been watching the city for some days now, having made themselves a temporary home in the dusty holes of the dried-up river bed. They were saddened as they realized that all their wanderings had brought them no nearer to understanding human behaviour. The walled city and the mass of people who clustered around it were a source of fear and loathing to them, yet they felt drawn to it, and had been unable to leave.

The Wanderers had come here after leaving the giant burrow beneath their desert home. They had known that Gemma was in the vicinity, and had been mystified when they realized that Arden had ridden off in the opposite direction. Now they waited with increasing impatience, wanting to rejoin the one human who could speak to them and whose spirit had, until recently, called to them, but unable to risk approaching the monstrous burrow which held her.

Gem-ma is still within? Ox asked.

I do not know, Ul told the clan-leader, *but I do not sense that she has left.*

Ul was one of the senior females, a relator of myths, and it was her dream-sense that had guided them on their journeyings thus far. It was she who had led them into the giant burrow and located Arden within its labyrinthine depths, and she who had insisted that they follow Gemma to Great Newport.

The meyrkats decided to go in search of food and then, as the day grew warmer, returned to their holes

321

to rest. They had been used to much hotter temperatures when living in the desert, but a midday rest was an in-grained habit. Two of them, Av and Ed, remained above ground on look-out duty. They did not know what dangers lurked in this alien place, and the two sentries scanned the area constantly, talking as they watched.

We must make a new happy-lie-all-know for when we find Gem-ma, Ed stated. *Our promise must be kept.*

Jokes had become something of an obsession with Ed, ever since Gemma had first introduced the concept to the clan. He was forever trying to invent them and had made some progress, but occasionally drove his clan-members to desperation with his seemingly pointless chatter.

Two clans find the same burrow, he began. *It is good, and neither will give it up, so there is fighting. Then a talon-killer flies in. He talks to the leaders of both clans—*

Talk? To a talon-killer? That's stupid! Av retorted. The desert eagle was the meyrkats' most feared and hated enemy.

They agree that— Ed continued, ignoring the inter-ruption, but stopped when it became obvious that Av was no longer listening to him. Her attention was else-where – her sharp eyes had seen a man approaching.

The meyrkats stood very still, their brown fur camouflaging them in the dusty earth, but the man walked straight towards them. He limped slightly.

Ard-en? Ed wondered.

Yes! Av confirmed, and the two bounded joyfully towards Gemma's friend.

* * *

Arden saw them coming, two balls of fur bouncing along on stiff legs, their tails erect. His heart lifted at the sight. *I've found them!* he thought jubilantly, and greeted them in the only way he knew – by sitting down on the ground and stretching out one leg. Av jumped over the offered limb, peeping with excitement. Ed followed, adding a somersault of his own invention as he landed. Arden laughed at their obvious delight.

'Where are the rest of the clan?' he asked, thinking to himself that speaking to animals was becoming a bit of a habit.

His question was soon answered, whether it had been understood or not, because the pair led him directly to their burrow. Arden was soon surrounded by meyrkats, all in a state of high excitement.

How do I persuade them to go into the city? he wondered. He waited for a lull in the activity about him, then pointed towards Great Newport. The meyrkats followed his sign, turning to look at the distant, broken walls.

'Gemma is in there,' Arden said loudly, 'and she needs your help. Will you come with me?'

There was some consternation among the animals, and they glanced back and forth, giving piping calls of distress. Arden wondered if they could somehow have recognized Gemma's name, and repeated it slowly, pointing once more.

'We can enter it underground, like a burrow,' he explained further. 'I'll show you.'

He stood up and walked a few paces toward the city, then turned round and beckoned to the clan. They hesitated, then, to Arden's great relief, began to follow.

Two hours later, after a journey in which he had received some very strange looks, and had had to do a great deal of explaining to incredulous members of Jordan's Underground movement, Arden was shown into the organization's headquarters. Paule and Hewe were inside; they looked bleary-eyed and haggard.

'Gods!' Hewe exclaimed. 'Where did you spring from?'

'It's a long story,' Arden replied. 'Hasn't Jordan told you?'

'We haven't seen him for days,' Paule replied. 'Have you?'

'Yes.'

'Tell us!' Hewe demanded urgently.

'All right, but can my friends come in first?' Arden asked.

'Of course.'

Arden pulled the door wide open. Peeping sounds came from the dark corridor outside.

The meyrkats filed slowly into the room, glancing about nervously with their bright black eyes.

CHAPTER FORTY

Arden spent the rest of that afternoon exchanging news with Hewe and Paule. They were each astonished by the other's tale. Arden could not understand why Jordan had not returned, and worried that something had gone wrong in the Lightless Kingdom. He learnt of the destruction of the Guild, the ensuing chaos and the incredible erection of the tower, but the news which stirred and frightened him most was that about Gemma. Her disappearance and subsequent incarceration – in all probability in the tower itself – made his blood run cold. He wanted to attack the steel stronghold right away, but cooler heads dissuaded him.

'It's impregnable,' Paule said. 'The land around it has been devastated, and anyone who tries to approach too close is killed. The tower itself has weapons that are mind-boggling.'

'I know,' Arden replied. 'I saw it in action. But there must be something we can do – we can't just sit here and let it destroy everything. And Gemma's trapped in there!'

'I can't tell you how badly we feel about that,' Paule said. 'After all, it was our idea. But I don't see how we can get her out.'

'We're working on some ideas,' Hewe went on, 'but the guards at the tower have weapons that defy description. No armour we've got is proof against their metal arrows, and they're deadly accurate, even at night.'

'Some of our people think that the helmets the

soldiers are wearing are devices to help them see in the dark,' Paule added.

'What about underground?' Arden asked, desperate for a glimmer of hope.

'That's our only chance, if a slim one,' Hewe replied. 'The guards are just as deadly, but they can't cover every tunnel, and at least we get *some* cover.'

'Let's go then!' Arden urged.

'We're planning it,' Paule said soberly. 'We've already lost an awful lot of men, and have made no progress. I'm not about to allow more to die that way. Those tunnels have become a hell-hole.'

'You'll be the first to know as soon as we're ready to try again,' Hewe said sympathetically.

'Make it soon,' Arden pleaded.

Their discussion moved on to the Lightless Kingdom and its people, and then to the wizards' floating city and what Arden had learnt there.

'We'd had several reported sightings,' Paule said, 'but no one could get close. No matter how fast they chased it, it always got away.'

'I couldn't get *away* from it,' Arden responded. He told them about the alternative futures, and the crucial role that the meyrkats appeared to play. The creatures were standing quietly along one wall, glancing about at their unfamiliar surroundings, but always returning their gaze to Arden; he was their one link with their former lives, and they looked to him for guidance.

'What can *they* do?' Paule asked.

'I've no idea,' Arden replied. 'Nor did Wynut and Shanti. But Gemma can talk to them, so I think we'd better include them in our plans.'

Hewe shrugged. 'Why not? At least they'll be used to tunnels.'

Throughout the afternoon, their discussions had been punctuated by reports from the city, informing them how their plans for re-establishing order were going, and giving the latest update on the list of casualties.

Now a white-faced Egan burst into the room, and the meyrkats dived for shelter beneath various pieces of furniture.

'The tower's attacked again,' he said breathlessly.

'We haven't heard any explosion,' Hewe replied; the last one had meant a rude awakening for himself and Paule.

'Nothing so simple,' Egan went on. 'This time it was a white beam, spread wide. A whole sector of the city just disappeared!'

'What?'

'If I hadn't seen it with my own eyes . . .' Egan shook himself. 'It just vanished. There was nothing there, nothing at all! It must have lasted a quarter of an hour, then the light went out and the city came back.'

'Intact?'

'Yes, but—'

'But what?'

'Everyone . . . everyone who had been in that sector . . . When they came back, they were raving, quite mad. Their minds had gone.' Egan's face mirrored the horror he had witnessed.

'Like the island,' Hewe said, looking at Arden.

'Is there no end to the powers of that thing?' Paule asked bitterly. 'We've got to get in there and destroy it – fast.'

'While there's still some of us left,' Hewe agreed firmly.

Arden joined their planning with a heavy heart. It was beginning to look as though he and the meyrkats had come too late.

*   *   *

Gemma lay on the bed in her cell, wondering what new horror was being perpetrated by the power that surrounded her and the megalomaniac who controlled it. She wished she could find some fault in Mendle's logic

327

but could not, however hard she tried. She knew with dreadful certainty that it would happen exactly the way he had described; she would be powerless to prevent it.

She thought back in desperation over the events of her imprisonment but could find nothing to give her hope. She had followed Mendle from the blue-flame chamber, leading through a door he had opened by pointing a small mechanical object at it. Then she had been a witness to the incredible rise of the tower. Though she had not known at the time what it was, she had realized that some gigantic machinery was at work. The whole world vibrated and hummed. Great slabs of steel moved, as Mendle exulted at the culmination of his plans. All the effort that had gone into the months of designing his masterpiece became worthwhile as the massive underground construction moved in response to his commands. Power flowed, machinery sprang into life, fitting the pieces together, then raising them heavenward. Mendle's vision was a reality at last.

After that, Gemma had been locked up in this small metal-walled room, and left to ponder her fate. She kept thinking back to the book; there *had* to be a solution, but she could not find it. She was the Key to the Dream and she would be forced to help destroy all those she loved, and all that she valued. There was no escape.

Her own history in the tome had laid special emphasis on her role in the magical rite that had precipitated The Levelling. Perhaps there was the clue as to why she had become the focus of any future magic.

In the book, all the other members of the mysterious circles had been called the Servants of the Earth. That name evoked memories of the role of the Servants in that earlier conflict, but this time the enemy sought to *destroy* magic utterly, not dominate by its use. In any case, it now seemed that, in effect, she was part of the enemy.

What group are you a part of? Ashlin had asked her a lifetime ago. Now she knew the answer, but not only

328

did it do her no good, the very fact secured the doom of herself, her friends, and magic itself.

Gemma began to cry quietly, wondering if Ashlin was able to survive without her protection; if indeed he was still alive. And she missed Arden dreadfully. He had always been *her* protector, but more than that, she regretted the fact that she had never told him that she loved him. And now it was too late.

So many people have suffered because of me, she thought miserably. *And it will be even worse now*.

She thought again of killing herself, but knew that even if she had the means, she would not be able to achieve that last act of defiance.

*   *   *

The Underground's attack began in the late afternoon of the following day. Paule and Hewe had gathered together all the loyal men and women who had not fled from the city, and who were still willing and able to fight. Maps of the underground tunnels and chambers had been drawn up as quickly and as accurately as possible, and the movements of the guards' patrols studied by volunteers.

It appeared that the blue-flame hall into which Gemma had disappeared was directly underneath the tower, and it was towards this room that their attentions were directed. Plans were drawn up to present a threat on all sides at once, in the hope that the defenders would leave at least one approach unguarded – or at least sufficiently weak so that they could be overwhelmed.

'Even if we can't get into the room itself,' Paule said at their final council of war, 'there must be other ways into that tower – all we have to do is find them.'

'If we get that far,' Hewe added.

Roughly speaking, their plan was for a four-pronged advance. Hewe would lead a party towards the tower's foundations from the west, Egan would approach from the north, and Davin, a veteran soldier, from the south. Paule, with Ashlin, Arden and the meyrkats among his charges, would go in from the east.

Their attacks would be as close to the same time as possible, and a system of signals had been devised to let each know how the others were faring, and what their movements were. The ideal result would be an overwhelming defeat of the defenders, but that was considered highly unlikely. The soldiers' superior weapons far outweighed the greater numbers of their opponents. The next best outcome would be for two or three of the Underground's groups to engage the enemy, then retreat, drawing the guards away from the base of the tower and allowing the remaining attackers to penetrate the stronghold. Exactly how this would work would be left until they saw how each party was progressing, but if it *were* possible, Paule's eastern section should be the ones to get through.

It was clear almost from the onset that their plan was going badly wrong. Their stealthy approach had been made almost exclusively without the use of torches, but the guards had seen them coming even so, and had picked off several of their number before the enemy was even sighted. One man came spinning back past Arden, blood spraying from his smashed shoulder and jaw. His body crashed to the floor, sending meyrkats scurry-ing in all directions. Arden and Paule exchanged fearful glances in the near darkness. They pressed on slowly, raising their own more primitive crossbows, and scored one or two successes. Their casualties continued to mount steadily, and Paule himself was hit in the arm. He dealt with the wound as best he could, swearing under his breath.

'How can they see so clearly?' Arden whispered. 'I can hardly see my hand in front of my face.'

Sounds of fighting and signal calls came from the tunnels about them.

'Egan and Davin are pulling back,' Paule said, frowning. 'They haven't given us much time.' He winced as Arden pulled his bandage tight. 'Let's go.'

A little while later, Paule breathed, 'We're close now. Keep low.'

They crouched down, wriggling forward as quietly as possible.

Another signal echoed through the tunnels – Hewe was being forced to retreat. Paule went on, crawling now, with Arden and the meyrkats right behind him. As they rounded a corner, they saw the blue-flame barrier just as a hail of metal arrows flew towards them. Paule was cut to pieces where he lay, and several others were fatally wounded. Arden and Ashlin escaped that first salvo, but realized within moments that they had fallen into a trap. There were unseen guards in front and behind them; they had nowhere to run, nowhere to hide. Some of the men panicked and tried to make a run for it but were cut down almost as soon as they made their move. Those that remained huddled in dark corners, keeping perfectly still.

'Where *are* they?' Ashlin whispered. 'I can't see any of them.'

Arden motioned him to silence, but Ashlin, who had grown thin and pale in the last few days, started coughing, and was unable to stop. Arden tried to cover his mouth with his hand, but to no avail. Ashlin rose suddenly, and ran recklessly towards the elemental wall. He was hit several times before he reached it, but his insane momentum carried him on. His body crashed into the blue light, creating an angry hissing noise and a bright shower of sparks. Then he fell to the floor, and the last few moments of his life ebbed away.

He tried to say Gemma's name, but did not have the strength; all that emerged was a feeble death-rattle.

Arden watched his friend's demise with horror, but soon had other things on his mind. In the increased

331

light provided by the sparks, he had seen dark shapes moving within the shadows. At first he had assumed they were guards, but now he was not so sure. As the darkness returned, there were the sounds of violent struggle all around, and several guards fell from their hiding places, steel shafts protruding from their chests. Screams and shouts resounded in the air about him.

'What's going on?' one of Arden's remaining colleagues asked in a terrified voice.

Someone appeared at Arden's side.

'Come on,' the man urged. 'Let's get out of here while we still can.'

'Jordan!'

'Let's go!' The Underground's leader pulled Arden to his feet. 'We didn't come all this way to let you get killed now.' He gave Arden a push, and they left with the remnants of Paule's group. Arden glanced back and saw several figures wrapped entirely in shiny black tape. Not even their eyes were exposed.

'They came?' he exclaimed. 'They came here?'

'I didn't go to talk to them just for the sake of it,' Jordan remarked, and they hurried on, away from the scene of carnage.

An hour later, the surviving members of the Underground gathered together with their new allies. The soldiers from the Lightless Kingdom stood silently, totally encased in black.

'So we meet again, Arden,' one of them said, her voice muffled by the tape.

'J'vina?'

She bowed slightly, and introduced her colleagues.

'D'vor, V'dal, C'lin and T'via.'

'Where's C'tis?'

'She's here, a little way back. Ready to look after the wounded. I think she will have a busy night.'

'Our casualties have been very high,' Hewe admitted. 'Will she tend our people?'

'Of course,' D'vor replied.

'I can't thank you enough for your timely appearance,' Arden told them.

'It is our pleasure,' J'vina replied, 'but it seems we still have much work to do.'

'True enough,' Jordan said. 'This night has achieved little. With your help, we will do better next time.'

The gathering dispersed to lick the wounds and begin planning their next move.

It was not until much later that Arden realized that some of their number were not accounted for.

'Where are the meyrkats?' he asked suddenly.

CHAPTER FORTY-ONE

No one had seen the meyrkats since the beginning of
the retreat. The Lightless Kingdom people had noticed
some movement but had assumed it to be rats, so hadn't
taken any notice. Arden was worried about the animals'
safety, and wanted to go back and look for them. He
explained their significance to Jordan, but was forced
to admit that he did not know what purpose the meyrkats were supposed to serve, merely that they *had* to
be present.

'They're still here,' Hewe pointed out. 'Perhaps they
know what they're doing better than we do.'

'It would be madness to go back now,' Jordan told
Arden. He was still reeling from the loss of Paule and
so many other friends. 'And we need time to regroup
and think again.'

Their council of war was held in a dank underground
room, well away from the tower. In deference to their
guests, it was lit only by the dimmest, shrouded lamps.
Jordan was brought up to date, and recovered a little
from the shocks of recent events.

'I should have been here,' he said quietly at one point,
the hurt showing in his eyes. However, that was the
only outward sign of regret he allowed himself, and he
was soon telling his own tale.

'I travelled with our friends here,' he began. 'And
quite a journey it was, too – but I'll save that for
another time. I talked to their prophets, and they agreed
to help us in return for a promise to at least *try* to do
something about the pollution that is destroying their

realm. They also believe for some reason that they're
going to be invaded from the south . . .' In the shadows
J'vina grunted derisively. '. . . and I agreed to an alliance
should it come to war. *If* we succeed here first,' he
added. 'The prophets took a lot of convincing, but we
managed it.' He nodded in acknowledgement to the
silent figures of D'vor and V'dal. 'Naturally enough,'
he said, turning to Arden, 'they chose your control
party and a few others to come to Newport as their
advance party.'

'Your arrival was very welcome,' Arden put in, with
considerable understatement. 'Having someone who
can see as well as the guards is invaluable.'

'We only wish we could have arrived in time to save
more of your group,' D'vor replied heavily.

'If I'd known events would move this fast,' Jordan
went on, 'I'd have tried for a bigger force – and made
sure we got here sooner.'

'We could send for reinforcements now,' D'vor
suggested.

'That would take days,' Jordan replied regretfully,
'and I don't think we have that much time. Though I
appreciate the offer.'

'How did you get here?' Arden asked, after a
moment's pause.

'We walked,' Jordan replied. 'At night.'

There were muffled sounds of amusement from the
control group.

'I'm afraid Jordan found us rather difficult travelling
companions,' C'lin remarked.

'There was no way we could enter the upworld while
the sky burns,' V'dal explained, 'but we found by
experiment that with a complete silkfish covering,
including a layer over our eyes, we could tolerate what
you call starlight. Even so, it was a relief to reach the
civilized tunnels beneath your city.'

'You've come to no harm?' Arden asked, while others
smiled at V'dal's description of Newport's underworld.

'Not that I can tell,' V'dal replied. 'C'tis will do more tests when we have proper dark.'

The sinister appearance of the envoys from the Lightless Kingdom had been the subject of much whispered comment and later, when the party had split up, Jordan and Arden were quizzed about the real nature of their new-found friends.

'Looking like that, they're enough to scare the hell out of anyone,' Hewe remarked. 'You mean to tell me that underneath that stuff they're fair-skinned and blond?'

'Like white flame,' Jordan replied.

'With eyes like the full moon,' Arden added.

Hewe stared at them.

'You're not going to turn poetic on me, are you?' he groaned.

*　　*　　*

The meyrkats huddled together in a small steel burrow. They had seen several promising holes which they longed to explore, sensing Gemma's nearness and eager to greet her again. However, these entrances were too close to the frightening blue flames, and there were men guarding the cavern. One meyrkat had already been robbed of his body warmth, sent skidding bloodily across the floor by forces they could neither see nor understand. And so the remaining wanderers lay still and silent, waiting for another opportunity.

Ed tried to distract them by testing his latest joke.

. . . the talon-killer talks to the leader of both clans, and they agree that the two of them will have a race, the winner's clan to get the burrow. The talon-killer will be the judge.

What do you get out of this? one leader asks the talon-killer.

I will eat the loser, he replies.

A collective shudder ran through the meyrkats' minds.

This is not a happy-lie, Ox stated firmly.

Ed took the hint and abandoned his story.

As the meyrkats waited nervously, the strange metal burrow vibrated and echoed hollowly.

*   *   *

'The tower's destroyed another section of the city wall,' Egan reported. 'It's even worse than last time.'

'We'll have to try again now,' Jordan decided. 'Ready or not. There'll be nothing left to fight for soon.'

'Do D'vor's people know what to do?' Arden asked.

'They've been briefed,' Hewe told him.

'Then let's go,' Jordan said.

This time, their plan was to lure away as many guards as possible, while avoiding any actual combat, so that the control group and Arden could try to get into the tower. All they hoped for was that their efforts would meet with better fortune this time.

*   *   *

The elevator brought Gemma to the very pinnacle of the tower. Stepping out, she looked around, and immediately felt dizzy. The elevator withdrew. Insubstantial railings around the rim were all that separated Gemma from the vertiginous drop on all sides. She stayed near the centre, trying not to cling to the elevator's casing, and trembling at the thought of such a fall. Far, far below, the buildings of Great Newport looked like miniscule toys, with tiny, ant-like creatures moving to and fro between them. Beyond that, land and sea stretched into the distant, early morning haze.

Mendle was already there, leaning nonchalantly on the railings. In his hand he carried the strange gadget with which he had opened the blue-flame wall.

'Welcome, my dear. It is quite a view, don't you think?'

337

Gemma did not reply.

'You are in no danger,' Mendle reassured her. 'I would not allow you to fall. Besides, these railing are not the only protection against such an unfortunate occurrence.' He pressed a button, and a faint blue shimmering became visible, forming a wall around the platform. 'At the moment we are standing *inside* the tower, in spite of appearances to the contrary. However, in a few moments I will alter the nature of this shield, and while it will still be impossible for us to fall – or to jump – it *will* allow your friends to make their magical contact. The time has come, you see.'

Gemma walked slowly to the rail, keeping as far from Mendle as possible. Trying not to look down, she stretched out a hand and pushed against the ghostly screen. It gave way a fraction, then became as hard as steel. She turned back to face her captor, holding on to the rail behind her with both hands. Her mind was in turmoil, dreading her enforced treachery but unable to think of a way to prevent it.

'You will come to no harm,' Mendle went on smoothly. 'It will be a simple transaction between your circles and myself. Their power will pass through you, but will not affect you.'

'And afterwards?' she asked weakly.

'Afterwards, this monument will become a beacon of unrivalled power that all the world will have to recognize. I have been preparing for this for many years. No one, not even my colleagues in the south, will be able to question my authority now.' He laughed, and pressed another button.

The shield around them flickered, becoming almost white. For the first time, Gemma felt the wind blowing around them; it was cool and fresh, but she paid it little heed. The world about her seemed unreal, and her brain felt as though it was going to explode. Across the metal circle, Mendle nodded contentedly, pushing even more buttons.

It was Cai who made himself heard first.

Where have you been? I have not been able to sense you for so long. But now you feel clearer than ever.

Stay away. Leave me alone, she replied miserably, her heart aching at the longed-for sound of his voice.

Why? What's wrong? It was clear that he was hurt by her rejection. *Let me help you.*

No! Please – just go!

Together we are strong. There are many of us. Let us help you, Cai insisted.

That strength only guarantees our defeat, Gemma replied desperately. *It will be the end of everything.*

You mustn't give up hope. We will all help you, he repeated.

She tried to hide from him, but could not. In agony now, she saw the inevitable fall of her friends, of herself, and of magic. She could do nothing to stop it. Abandoning herself to the clamour, she sank helplessly into her predestined role. Protest was useless. Each circle came quickly to her aid, then found that what they gave was not enough – and so gave more.

Gemma saw a succession of faces – some human, some animal; some she recognized, while others were unknown to her. She saw Cai, the swarm buzzing angrily about his head. She saw Mallory stirring restlessly in her sleep, the embryonic life within her reacting to secret stimuli. She glimpsed Kris and Jordan and Wray. She beheld visions from her past: a man with golden hair and glowing eyes, his hand entwined in that of a beautiful violet-eyed woman; an ancient hermit with white hair and patchwork clothes surrounded by animals of all kinds. She saw sights she could never have imagined; white-faced, black-eyed men and women; wolves howling amid snow-clad pines; painted warriors dancing under a blood-red sky. She recognized Adria, and saw that the old woman was trying to tell her something – but could not hear for the clamour in her head. She saw Arden for an instant,

339

utter confusion on his face, and her heart yearned for him. And so it went on, an endless stream of characters who shared only one thing – they were part of a network which was now being ruthlessly exploited. The Servants of the Earth were all rushing to their destruction.

Gemma opened her eyes, tears streaming down her face, and looked at Mendle. His steel face was as impassive as ever, but he was almost dancing with glee. *He's won*, Gemma thought dismally and closed her eyes again to shut away the terrible sight.

And then she saw the meyrkats.

You too? she mourned, wondering how they would survive without their mental communication.

But this was different! The meyrkats were not a momentary glimpse like all the rest, and did not fade from her vision. They stayed within her mind, a stable rock of sanity amid the shifting sands. The clan was singing, their strange voices echoing unnaturally, growing ever stronger. They were somehow immune to the process which was draining the others of their power. *How can this be?*

The meyrkats were close to her. She felt their nearness, and the first faint spark of hope kindled within her despair. The singing rose in volume once more – it was as though the clan became stronger as the others grew weak.

Gemma cautiously opened her eyes. Mendle was studying the instrument in his hand carefully, and his earlier, relaxed attitude seemed to have disappeared. He pushed various buttons experimentally.

In that instant, Gemma understood what was happening, and called out to all the circles. Whereas before she had tried to refuse their ill-fated gifts, now she welcomed them, and the influx ran through her like a river of light. At last she had the means of using the power – *she* could direct it, store it, use it. And all because one of the circles of magic had not been lost to her.

The meyrkats were *inside* the tower.

Mendle still did not realize what was happening. He studied his controls, puzzled that the levels of power he had stored were no longer rising so quickly. The flow was as strong, if not stronger, than before, but the tower's banks were filling only slowly. Had he overlooked some aspect of the systems? No, that was impossible. There was more than enough capacity. What then?

His consternation deepened as the levels of stored magical energy actually began to decline, even though it was still pouring in from outside. Uncertain now, he looked up from his readings and stared at Gemma. She stood unmoving, her eyes closed, gripping the rail tightly. And yet there was about her an aura of excitement; it was as though sparks were flying from her fiery red hair.

'What are you doing, you bitch!' Mendle shouted, moving towards her menacingly.

As Gemma opened her eyes, Mendle stopped in his tracks, held by her unnerving gaze. He stared into the depths of her soft grey eyes and saw his death encompassed within.

He pushed the control buttons feverishly, hoping to seal Gemma from the sources of her power. The screen shimmered blue, then white.

'Stop it! I command you!' he screamed hysterically.

Gemma just smiled and closed her eyes again, as if he was of no importance.

Gem-ma, are you well? Ed's voice sounded in her head.

I am well, now that you are here, she replied, feeling with delight the extraordinary strength of the link between herself and the clan. They were hundreds of paces below her, behind layers of impervious steel and incomprehensible machinery, yet their voices were clear and jubilant.

This burrow goes the wrong way, Av stated. *Up, not*

341

down.

We do not like it, Ox added.

Neither do I, Gemma replied. *We will leave soon,* she promised, *but first I must finish my business here.*

She opened her eyes.

'Reverse it,' she commanded. 'Return their power to them.'

'I . . . I can't. It's all mixed up,' Mendle stuttered.

'Release it then. I will separate it.'

'All at once? It will blow us from the face of the earth!' Mendle was terrified.

'Now!' Gemma ordered.

'You do it!' he cried, and dashed the control unit to the floor, stamping on it until only fragments remained.

The light of fury exploded within Gemma. What had once been a fountain was now a volcano of pure energy which burst forth in an unstoppable torrent. Yet each strand remained separate, each circle defined; each accepted its due.

The wind blew across the top of the tower, making the now unprotected railings sing. The shield had gone.

Mendle lunged towards Gemma, madness glowing red within his eye sockets. With an incoherent cry, his hands locked around her throat with a grip like steel. *My face is not the only thing that has changed.* But Gemma felt no fear. For an instant there was pity, then contempt filled her, and she swept this feeble creature aside. She looked down on him as he sprawled next to the railing.

'Go,' she said quietly. 'You have outlived your place in this world.'

'No, please,' he whispered in a cracked and terrified voice.

'Now you know what it is like to have another control your actions,' Gemma said coldly.

Mendle rose, his limbs working slowly and painfully. Climbing up on to the rail, he balanced himself precariously for a few moments, then stepped forward into the abyss.

342

Gemma watched him fall, his body becoming ever smaller and more insignificant. She turned away before he hit the ground.

Ox! she called. *Gather the clan. I am coming down.*

We will wait for you, came his joyful response.

The elevator came at Gemma's command and, with one last look around the empty platform, she stepped inside and began her return to the earth.

CHAPTER FORTY-TWO

At first, the new assault on the tower appeared unsuccessful. Arden's control group took the lead and, as they were able to move easily in almost complete darkness, they had some success, clearing out a sentry post and setting up their own position. Arden examined the strange weapons of the dead men, but could make neither head nor tail of them. Elsewhere, the attack fared less well. Several men were lost, cut down by unseen foes, and only a few of the enemy were drawn away from their defensive posts.

However, as the sun rose on the world outside, the tower's guards grew agitated. There were evidently things happening behind them that gave cause for concern. The attackers took advantage of this temporary confusion, and D'vor and his group moved to the entrance of the room next to the elemental wall. The guard's stronghold was beside that, but there was no way of attacking it other than a frontal assault – and that would be suicidal. In any case, the blue flames were blinding to the people of the Lightless Kingdom, in spite of their protective coverings. So they stopped for a few moments to discuss their progress.

While they were talking, consternation broke out in the defenders' stronghold, and shouts were heard.

'The barriers are moving!'

'It's out of control.'

'Get inside!'

'Leave them, you idiot!'

Arden and J'vina exchanged glances.

'What's going on?' he wondered.

'Let's find out,' she replied, and before anyone could stop her, she left their shelter and ran across the room, staying close to the darkest wall.

'Come on,' D'vor urged. 'She can't do this alone.'

They followed her, moving quickly but stealthily, and in moments were clambering into the deserted guard post.

'There are barriers here,' J'vina reported from up ahead. 'Steel, at a guess. I can't move them.'

'Perhaps you need keys,' V'dal suggested.

'Great! So how do we get in?' J'vina replied.

Her question was answered when the metal panel in front of her rose of its own accord.

'C'lin, go and tell Jordan that we're in,' D'vor ordered quickly. 'Bring them here. Everyone else inside – fast!'

As the soldier left, the others scrambled onward, coming upon a scene of utter devastation. Guards lay dead on all sides, their weapons smashed or cast aside. The walls of the chamber were scarred and dented, as though they had been pounded by fiery, metal fists.

'Someone's done our work for us,' J'vina remarked, turning one of the bodies over with her foot.

'Looks like they turned on each other,' V'dal commented thoughtfully. 'As if they all suddenly went mad.'

Indeed, the staring eyes and grimaces of the dead guards' faces gave a strong impression of insanity.

Jordan, Hewe and several others entered the room then, taking in the gory scene at a glance.

'Good work,' Hewe said with satisfaction. 'The other guards are deserting the place.'

'Come on,' Arden said, pointing to a spiral staircase. 'We have to find Gemma.'

So they began the long, slow task of searching floor after floor of empty, echoing rooms.

*　　*　　*

As Gemma stepped from the elevator, the meyrkats greeted her jubilantly, leaping into the air, peeping happily. They sounded almost unbearably loud inside her head.

Gem-ma, we sing!

The clan stands tall.

Welcome, clan-friend.

She knelt down to touch them, rubbing her fingers in the soft fur at the back of their necks.

Thank you, she said quietly. *You have saved us all.*

Gemma could already feel the power slipping away from her; that intoxicating feeling of invulnerability was receding, and she felt its loss keenly, but welcomed the return of her own humanity. *I am not meant to be so powerful,* she thought. The real Gemma would never have dealt so ruthlessly with Mendle. She shuddered at the memory of his pathetic plea and his subsequent death-plunge, then put it firmly aside.

How did you get in here?

Through the small burrows, Av answered. *Look, we'll show you.*

She bounded over to a small opening in the wall. The grille that had covered it lay bent and broken nearby. Gemma peered inside, and saw several different coloured cables. Although she had no idea what they were, she realized that they must run throughout the tower. Their channels had provided the meyrkats with a perfect entry – one which had been too small for Mendle to bother sealing.

I'm glad you arrived when you did, Gemma said with feeling. *Now you must come with me.*

Will you help me with the ending of my joke? Ed asked. *I can't get it right.*

Gemma laughed.

Of course I will. If I can. But first I have some reading to do.

*   *   *

Each floor of the tower revealed more machinery that Arden and his group were afraid to touch, but each room was otherwise as empty as the next. Arden's hopes began to fade. *Gemma!* he pleaded silently. *After all this you must be here.* They toiled on up the endless flights of stairs.

'We must be near the top now,' Hewe said, breathing heavily.

Arden was the first to see the tower's next astonishing offering. Entering the circular, windowless room, he gazed in awe at the banks of multi-coloured switches and flashing lights. The others filed in behind him and stood, open-mouthed.

Everyone jumped as a metallic voice shattered the silence.

'Mendle! Mendle! What's going on? The circuits have gone crazy. Can you hear us! Mendle!'

'Mendle?' Arden breathed, his heart pounding.

'I thought he was dead,' Jordan said. 'Where's that noise coming from?'

'There!' T'via cried, pointing with a black, claw-like hand. 'On the wall. Those pictures are alive!'

They looked to where she indicated, and froze. On the wall above one of the panels was a large, moving picture of a man who was pushing buttons and turning this way and that as he looked at unseen objects. His mouth opened and sound filled the room once more.

'Mendle! Can you hear me?' The picture-man turned aside and spoke to someone else. 'It's no good. He's not responding. Shall we send the fliers?'

Then the picture went blank, and the screen emitted a faint hissing noise.

'This is beyond magic,' Hewe whispered.

'It's evil!' T'via exclaimed. 'It must be destroyed!' She plunged forward, attacking the now vanished picture with her sword. The screen exploded in a shower of sparks, shattering into a thousand brittle pieces. T'via staggered back, clearly shocked, but her actions had

347

broken the spell. The fear and superstitions of the onlookers rose up to claim them and they set about smashing everything in the macabre room.

'No!' Jordan cried, trying to halt the destruction. 'We could learn from this.' But it was too late – his companions would not listen. Even Hewe, his trusted lieutenant, was berserk with an unnatural terror. Before long, the contents of the room lay crushed and scattered on the floor.

Jordan looked on sadly as the orgy of destruction came to an end. He watched the participants lose the manic energy that had possessed them and stand limply amid the devastation. Arden was first to recover. He left the room without a word, climbing the last few levels of the gigantic tower.

The top floor was as empty as the rest. Arden took a quick look around, and swore violently.

'There's only one place left,' he said savagely. 'And we should have tried there first!'

He started back down, muttering to himself.

'If Gemma's gone, then so has the Overlord,' Hewe said quietly to Jordan.

'Either that, or they're both in the blue-flame hall,' Jordan replied. 'And we still don't know how to get in there.'

'We'll see about that!' Arden called over his shoulder, then went on, taking the steps three at a time.

*   *   *

Gemma stood before the book for some time, wondering whether she had the courage to open it and read those fateful words again. They had caused her such anguish, but now . . .

She had used the last of her waning power to open a door in the elemental shield that still protected this ancient, timeless room. The meyrkats, now aware of the part they played in her progress, had followed her inside and stood clustered about her feet.

At last, Gemma opened the book, and was not at all surprised when it fell open at the page she wanted. She read.

' "The signal marking the beginning of the change was the return of the Bringer of Destruction to the Apex City, and his accession to its highest power. Although the actions of his associates achieved nothing except an orgy of bloodletting, he was nonetheless able to build a secure, seemingly impregnable fortress of steel." '

Gemma's heart skipped a beat. *Seemingly impregnable.* That was not what she had read before. She went on, her spirits soaring.

' "From there, he set in motion the experiments and processes which would lead to the new age.

' "Only one power could have opposed his progress, and that nearly failed through ignorance and clinging to outmoded ideals. However, the Servants of the Earth achieved a temporary victory . . ." '

Her hopes fell. *Temporary victory?*

' ". . . when the Key to the Dream, who had been imprisoned in the steel fortress, was able to reassert the doctrines of magic and turn the Bringer of Destruction's power upon himself.

' "However, this setback merely spurred the forces of the Far South to even greater efforts, and their influence soon spread throughout the world. The old order was destroyed.

' "The Age of Chaos began." '

Gemma could not believe it. *All for nothing?* Her mind became numb, unable to reach past this thought. *All for nothing? It can't be possible. It can't!*

At her feet, the meyrkats stirred uneasily, aware of Gemma's agitation.

No! The denial came from deep within her, but also from all the friends, known and unknown, who had come to her help, and from all the circles of magic who had entrusted her with their power without thought of the consequences. Gemma could not contact them now – the elemental screen denied her that – but their agreement was certain nevertheless.

'This book has been changed once,' she said aloud. 'And it can be done again!'

The meyrkats, sensing her new resolve, yelped their agreement.

Then Gemma felt the blue-flame wall stir behind her, and turned to look at it, new fears kindling in her heart. The shimmering pattern wavered, then bulged, and a figure formed within the blue light, unfocused at first, but becoming increasingly clear. The image of Arden stepped into the room, flecks of blue still burning in his hair and on his shoulders.

Gemma's knees turned to jelly. This was too cruel!

'Wasn't once enough?' she cried, her voice cracking with misery. 'Why must you taunt me with these demons?'

She closed her eyes, shutting out the false vision, praying that it would disappear. 'Your games mock me – and him,' she said. 'Return to your proper state.'

The elemental spoke, its voice hoarse.

'Gemma, my love, I'm no demon.'

Something in that well-remembered voice forced her to look up, tears brimming in her eyes. She hardly dared breathe.

She forced herself to walk towards him, stretching out a shaking hand to touch his chest. She almost fainted when she felt its warm solidity.

'You *are* real,' she whispered, then fell into his welcoming arms, sobbing uncontrollably.

'Of course I'm real,' he said softly, holding her tight. 'You're safe now, my love.'

After a few moments, she drew back a little, looking at him with tear-bright eyes.

'Safe for now,' she breathed. 'But it's not over yet. Arden, we have to go to the Far South.'

'I don't care *where* we have to go – to the Far South,

350

even to hell itself – as long as we're together. If you decide on any more crazy kite flights, you'll be taking along a passenger this time!'

She laughed with him then, as she had thought she would never laugh again.

'Thank you,' she said.

'What for?'

'For living, for being real, for bringing the light back into my life.'

Then Gemma turned her face up for his kiss. Long moments passed.

The meyrkats shifted uneasily, delighted that their two friends were reunited, but concerned about their current actions.

Gem-ma? Ed asked, sounding rather worried. *Can you still breathe?*

THE END

A SELECTED LIST OF SCIENCE FICTION AND FANTASY TITLES AVAILABLE FROM CORGI BOOKS

THE PRICES SHOWN BELOW WERE CORRECT AT THE TIME OF GOING TO PRESS.
HOWEVER TRANSWORLD PUBLISHERS RESERVE THE RIGHT TO SHOW NEW
RETAIL PRICES ON COVERS WHICH MAY DIFFER FROM THOSE PREVIOUSLY
ADVERTISED IN THE TEXT OR ELSEWHERE.

☐ 12566 0	THE WIZARDS AND THE WARRIORS	*Hugh Cook*	£3.99
☐ 13130 X	THE WORDSMITHS AND THE WAR GUILD	*Hugh Cook*	£2.99
☐ 13131 8	THE WOMEN AND THE WARLORDS	*Hugh Cook*	£3.50
☐ 13327 2	THE WALRUS AND THE WARWOLF	*Hugh Cook*	£3.95
☐ 13439 2	THE WICKED AND THE WITLESS	*Hugh Cook*	£3.99
☐ 13017 6	MALLOREON 1: GUARDIANS OF THE WEST	*David Eddings*	£3.50
☐ 13018 4	MALLOREON 2: KING OF THE MURGOS	*David Eddings*	£3.99
☐ 12284 X	BOOK ONE OF THE BELGARIAD: PAWN OF PROPHECY	*David Eddings*	£2.99
☐ 12348 X	BOOK TWO OF THE BELGARIAD: QUEEN OF SORCERY	*David Eddings*	£2.99
☐ 12382 X	BOOK THREE OF THE BELGARIAD: MAGICIAN'S GAMBIT	*David Eddings*	£2.99
☐ 12435 4	BOOK FOUR OF THE BELGARIAD: CASTLE OF WIZARDRY	*David Eddings*	£2.99
☐ 12447 8	BOOK FIVE OF THE BELGARIAD: ENCHANTERS' END GAME	*David Eddings*	£3.50
☐ 12679 9	MASTER OF THE FIVE MAGICS	*Lyndon Hardy*	£2.95
☐ 12680 2	SECRET OF THE SIXTH MAGIC	*Lyndon Hardy*	£2.95
☐ 13440 6	RIDDLE OF THE SEVEN REALMS	*Lyndon Hardy*	£3.99
☐ 13101 6	SERVANTS OF ARK I: THE FIRST NAMED	*Jonathan Wylie*	£2.99
☐ 13134 2	SERVANTS OF ARK II: THE CENTRE OF THE CIRCLE	*Jonathan Wylie*	£2.99
☐ 13161 X	SERVANTS OF ARK III: THE MAGE-BORN CHILD	*Jonathan Wylie*	£2.99
☐ 13416 3	THE UNBALANCED EARTH I: DREAMS OF STONE	*Jonathan Wylie*	£2.99
☐ 13417 1	THE UNBALANCED EARTH II: THE LIGHTLESS KINGDOM	*Jonathan Wylie*	£2.99

All Corgi/Bantam Books are available at your bookshop or newsagent, or can be ordered from the following address:

Corgi/Bantam Books,
Cash Sales Department,
P.O. Box 11, Falmouth, Cornwall TR10 9EN

Please send a cheque or postal order (no currency) and allow 60p for postage and packing for the first book plus 25p for the second book and 15p for each additional book ordered up to a maximum charge of £1.90 in UK.

B.F.P.O. customers please allow 60p for the first book, 25p for the second book plus 15p per copy for the next 7 books, thereafter 9p per book.

Overseas customers, including Eire, please allow £1.25 for postage and packing for the first book, 75p for the second book, and 28p for each subsequent title ordered.